# **FREE** Study Skills Videos/

Dear Customer,

Thank you for your purchase from Mometrix! We consider it an honor and a privilege that you have purchased our product and we want to ensure your satisfaction.

As a way of showing our appreciation and to help us better serve you, we have developed Study Skills Videos that we would like to give you for FREE. These videos cover our *best practices* for getting ready for your exam, from how to use our study materials to how to best prepare for the day of the test.

All that we ask is that you email us with feedback that would describe your experience so far with our product. Good, bad, or indifferent, we want to know what you think!

To get your FREE Study Skills Videos, you can use the **QR code** below, or send us an **email** at studyvideos@mometrix.com with *FREE VIDEOS* in the subject line and the following information in the body of the email:

- The name of the product you purchased.
- Your product rating on a scale of 1-5, with 5 being the highest rating.
- Your feedback. It can be long, short, or anything in between. We just want to know your impressions and experience so far with our product. (Good feedback might include how our study material met your needs and ways we might be able to make it even better. You could highlight features that you found helpful or features that you think we should add.)

If you have any questions or concerns, please don't hesitate to contact me directly.

Thanks again!

Sincerely,

Jay Willis
Vice President
jay.willis@mometrix.com
1-800-673-8175

# ASP Safety Fundamentals

## Exam Secrets Study Guide

### Exam Review and ASP Practice Test for the Associate Safety Professional Test

Written and edited by Mometrix Test Prep

Printed in the United States of America

This paper meets the requirements of ANSI/NISO Z39.48-1992 (Permanence of Paper).



Paperback
ISBN 13: 978-1-5167-1473-5
ISBN 10: 1-5167-1473-3

# Dear Future Exam Success Story

First of all, **THANK YOU** for purchasing Mometrix study materials!

Second, congratulations! You are one of the few determined test-takers who are committed to doing whatever it takes to excel on your exam. **You have come to the right place.** We developed these study materials with one goal in mind: to deliver you the information you need in a format that's concise and easy to use.

In addition to optimizing your guide for the content of the test, we've outlined our recommended steps for breaking down the preparation process into small, attainable goals so you can make sure you stay on track.

We've also analyzed the entire test-taking process, identifying the most common pitfalls and showing how you can overcome them and be ready for any curveball the test throws you.

Standardized testing is one of the biggest obstacles on your road to success, which only increases the importance of doing well in the high-pressure, high-stakes environment of test day. Your results on this test could have a significant impact on your future, and this guide provides the information and practical advice to help you achieve your full potential on test day.

**Your success is our success**

**We would love to hear from you!** If you would like to share the story of your exam success or if you have any questions or comments in regard to our products, please contact us at **800-673-8175** or **support@mometrix.com**.

Thanks again for your business and we wish you continued success!

Sincerely,
The Mometrix Test Preparation Team

**Need more help? Check out our flashcards at:**
**http://MometrixFlashcards.com/ASP**

# TABLE OF CONTENTS

# Introduction

**Thank you for purchasing this resource**! You have made the choice to prepare yourself for a test that could have a huge impact on your future, and this guide is designed to help you be fully ready for test day. Obviously, it's important to have a solid understanding of the test material, but you also need to be prepared for the unique environment and stressors of the test, so that you can perform to the best of your abilities.

For this purpose, the first section that appears in this guide is the **Secret Keys**. We've devoted countless hours to meticulously researching what works and what doesn't, and we've boiled down our findings to the five most impactful steps you can take to improve your performance on the test. We start at the beginning with study planning and move through the preparation process, all the way to the testing strategies that will help you get the most out of what you know when you're finally sitting in front of the test.

We recommend that you start preparing for your test as far in advance as possible. However, if you've bought this guide as a last-minute study resource and only have a few days before your test, we recommend that you skip over the first two Secret Keys since they address a long-term study plan.

If you struggle with **test anxiety**, we strongly encourage you to check out our recommendations for how you can overcome it. Test anxiety is a formidable foe, but it can be beaten, and we want to make sure you have the tools you need to defeat it.

# Secret Key #1 – Plan Big, Study Small

There's a lot riding on your performance. If you want to ace this test, you're going to need to keep your skills sharp and the material fresh in your mind. You need a plan that lets you review everything you need to know while still fitting in your schedule. We'll break this strategy down into three categories.

## Information Organization

Start with the information you already have: the official test outline. From this, you can make a complete list of all the concepts you need to cover before the test. Organize these concepts into groups that can be studied together, and create a list of any related vocabulary you need to learn so you can brush up on any difficult terms. You'll want to keep this vocabulary list handy once you actually start studying since you may need to add to it along the way.

## Time Management

Once you have your set of study concepts, decide how to spread them out over the time you have left before the test. Break your study plan into small, clear goals so you have a manageable task for each day and know exactly what you're doing. Then just focus on one small step at a time. When you manage your time this way, you don't need to spend hours at a time studying. Studying a small block of content for a short period each day helps you retain information better and avoid stressing over how much you have left to do. You can relax knowing that you have a plan to cover everything in time. In order for this strategy to be effective though, you have to start studying early and stick to your schedule. Avoid the exhaustion and futility that comes from last-minute cramming!

## Study Environment

The environment you study in has a big impact on your learning. Studying in a coffee shop, while probably more enjoyable, is not likely to be as fruitful as studying in a quiet room. It's important to keep distractions to a minimum. You're only planning to study for a short block of time, so make the most of it. Don't pause to check your phone or get up to find a snack. It's also important to **avoid multitasking**. Research has consistently shown that multitasking will make your studying dramatically less effective. Your study area should also be comfortable and well-lit so you don't have the distraction of straining your eyes or sitting on an uncomfortable chair.

The time of day you study is also important. You want to be rested and alert. Don't wait until just before bedtime. Study when you'll be most likely to comprehend and remember. Even better, if you know what time of day your test will be, set that time aside for study. That way your brain will be used to working on that subject at that specific time and you'll have a better chance of recalling information.

Finally, it can be helpful to team up with others who are studying for the same test. Your actual studying should be done in as isolated an environment as possible, but the work of organizing the information and setting up the study plan can be divided up. In between study sessions, you can discuss with your teammates the concepts that you're all studying and quiz each other on the details. Just be sure that your teammates are as serious about the test as you are. If you find that your study time is being replaced with social time, you might need to find a new team.

# Secret Key #2 – Make Your Studying Count

You're devoting a lot of time and effort to preparing for this test, so you want to be absolutely certain it will pay off. This means doing more than just reading the content and hoping you can remember it on test day. It's important to make every minute of study count. There are two main areas you can focus on to make your studying count.

## Retention

It doesn't matter how much time you study if you can't remember the material. You need to make sure you are retaining the concepts. To check your retention of the information you're learning, try recalling it at later times with minimal prompting. Try carrying around flashcards and glance at one or two from time to time or ask a friend who's also studying for the test to quiz you.

To enhance your retention, look for ways to put the information into practice so that you can apply it rather than simply recalling it. If you're using the information in practical ways, it will be much easier to remember. Similarly, it helps to solidify a concept in your mind if you're not only reading it to yourself but also explaining it to someone else. Ask a friend to let you teach them about a concept you're a little shaky on (or speak aloud to an imaginary audience if necessary). As you try to summarize, define, give examples, and answer your friend's questions, you'll understand the concepts better and they will stay with you longer. Finally, step back for a big picture view and ask yourself how each piece of information fits with the whole subject. When you link the different concepts together and see them working together as a whole, it's easier to remember the individual components.

Finally, practice showing your work on any multi-step problems, even if you're just studying. Writing out each step you take to solve a problem will help solidify the process in your mind, and you'll be more likely to remember it during the test.

## Modality

*Modality* simply refers to the means or method by which you study. Choosing a study modality that fits your own individual learning style is crucial. No two people learn best in exactly the same way, so it's important to know your strengths and use them to your advantage.

For example, if you learn best by visualization, focus on visualizing a concept in your mind and draw an image or a diagram. Try color-coding your notes, illustrating them, or creating symbols that will trigger your mind to recall a learned concept. If you learn best by hearing or discussing information, find a study partner who learns the same way or read aloud to yourself. Think about how to put the information in your own words. Imagine that you are giving a lecture on the topic and record yourself so you can listen to it later.

For any learning style, flashcards can be helpful. Organize the information so you can take advantage of spare moments to review. Underline key words or phrases. Use different colors for different categories. Mnemonic devices (such as creating a short list in which every item starts with the same letter) can also help with retention. Find what works best for you and use it to store the information in your mind most effectively and easily.

# Secret Key #3 – Practice the Right Way

Your success on test day depends not only on how many hours you put into preparing, but also on whether you prepared the right way. It's good to check along the way to see if your studying is paying off. One of the most effective ways to do this is by taking practice tests to evaluate your progress. Practice tests are useful because they show exactly where you need to improve. Every time you take a practice test, pay special attention to these three groups of questions:

- The questions you got wrong
- The questions you had to guess on, even if you guessed right
- The questions you found difficult or slow to work through

This will show you exactly what your weak areas are, and where you need to devote more study time. Ask yourself why each of these questions gave you trouble. Was it because you didn't understand the material? Was it because you didn't remember the vocabulary? Do you need more repetitions on this type of question to build speed and confidence? Dig into those questions and figure out how you can strengthen your weak areas as you go back to review the material.

Additionally, many practice tests have a section explaining the answer choices. It can be tempting to read the explanation and think that you now have a good understanding of the concept. However, an explanation likely only covers part of the question's broader context. Even if the explanation makes perfect sense, **go back and investigate** every concept related to the question until you're positive you have a thorough understanding.

As you go along, keep in mind that the practice test is just that: practice. Memorizing these questions and answers will not be very helpful on the actual test because it is unlikely to have any of the same exact questions. If you only know the right answers to the sample questions, you won't be prepared for the real thing. **Study the concepts** until you understand them fully, and then you'll be able to answer any question that shows up on the test.

It's important to wait on the practice tests until you're ready. If you take a test on your first day of study, you may be overwhelmed by the amount of material covered and how much you need to learn. Work up to it gradually.

On test day, you'll need to be prepared for answering questions, managing your time, and using the test-taking strategies you've learned. It's a lot to balance, like a mental marathon that will have a big impact on your future. Like training for a marathon, you'll need to start slowly and work your way up. When test day arrives, you'll be ready.

Start with the strategies you've read in the first two Secret Keys—plan your course and study in the way that works best for you. If you have time, consider using multiple study resources to get different approaches to the same concepts. It can be helpful to see difficult concepts from more than one angle. Then find a good source for practice tests. Many times, the test website will suggest potential study resources or provide sample tests.

# Practice Test Strategy

If you're able to find at least three practice tests, we recommend this strategy:

## Untimed and Open-Book Practice

Take the first test with no time constraints and with your notes and study guide handy. Take your time and focus on applying the strategies you've learned.

## Timed and Open-Book Practice

Take the second practice test open-book as well, but set a timer and practice pacing yourself to finish in time.

## Timed and Closed-Book Practice

Take any other practice tests as if it were test day. Set a timer and put away your study materials. Sit at a table or desk in a quiet room, imagine yourself at the testing center, and answer questions as quickly and accurately as possible.

Keep repeating timed and closed-book tests on a regular basis until you run out of practice tests or it's time for the actual test. Your mind will be ready for the schedule and stress of test day, and you'll be able to focus on recalling the material you've learned.

# Secret Key #4 – Pace Yourself

Once you're fully prepared for the material on the test, your biggest challenge on test day will be managing your time. Just knowing that the clock is ticking can make you panic even if you have plenty of time left. Work on pacing yourself so you can build confidence against the time constraints of the exam. Pacing is a difficult skill to master, especially in a high-pressure environment, so **practice is vital**.

Set time expectations for your pace based on how much time is available. For example, if a section has 60 questions and the time limit is 30 minutes, you know you have to average 30 seconds or less per question in order to answer them all. Although 30 seconds is the hard limit, set 25 seconds per question as your goal, so you reserve extra time to spend on harder questions. When you budget extra time for the harder questions, you no longer have any reason to stress when those questions take longer to answer.

Don't let this time expectation distract you from working through the test at a calm, steady pace, but keep it in mind so you don't spend too much time on any one question. Recognize that taking extra time on one question you don't understand may keep you from answering two that you do understand later in the test. If your time limit for a question is up and you're still not sure of the answer, mark it and move on, and come back to it later if the time and the test format allow. If the testing format doesn't allow you to return to earlier questions, just make an educated guess; then put it out of your mind and move on.

On the easier questions, be careful not to rush. It may seem wise to hurry through them so you have more time for the challenging ones, but it's not worth missing one if you know the concept and just didn't take the time to read the question fully. Work efficiently but make sure you understand the question and have looked at all of the answer choices, since more than one may seem right at first.

Even if you're paying attention to the time, you may find yourself a little behind at some point. You should speed up to get back on track, but do so wisely. Don't panic; just take a few seconds less on each question until you're caught up. Don't guess without thinking, but do look through the answer choices and eliminate any you know are wrong. If you can get down to two choices, it is often worthwhile to guess from those. Once you've chosen an answer, move on and don't dwell on any that you skipped or had to hurry through. If a question was taking too long, chances are it was one of the harder ones, so you weren't as likely to get it right anyway.

On the other hand, if you find yourself getting ahead of schedule, it may be beneficial to slow down a little. The more quickly you work, the more likely you are to make a careless mistake that will affect your score. You've budgeted time for each question, so don't be afraid to spend that time. Practice an efficient but careful pace to get the most out of the time you have.

# Secret Key #5 – Have a Plan for Guessing

When you're taking the test, you may find yourself stuck on a question. Some of the answer choices seem better than others, but you don't see the one answer choice that is obviously correct. What do you do?

The scenario described above is very common, yet most test takers have not effectively prepared for it. Developing and practicing a plan for guessing may be one of the single most effective uses of your time as you get ready for the exam.

In developing your plan for guessing, there are three questions to address:

- When should you start the guessing process?
- How should you narrow down the choices?
- Which answer should you choose?

## When to Start the Guessing Process

Unless your plan for guessing is to select C every time (which, despite its merits, is not what we recommend), you need to leave yourself enough time to apply your answer elimination strategies. Since you have a limited amount of time for each question, that means that if you're going to give yourself the best shot at guessing correctly, you have to decide quickly whether or not you will guess.

Of course, the best-case scenario is that you don't have to guess at all, so first, see if you can answer the question based on your knowledge of the subject and basic reasoning skills. Focus on the key words in the question and try to jog your memory of related topics. Give yourself a chance to bring the knowledge to mind, but once you realize that you don't have (or you can't access) the knowledge you need to answer the question, it's time to start the guessing process.

It's almost always better to start the guessing process too early than too late. It only takes a few seconds to remember something and answer the question from knowledge. Carefully eliminating wrong answer choices takes longer. Plus, going through the process of eliminating answer choices can actually help jog your memory.

**Summary**: Start the guessing process as soon as you decide that you can't answer the question based on your knowledge.

## How to Narrow Down the Choices

The next chapter in this book (**Test-Taking Strategies**) includes a wide range of strategies for how to approach questions and how to look for answer choices to eliminate. You will definitely want to read those carefully, practice them, and figure out which ones work best for you. Here though, we're going to address a mindset rather than a particular strategy.

Your odds of guessing an answer correctly depend on how many options you are choosing from.

| Number of options left | 5 | 4 | 3 | 2 | 1 |
|---|---|---|---|---|---|
| Odds of guessing correctly | 20% | 25% | 33% | 50% | 100% |

You can see from this chart just how valuable it is to be able to eliminate incorrect answers and make an educated guess, but there are two things that many test takers do that cause them to miss out on the benefits of guessing:

- Accidentally eliminating the correct answer
- Selecting an answer based on an impression

We'll look at the first one here, and the second one in the next section.

To avoid accidentally eliminating the correct answer, we recommend a thought exercise called **the $5 challenge**. In this challenge, you only eliminate an answer choice from contention if you are willing to bet $5 on it being wrong. Why $5? Five dollars is a small but not insignificant amount of money. It's an amount you could afford to lose but wouldn't want to throw away. And while losing $5 once might not hurt too much, doing it twenty times will set you back $100. In the same way, each small decision you make—eliminating a choice here, guessing on a question there—won't by itself impact your score very much, but when you put them all together, they can make a big difference. By holding each answer choice elimination decision to a higher standard, you can reduce the risk of accidentally eliminating the correct answer.

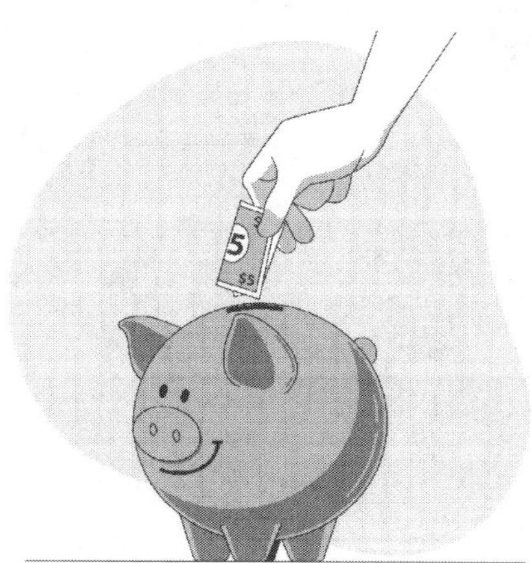

The $5 challenge can also be applied in a positive sense: If you are willing to bet $5 that an answer choice *is* correct, go ahead and mark it as correct.

**Summary**: Only eliminate an answer choice if you are willing to bet $5 that it is wrong.

## Which Answer to Choose

You're taking the test. You've run into a hard question and decided you'll have to guess. You've eliminated all the answer choices you're willing to bet $5 on. Now you have to pick an answer. Why do we even need to talk about this? Why can't you just pick whichever one you feel like when the time comes?

The answer to these questions is that if you don't come into the test with a plan, you'll rely on your impression to select an answer choice, and if you do that, you risk falling into a trap. The test writers know that everyone who takes their test will be guessing on some of the questions, so they intentionally write wrong answer choices to seem plausible. You still have to pick an answer though, and if the wrong answer choices are designed to look right, how can you ever be sure that you're not falling for their trap? The best solution we've found to this dilemma is to take the decision out of your hands entirely. Here is the process we recommend:

**Once you've eliminated any choices that you are confident (willing to bet $5) are wrong, select the first remaining choice as your answer.**

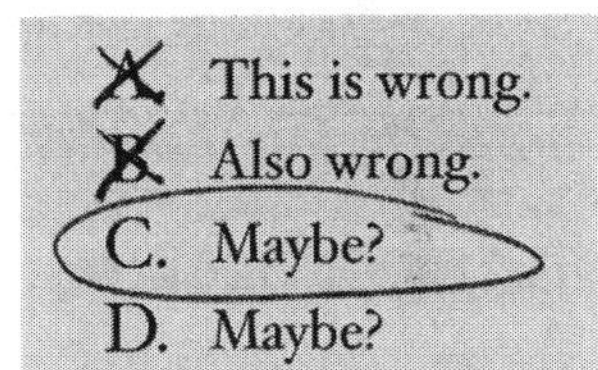


Whether you choose to select the first remaining choice, the second, or the last, the important thing is that you use some preselected standard. Using this approach guarantees that you will not be enticed into selecting an answer choice that looks right, because you are not basing your decision on how the answer choices look.

This is not meant to make you question your knowledge. Instead, it is to help you recognize the difference between your knowledge and your impressions. There's a huge difference between thinking an answer is right because of what you know, and thinking an answer is right because it looks or sounds like it should be right.

**Summary**: To ensure that your selection is appropriately random, make a predetermined selection from among all answer choices you have not eliminated.

# Test-Taking Strategies

This section contains a list of test-taking strategies that you may find helpful as you work through the test. By taking what you know and applying logical thought, you can maximize your chances of answering any question correctly!

It is very important to realize that every question is different and every person is different: no single strategy will work on every question, and no single strategy will work for every person. That's why we've included all of them here, so you can try them out and determine which ones work best for different types of questions and which ones work best for you.

## Question Strategies

### ✓ Read Carefully

Read the question and the answer choices carefully. Don't miss the question because you misread the terms. You have plenty of time to read each question thoroughly and make sure you understand what is being asked. Yet a happy medium must be attained, so don't waste too much time. You must read carefully and efficiently.

### ✓ Contextual Clues

Look for contextual clues. If the question includes a word you are not familiar with, look at the immediate context for some indication of what the word might mean. Contextual clues can often give you all the information you need to decipher the meaning of an unfamiliar word. Even if you can't determine the meaning, you may be able to narrow down the possibilities enough to make a solid guess at the answer to the question.

### ✓ Prefixes

If you're having trouble with a word in the question or answer choices, try dissecting it. Take advantage of every clue that the word might include. Prefixes and suffixes can be a huge help. Usually, they allow you to determine a basic meaning. *Pre-* means before, *post-* means after, *pro-* is positive, *de-* is negative. From prefixes and suffixes, you can get an idea of the general meaning of the word and try to put it into context.

### ✓ Hedge Words

Watch out for critical hedge words, such as *likely, may, can, sometimes, often, almost, mostly, usually, generally, rarely,* and *sometimes.* Question writers insert these hedge phrases to cover every possibility. Often an answer choice will be wrong simply because it leaves no room for exception. Be on guard for answer choices that have definitive words such as *exactly* and *always.*

### ✓ Switchback Words

Stay alert for *switchbacks.* These are the words and phrases frequently used to alert you to shifts in thought. The most common switchback words are *but, although,* and *however.* Others include *nevertheless, on the other hand, even though, while, in spite of, despite,* and *regardless of.* Switchback words are important to catch because they can change the direction of the question or an answer choice.

### ☑ Face Value

When in doubt, use common sense. Accept the situation in the problem at face value. Don't read too much into it. These problems will not require you to make wild assumptions. If you have to go beyond creativity and warp time or space in order to have an answer choice fit the question, then you should move on and consider the other answer choices. These are normal problems rooted in reality. The applicable relationship or explanation may not be readily apparent, but it is there for you to figure out. Use your common sense to interpret anything that isn't clear.

## Answer Choice Strategies

### ☑ Answer Selection

The most thorough way to pick an answer choice is to identify and eliminate wrong answers until only one is left, then confirm it is the correct answer. Sometimes an answer choice may immediately seem right, but be careful. The test writers will usually put more than one reasonable answer choice on each question, so take a second to read all of them and make sure that the other choices are not equally obvious. As long as you have time left, it is better to read every answer choice than to pick the first one that looks right without checking the others.

### ☑ Answer Choice Families

An answer choice family consists of two (in rare cases, three) answer choices that are very similar in construction and cannot all be true at the same time. If you see two answer choices that are direct opposites or parallels, one of them is usually the correct answer. For instance, if one answer choice says that quantity *x* increases and another either says that quantity *x* decreases (opposite) or says that quantity *y* increases (parallel), then those answer choices would fall into the same family. An answer choice that doesn't match the construction of the answer choice family is more likely to be incorrect. Most questions will not have answer choice families, but when they do appear, you should be prepared to recognize them.

### ☑ Eliminate Answers

Eliminate answer choices as soon as you realize they are wrong, but make sure you consider all possibilities. If you are eliminating answer choices and realize that the last one you are left with is also wrong, don't panic. Start over and consider each choice again. There may be something you missed the first time that you will realize on the second pass.

### ☑ Avoid Fact Traps

Don't be distracted by an answer choice that is factually true but doesn't answer the question. You are looking for the choice that answers the question. Stay focused on what the question is asking for so you don't accidentally pick an answer that is true but incorrect. Always go back to the question and make sure the answer choice you've selected actually answers the question and is not merely a true statement.

### ☑ Extreme Statements

In general, you should avoid answers that put forth extreme actions as standard practice or proclaim controversial ideas as established fact. An answer choice that states the "process should be used in certain situations, if…" is much more likely to be correct than one that states the "process should be discontinued completely." The first is a calm rational statement and doesn't even make a definitive, uncompromising stance, using a hedge word *if* to provide wiggle room, whereas the second choice is far more extreme.

### ⊘ Benchmark

As you read through the answer choices and you come across one that seems to answer the question well, mentally select that answer choice. This is not your final answer, but it's the one that will help you evaluate the other answer choices. The one that you selected is your benchmark or standard for judging each of the other answer choices. Every other answer choice must be compared to your benchmark. That choice is correct until proven otherwise by another answer choice beating it. If you find a better answer, then that one becomes your new benchmark. Once you've decided that no other choice answers the question as well as your benchmark, you have your final answer.

### ⊘ Predict the Answer

Before you even start looking at the answer choices, it is often best to try to predict the answer. When you come up with the answer on your own, it is easier to avoid distractions and traps because you will know exactly what to look for. The right answer choice is unlikely to be word-for-word what you came up with, but it should be a close match. Even if you are confident that you have the right answer, you should still take the time to read each option before moving on.

## General Strategies

### ⊘ Tough Questions

If you are stumped on a problem or it appears too hard or too difficult, don't waste time. Move on! Remember though, if you can quickly check for obviously incorrect answer choices, your chances of guessing correctly are greatly improved. Before you completely give up, at least try to knock out a couple of possible answers. Eliminate what you can and then guess at the remaining answer choices before moving on.

### ⊘ Check Your Work

Since you will probably not know every term listed and the answer to every question, it is important that you get credit for the ones that you do know. Don't miss any questions through careless mistakes. If at all possible, try to take a second to look back over your answer selection and make sure you've selected the correct answer choice and haven't made a costly careless mistake (such as marking an answer choice that you didn't mean to mark). This quick double check should more than pay for itself in caught mistakes for the time it costs.

### ⊘ Pace Yourself

It's easy to be overwhelmed when you're looking at a page full of questions; your mind is confused and full of random thoughts, and the clock is ticking down faster than you would like. Calm down and maintain the pace that you have set for yourself. Especially as you get down to the last few minutes of the test, don't let the small numbers on the clock make you panic. As long as you are on track by monitoring your pace, you are guaranteed to have time for each question.

### ⊘ Don't Rush

It is very easy to make errors when you are in a hurry. Maintaining a fast pace in answering questions is pointless if it makes you miss questions that you would have gotten right otherwise. Test writers like to include distracting information and wrong answers that seem right. Taking a little extra time to avoid careless mistakes can make all the difference in your test score. Find a pace that allows you to be confident in the answers that you select.

### ✓ Keep Moving

Panicking will not help you pass the test, so do your best to stay calm and keep moving. Taking deep breaths and going through the answer elimination steps you practiced can help to break through a stress barrier and keep your pace.

## Final Notes

The combination of a solid foundation of content knowledge and the confidence that comes from practicing your plan for applying that knowledge is the key to maximizing your performance on test day. As your foundation of content knowledge is built up and strengthened, you'll find that the strategies included in this chapter become more and more effective in helping you quickly sift through the distractions and traps of the test to isolate the correct answer.

Now that you're preparing to move forward into the test content chapters of this book, be sure to keep your goal in mind. As you read, think about how you will be able to apply this information on the test. If you've already seen sample questions for the test and you have an idea of the question format and style, try to come up with questions of your own that you can answer based on what you're reading. This will give you valuable practice applying your knowledge in the same ways you can expect to on test day.

**Good luck and good studying!**

# Advanced Sciences and Math

## General Chemistry Concepts

### Nomenclature

**Chemical nomenclature** refers to the manner in which chemical compounds are named.

#### *Binary Molecular Compounds*

The names of binary molecular compounds follow this pattern: prefix + first element name (space) prefix + root of second element name + -ide.

If a prefix ends with *a* or *o* and the element name begins with *a* or *o*, the first *a* or *o* of the prefix is dropped. For example, $N_2O_5$ is named dinitrogen pentoxide. The prefix *mono-* is usually dropped unless more than one binary compound may be formed from the two elements involved.

| **Binary Molecular Compounds** | | | |
|---|---|---|---|
| # | Prefix | # | Prefix |
| 1 | mono- | 6 | hexa- |
| 2 | di- | 7 | hepta- |
| 3 | tri- | 8 | octa- |
| 4 | tetra- | 9 | nona- |
| 5 | penta- | 10 | deca- |

#### *Binary Ionic Compounds*

The names of binary ionic compounds follow this pattern: cation name (space) anion name.

The name of simple cations is usually the element name. For example, the $K^+$ cation is named potassium. Some cations exist in more than one form. In those cases, the charge of the ion follows the element as a Roman numeral in parentheses. For example, the $Cu^+$ ion is named copper(I) and the $Cu^{2+}$ ion is named copper(II). Simple anions are named with the root of the element name followed by the suffix *-ide.* For example, the $O^{2-}$ anion is named oxide, and the $F^-$ ion is named fluoride. The following are some examples of names of binary ionic compounds: KI is named potassium iodide, and FeO is named iron(II) oxide.

Examples:

*$N_2O_4$*

This is a binary molecular compound. Using the prefixes *di-* for 2 and *tetra-* for 4, this compound is named dinitrogen tetroxide. Note that the entire element name is retained for the cation, but the root plus *-ide* is used for the anion name.

*$S_2F_{10}$*

This is a binary molecular compound. Using the prefixes *di-* for 2 and *deca-* for 10, this compound is named disulfur decafluoride. Note that the entire element name is retained for the cation, but the root plus *-ide* is used for the anion name.

*$Fe_2O_3$*

This is a binary ionic compound. Iron forms two types of cations $Fe^{2+}$ and $Fe^{3+}$, but because the anion is $O^{2-}$, this must be the $Fe^{3+}$ ion in order to balance the charges. This compound is named iron(III) oxide.

*$CuCl_2$*

This is a binary ionic compound. Copper forms two types of cations $Cu^+$ and $Cu^{2+}$, but because the anion is $Cl^-$, this must be the $Cu^{2+}$ ion in order to balance the charges. This compound is named copper(II) chloride.

### Acids

Acids are generally categorized as binary acids or oxyacids. Binary acids are named by the pattern: *hydro-* + root of element + *-ic* (space) acid. For example, HI is named hydroiodic acid, and HCl is named hydrochloric acid. One exception is that in hydrosulfuric acid ($H_2S$), the entire element name sulfur is used. The names of oxyacids depend on the endings of their polyatomic anions. If the polyatomic anions end in *-ate*, then the acid names end in *-ic*. If the anions end in *-ite*, the acid names end in *-ous*. The naming pattern for an oxyacid is as follows: anion root + ending (space) acid. For example, $H_2CO_3$ is named carbonic acid because the carbonate ion ends in *-ate*, and $H_2SO_3$ is named sulfurous acid because the sulfite ion ends in *-ite.*

### Hydrates

Hydrates form from salts (ionic compounds) that attract water. Hydrates are named from their salt (ionic compound) name and the number of water molecules involved in the following pattern:

salt name (space) prefix + hydrate.

For example, the name of $CuSO_4{\cdot}5H_2O$ is copper(II) sulfate pentahydrate, and the name of $CoCl_2{\cdot}6H_2O$ is cobalt(II) chloride hexahydrate.

### Salts

Salts are ionic compounds with any cation except $H^+$ from an aqueous base and any anion except $OH^-$ from an aqueous acid. Salts are named like regular ionic compounds with the name of the cation followed by the name of the anion. Examples of salts include sodium chloride (NaCl), potassium fluoride (KF), magnesium iodide ($MgI_2$), sodium acetate ($NaC_2H_3O_2$), and ammonium carbonate ($(NH_4)_2CO_3$).

### Bases

Bases typically are ionic compounds with a hydroxide anion and are named following the conventions of naming ionic compounds. For example, NaOH is named sodium hydroxide and $Mg(OH)_2$ is named magnesium hydroxide.

## Chemical Reactions

### Basic Mechanisms

Chemical reactions normally occur when electrons are transferred from one atom or molecule to another. Reactions and reactivity depend on the **octet rule**, which describes the tendency of atoms to gain or lose electrons until their outer energy levels contain eight. The changes in a reaction may be in **composition** or **configuration** of a compound or substance, and result in one or more products being generated which were not present in isolation before the reaction occurred. For instance, when oxygen reacts with methane ($CH_4$), water and carbon dioxide are the products; one set of substances ($CH_4 + O$) was transformed into a new set of substances ($CO_2 + H_2O$).

Reactions depend on the presence of a **reactant**, or substance undergoing change, a **reagent**, or partner in the reaction less transformed than the reactant (such as a catalyst), and **products**, or the final result of the reaction. **Reaction conditions**, or environmental factors, are also important components in reactions. These include conditions such as temperature, pressure, concentration, whether the reaction occurs in solution, the type of solution, and presence or absence of catalysts. Chemical reactions are usually written in the following format: Reactants → Products.

### *Combination Reactions*

In a **combination reaction**, two or more reactants combine to make one product. This can be seen in the equation $A + B \rightarrow AB$. These reactions are also known as synthesis or addition reactions. An example is burning hydrogen in air to produce water. The equation is $2H_2\ (g) + O_2\ (g) \rightarrow 2H_2O\ (l)$. Another example is when water and sulfur trioxide react to form sulfuric acid. The equation is $H_2O + SO_3 \rightarrow H_2SO_4$.

### *Decomposition Reactions*

**Decomposition** (or desynthesis, decombination, or deconstruction) **reactions** are considered chemical reactions whereby a reactant is broken down into two or more products. This can be seen in the equation $AB \rightarrow A + B$. These reactions are also called analysis reactions. When a compound or substance separates into these simpler substances, the byproducts are often substances that are different from the original. Decomposition can be viewed as the opposite of combination reactions. These reactions are also called analysis reactions. Most decomposition reactions are **endothermic,** meaning that heat needs to be added for the chemical reaction to occur. **Thermal decomposition** is caused by heat. **Electrolytic decomposition** is due to electricity. An example of this type of reaction is the decomposition of water into hydrogen and oxygen gas. The equation is $2H_2O \rightarrow 2H_2 + O_2$. Separation processes can be mechanical or chemical, and usually involve reorganizing a mixture of substances without changing their chemical nature. The separated products may differ from the original mixture in terms of chemical or physical properties. Types of separation processes include filtration, crystallization, distillation, and chromatography. Decomposition breaks down one compound into two or more compounds or substances that are different from the original; separation sorts the substances from the original mixture into like substances.

### *Single Replacement Reactions*

**Single substitution**, **displacement,** or **replacement reactions** occur when one reactant is displaced by another to form the final product ($A + BC \rightarrow B + AC$). Single substitution reactions can be cationic or anionic. When a piece of copper (Cu) is placed into a solution of silver nitrate ($AgNO_3$), the solution turns blue. The copper appears to be replaced with a silvery-white material. The equation is $2AgNO_3 + Cu \rightarrow Cu(NO_3)_2 + 2Ag$. When this reaction takes place, the copper dissolves and the silver in the silver nitrate solution precipitates (becomes a solid), thus resulting in copper nitrate and silver. Copper and silver have switched places in the nitrate.

### *Double Replacement Reactions*

**Double displacement**, **double replacement, substitution, metathesis,** or **ion exchange reactions** occur when ions or bonds are exchanged by two compounds to form different compounds ($AC + BD \rightarrow AD + BC$). An example of this is that silver nitrate and sodium chloride form two different products (silver chloride and sodium nitrate) when they react. The formula for this reaction is $AgNO_3 + NaCl \rightarrow AgCl + NaNO_3$.

Double replacement reactions are metathesis reactions. In a double replacement reaction, the chemical reactants exchange ions but the oxidation state stays the same. One of the indicators of this is the formation of a solid precipitate. In acid/base reactions, an **acid** is a compound that can donate a proton, while a **base** is a compound that can accept a proton. In these types of reactions, the acid and base react to form a salt and water. When the proton is donated, the base becomes water and the remaining ions form a salt. One method of determining whether a reaction is an oxidation/reduction or a metathesis reaction is that the oxidation number of atoms does not change during a metathesis reaction.

### *Combustion Reactions*

**Combustion**, or burning, is a sequence of chemical reactions involving **fuel** and an **oxidant** that produces heat and sometimes light. There are many types of combustion, such as rapid, slow, complete, turbulent, microgravity, and incomplete. Fuels and oxidants determine the compounds formed by a combustion reaction. For example, when rocket fuel consisting of hydrogen and oxygen combusts, it results in the formation of water vapor. When air and wood burn, resulting compounds include nitrogen, unburned carbon, and carbon compounds. Combustion is an **exothermic** process, meaning it releases energy. Exothermic energy is commonly released as heat, but can take other forms, such as light, electricity, or sound.

**Review Video: Combustion**
Visit mometrix.com/academy and enter code: 592219

### *Catalysts*

**Catalysts**, substances that help change the rate of reaction without changing their form, can increase reaction rate by decreasing the number of steps it takes to form products. The mass of the catalyst should be the same at the beginning of the reaction as it is at the end. The **activation energy** is the minimum amount required to get a reaction started. Activation energy causes particles to collide with sufficient energy to start the reaction. A **catalyst** enables more particles to react, which lowers the activation energy. Examples of catalysts in reactions are manganese oxide ($MnO_2$) in the decomposition of hydrogen peroxide, iron in the manufacture of ammonia using the Haber process, and concentrate of sulfuric acid in the nitration of benzene.

### Balancing a Chemical Equation

According to the law of conservation of mass, the mass of the products must always equal the mass of the reactants in a chemical reaction. Because mass is conserved, the number of each type of atom in the products must equal the number of each type of atom in the reactants. The key to balancing a chemical reaction is in balancing the number of each type of atom on both sides of the equation. Only the coefficients in front of the reactants and products may be changed to accomplish this, not the subscripts in the molecules themselves. Try balancing the largest number of a type of atom first. Also, check if any odd numbers need to be changed to even. Always leave the uncombined elements to balance until the end.

Below is an unbalanced example of the chemical reaction that occurs when propane gas is burned in air.

$$C_3H_8\,(g) + O_2(g) \rightarrow CO_2\,(g) + H_2O\,(g) + heat$$

To balance the equation, first determine the types and numbers of each type of atom on each side of the equation:

| | Reactants | Products |
|---|---|---|
| C | 3 | 1 |
| H | 8 | 2 |
| O | 2 | 3 |

Since hydrogen has the largest number of atoms, balance it first. Adding a coefficient of 4 to the $H_2O$ on the right side makes the number of hydrogen atoms the same on both sides.

$$C_3H_8\ (g) +\ O_2(g) \rightarrow\ CO_2\ (g) + 4H_2O\ (g) + heat$$

Oxygen has the next-highest number of atoms to balance, but because it is uncombined with other elements on the left side, it is better to balance carbon first. Adding a coefficient of 3 to the $CO_2$ on the right side makes the number of carbon atoms the same on both sides.

$$C_3H_8\ (g) +\ O_2(g) \rightarrow\ 3CO_2\ (g) + 4H_2O\ (g) + heat$$

All that's left now are the oxygen atoms. Adding a coefficient of 5 to the $O_2$ on the left side completes the balancing process, leaving the correct equation:

$$C_3H_8\ (g) +\ 5O_2(g) \rightarrow\ 3CO_2\ (g) + 4H_2O\ (g) + heat$$

## Ideal Gas Law

**Ideal gases** are assumed to be a set of randomly moving point particles that do not interact with each other. The collisions of ideal gases are assumed to be completely elastic, and the intermolecular forces are assumed to be zero. Real gases show more complex behaviors. The ideal gas laws tend to fail at low temperatures and high pressures when the effects of the particle size and intermolecular forces are more apparent. Also, the ideal gas assumptions do not account for phase transitions.

The ideal gas law combines Boyle's law, Charles's law, and Avogadro's law, which describe the relationships between temperature (*T*), volume (*V*), and pressure (*P*). According to Boyle's law, $V \propto \frac{1}{P}$. According to Charles's law, $V \propto T$. According to Avogadro's law, $V \propto n$. Combining these three relationships into one relationship yields $V \propto \frac{nT}{P}$. Multiplying through by *P* yields $PV \propto nT$, or $PV = nRT$, where *R* is the ideal gas constant of 0.0821 L·atm/(K·mol), *P* is the pressure in atm, *V* is the volume in L, *n* is the number of moles in mol, and *T* is the temperature in K.

**Review Video: Ideal Gas Law**
Visit mometrix.com/academy and enter code: 381353

Example:

*Consider a vehicle in a 22 °C garage. Its tires are inflated with 3.2 moles of air at 33 psi. Calculate the volume of air in its tires.*

Using the ideal gas law,

$$T = °\text{C} + 273 = 22 + 273 = 295\ \text{K}$$

$$P = 33\ \text{psi} \times \frac{1\ \text{atm}}{14.696\ \text{psi}} = 2.25\ \text{atm}$$

$$V = \frac{nRT}{P} = \frac{3.2\ \text{mol} \times 0.082\ \frac{\text{L} \cdot \text{atm}}{\text{K} \cdot \text{mol}} \times 295\ \text{K}}{2.25\ \text{atm}} = 34.48\ \text{L}$$

### pH

The **potential of hydrogen (pH)** is a measurement of the concentration of hydrogen ions in a substance in terms of the number of moles of $H^+$ per liter of solution. All substances fall between 0 and 14 on the pH scale. A lower pH indicates a higher $H^+$ concentration, while a higher pH indicates a lower $H^+$ concentration.

Pure water has a neutral pH, which is 7. Anything with a pH lower than pure water (<7) is considered **acidic**. Anything with a pH higher than pure water (>7) is a **base**. Drain cleaner, soap, baking soda, ammonia, egg whites, and sea water are common bases. Urine, stomach acid, citric acid, vinegar, hydrochloric acid, and battery acid are acids. A **pH indicator** is a substance that acts as a detector of hydrogen or hydronium ions. It is **halochromic**, meaning it changes color to indicate that hydrogen or hydronium ions have been detected.

**Review Video: pH**
Visit mometrix.com/academy and enter code: 187395

## Electrical Principles

### Ohm's Law and Power

**Electricity** has three primary parameters: voltage, current, and resistance.

**Electric voltage** is the difference in electric potential energy between two points per unit electric charge. It is measured in Volts (V), which are equal to a joule of energy per coulomb of charge.

**Electric current** is a flow of electric charge. It is measured in amperes, or amps (A), which are equal to a flow of one coulomb of charge per second.

**Electrical resistance** is the measure of how difficult it is to pass an electric current through a conductor. It is measured in Ohms (Ω), which are equal to a volt per ampere.

The relationship between these three quantities is known as **Ohm's law**. It states that current is directly proportional to voltage, and is given by the following equation, where $V$ is voltage, $I$ is current, and $R$ is resistance:

$$V = I \times R$$

Rearranging this equation allows the calculation of any of the three variables: $R = \frac{V}{I}$ or $I = \frac{V}{R}$.

**Electric power**, the rate of doing work, is given by the following equation, where $P$ is electric power, $I$ is current, and $V$ is voltage:

$$P = IV$$

Power is measured in Watts (W), which are equal to a joule of energy per second. Multiplying power by time results in total energy, usually given in kilowatt-hours (kWh). The power equation can be combined with Ohm's law to produce $P = \frac{V^2}{R}$ and $P = I^2R$.

For example, if a light bulb draws 500 mA from a 120V source for 8 hours, the energy it has used can be calculated by:

$$P = 0.5\text{ A} \times 120\text{ V} = 60\text{ W}$$

$$60\text{ W} \times 8\text{ hours} = 0.48\text{ kWh}$$

**Review Video: Ohm's Law and Power**
Visit mometrix.com/academy and enter code: 784016

## Circuits

**Circuit analysis** is the process of determining the currents through and voltages across all the elements in a network. Some methods include equivalent circuit calculations, voltage division, current division, loop analysis, and mesh analysis.

When resistors in a simple circuit are arranged in series, their equivalent resistance is the sum of all the resistance values. In the circuit below, three resistors are in series, and their equivalent resistance is:

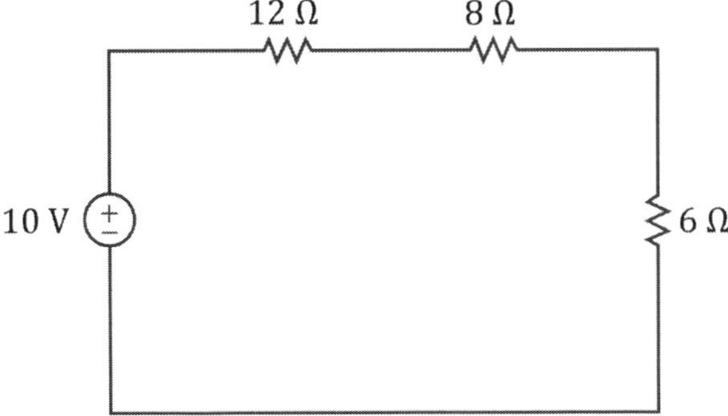


$$R_{eq} = R_1 + R_2 + \cdots + R_n = 12 + 8 + 6 = 26\ \Omega$$

For resistors in parallel, the equivalent resistance is the reciprocal of the sum of the reciprocals of the resistors. For the circuit below, the equivalent resistance is:

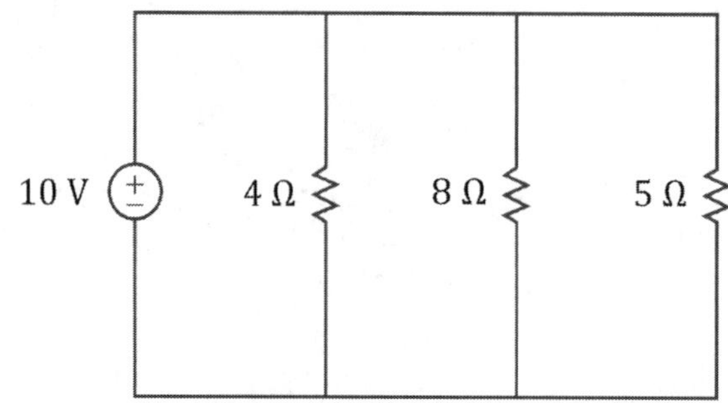


$$R_{eq} = \frac{1}{\frac{1}{R_1} + \frac{1}{R_2} + \cdots + \frac{1}{R_n}} = \frac{1}{\frac{1}{4} + \frac{1}{8} + \frac{1}{5}} = 1.74\ \Omega$$

**Voltage division** is a tool that allows the calculation of voltage across resistors in series. It uses the following equation, where $V_i$ is the voltage across the resistance $R_i$, $R_1$, $R_2$, etc are the other resistors in the circuit, and $V_{source}$ is the voltage source in the circuit:

$$V_i = V_{source} \times \frac{R_i}{R_1 + R_2 + \cdots + R_n}$$

For example, the voltage drop across the 1 kΩ resistor in the circuit below is calculated as:

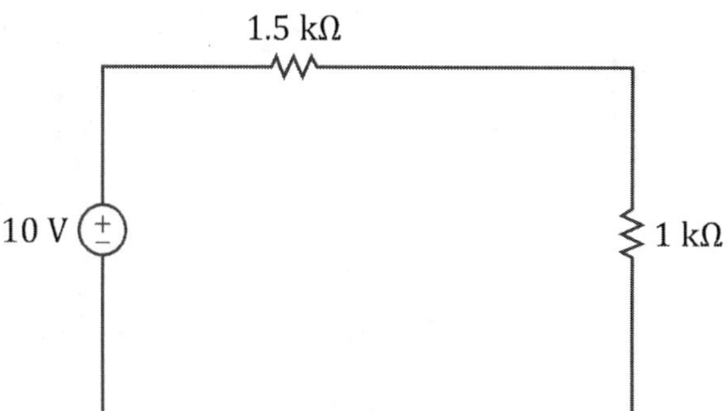


$$V_i = 10\text{V} \times \frac{1000}{1500 + 1000} = 4\text{V}$$

**Current division** is the splitting of currents between branches of a circuit. With resistances in parallel, the current through any branch can be calculated by the equation, where $I_i$ is the current through the resistance $R_i$, $R_1$, $R_2$, etc., are the other resistors in the circuit, and $I_{source}$ is the current in the main branch of the circuit:

$$I_i = I_{source} \times \left( \frac{\frac{1}{R_i}}{\frac{1}{R_1} + \frac{1}{R_2} + \cdots + \frac{1}{R_n}} \right)$$

For example, the current though the 50 Ω resistor in the circuit below is calculated as:

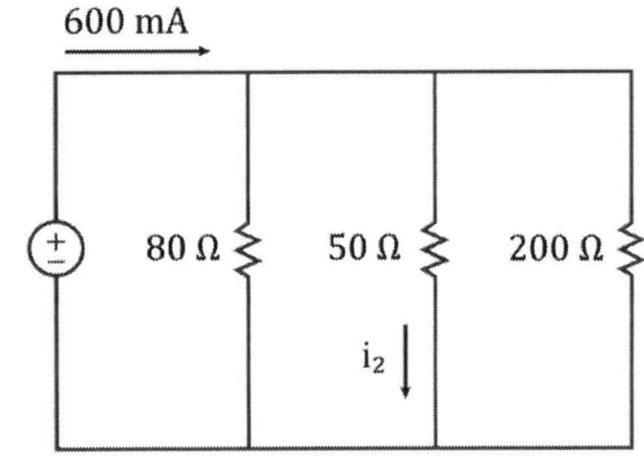


$$i_2 = 600 \text{ mA} \times \left( \frac{\frac{1}{50}}{\frac{1}{80} + \frac{1}{50} + \frac{1}{200}} \right) = 320 \text{ mA}$$

**Kirchoff's current law (KCL)** states that the amount of current flowing into a node must equal the amount of current flowing out of it, $I_{in} = I_{out}$. Summing all incoming current and setting it equal to the sum of all outgoing current will allow the calculation of any single current flow in the node. This is known as **nodal analysis**. For example, in the circuit below, all the current values are known except for $i_2$.

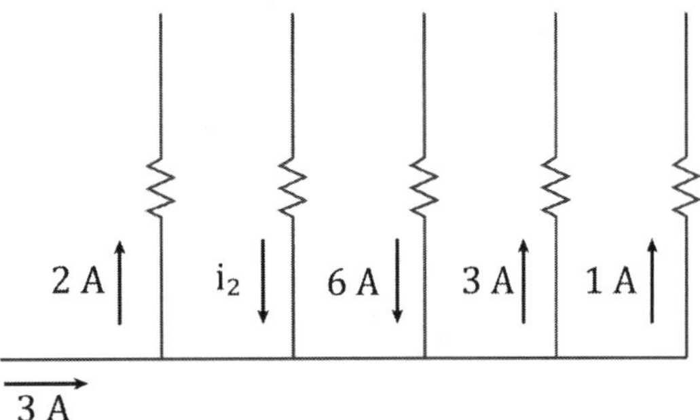


The equation of the node is:

$$3 + i_2 + 6 = 2 + 3 + 1$$

Thus $i_2$ must equal -3A.

**Kirchoff's voltage law (KVL)** states that the sum of the voltage drops across all devices in any closed loop of a circuit will always be zero. Using this information, an equation can be formulated which will allow the calculation of the volatge across any single element in a loop, assuming the other voltages are known. This is known as **mesh analysis**. For example, in the circuit below, all the voltages are known except for $V_{R_4}$.

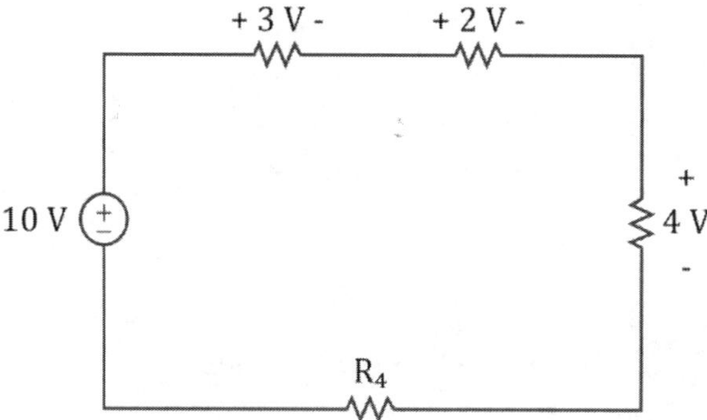


The equation for the loop is

$$0 = (\ 10) + 3 + 2 + 4 + V_{R_4}$$

Thus $V_{R_4}$ must equal 1 V.

## Inductors and Capacitors

**Inductors** are electrical devices that stores electric current. They are usually made of a coil of wire wrapped around a core of air, iron, or ferrite. **Inductance** is measured in henrys (H) or, more commonly, millihenrys (mH) and is proportional to the number of turns in the coil.

Likewise, **capacitors** are electrical devices that store electric charge. They are usually made of at least two electrical conductors separated by an insulator, or dielectric. **Capacitance** is measured in farads (F) or, more commonly, microfarads (μF) and is proportional to the surface area of the conductors, and inversely proportional to the separation between the plates.

**Alternating current** is an electric current in which the flow of electric charge periodically reverses direction. The nature of inductors and capacitors is to oppose changes in current and voltage, respectively. This opposition is referred to as **impedance** and is similar to resistance, also having units of ohms. However, unlike resistance, impedance is a complex value, meaning that it may have an imaginary component as well as a real component. For ideal capacitors and inductors, impedance is purely imaginary, and for ideal resistors, impedance is purely real.

It is only when combining the effects of these devices that the full expression for impedance, $Z$, is necessary: $Z = R + X \times i$, where $i = \sqrt{1}$. $X$ is a quantity known as reactance. The reactance of a capacitor is $X_C = \frac{1}{\omega C}$ where ω (omega) is the angular frequency of the current in radians per second. The reactance of an inductor is $X_L = \omega L$. Note that frequency in hertz must be mulipliied by $2\pi$ to get angular frequncy in radians per second.

For example, if a 50 mH inductor is connected to a 120 V, 60 Hz power supply, its reactance is

$$X_L = (2\pi \times 60) \times \left(50 \text{ mH} \times \frac{1 \text{ H}}{1000 \text{ mH}}\right) = 18.85 \ \Omega$$

Suppose this inductor has a real resistance of 0.01 ohms. Its impedance would then be $Z_L = 0.01 + 18.85i \ \Omega$.

# Principles of Radioactivity

## Decay and Half-Life

**Radioactive decay**, or radioactivity, is a set of processes that allow unstable atomic nuclei, or nuclides, to emit subatomic particles, or radiation. The decay is a random process, and it is not possible to predict an individual atom's decay. However, on a larger scale, radioactive material behaves in a predictable manner. Radioactive decay occurs at an exponential rate. This means that the amount of radioactive material, $N$, present after time $t$ is given by the following equation, where $N_0$ is the amount of material present at time $t = 0$, and $\lambda$ is the decay constant of the material:

$$N = N_0 e^{-\lambda t}$$

The time required for half the mass of a radioactive material to decay is known as its **half-life**. Half-life is the most commonly used measure of a material's rate of decay, and it can be as short as a fraction of a second or as long as millions of years. If the half-life of the material is known, **lambda**, the decay constant, can be calculated as $\lambda = \frac{\ln(2)}{t_{1/2}}$, where $t_{1/2}$ is the half-life. For example, suppose a sample of radium-224 starts at a mass of 10 grams. Its half-life is 3.63 days. The remaining mass of radium-224 after 8 days can be calculated by

$$\lambda = \frac{\ln(2)}{3.63 \text{ days}} = 0.191 \text{ disintegrations per day}$$

$$N = 10e^{-0.191 \times 8} = 2.17 \text{ g}$$

**Review Video: Radiation Calculations**
Visit mometrix.com/academy and enter code: 534888

## Source Strength

The source strength of a radioactive material is defined as the number of disintegrations per second and is measured in becquerels (Bq) or curies (Ci). One becquerel is one disintegration per second; one curie is $3.7 \times 10^{10}$ disintegrations per second. **Source strength** is given by the equation,

$$Q = \frac{\lambda m N_A}{W}$$

where:

- $Q$ is the number of disintegrations per second
- $\lambda$ is the decay constant
- $m$ is the mass of the radioisotope
- $N_A$ is Avogadro's number, $6.02 \times 10^{23}$ g/g-atoms
- $W$ is the atomic weight of the radioisotope

For example, if radium-224 has decay constant of $2.0289 \times 10^{-6}$ disintegrations per second and an atomic mass of 224.02 u, the mass of a $3.8 \times 10^{12}$ becquerel source of Ra-224 can be calculated:

$$m = \frac{QW}{\lambda N_A} = \frac{(3.8 \times 10^{12}) \times 224.02}{(2.2089 \times 10^{-6}) \times (6.02 \times 10^{23})} = 640 \text{ µg}$$

### Inverse Square Law

The **Inverse Square Law** is a mathematical description of what happens to the intensity of exposure as an individual moves further from a source of radiation. The intensity of radiation is inversely proportional to the distance squared. For every foot that a person moves away from a source of radiation, the intensity is reduced by the amount of change in distance squared. If a person is exposed to 100mr/hr of radiation at a distance of 4 feet, and they move to a distance 8 feet from the radiation source, the distance is effectually twice as far away, meaning the radiation will be a quarter as intense, or 25mr/hr. Similarly, if the same person were to move to a distance of 2 feet from the radiation source, the intensity would be quadrupled to be 400mr/hr of radiation. This illustrates how greatly the distance from the source of radiation affects the mount of exposure. Thus, distance from the source of radiation is a simple but effective way to minimize occupational exposure.

## Storage Capacity Calculations

**Static load** is the total weight that a storage rack is designed to hold, including safety factors. In practical applications, this total capacity may be adjusted based on floor construction and whether the warehouse is in a seismic zone. The load capacity is determined by an engineer or the manufacturer. Each beam pair must be labeled with the maximum load to notify employees of the capacity.

Example:

*Calculate the maximum static load for a four-level beam system rated at 4,000 pounds per level.*

The maximum static load is calculated by multiplying the load for each level by the number of levels: $4 \times 4{,}000 \text{ pounds} = 16{,}000 \text{ pounds}$.

## Rigging and Load Calculations

A **sling** is a rope, strap or chain that is used to connect a load to a lifting mechanism, such as a crane. In rigging, each sling is rated to a maximum weight limit. However, depending on how the sling is attached to the load, corrections to the rated load must be determined. In a multiple sling lift, the **tension factor (TF)** is the reduced capacity of a sling when it is not perpendicular to the load. In a **vertical hitch** system, two slings are attached to a single hook above the load.

Example:

*A two-sling vertical hitch system is to be used to lift a pipe weighing 3,600 pounds. Calculate the minimum vertical-rated capacity for each sling in order to make a safe lift if the slings are 10 feet long and the hitch will be 8 feet above the load.*

The load weighs 3,600 pounds. The load experienced by each sling in a vertical hitch system is determined by dividing the load by the number of slings (3,600 / 2 = 1,800). The tension factor can be determined from a table or be calculated by dividing the sling length by the hitch height from the load: TF = L / h = 10' / 8' = 1.25. Finally, the minimum sling rating is determined by multiplying the TF by the load carried by each sling: 1.25 x 1,800 = 2,250. Thus, each sling must be rated for a vertical lift of at least 2,250 pounds to safely lift the pipe.

In rigging, each sling is rated as to a maximum weight limit. The **working load limit (WLL)** is the maximum amount of weight a sling is designed to handle under normal conditions. However, depending on how the sling is attached to the load, the sling's capacity must be calculated using the WLL to ensure the rigging will not fail during the lift. In a **vertical hitch**, the sling is directly attached to both the lifting mechanism and the load. In a **choker hitch**, the sling is passed through an engineered loop ("hitch") and the other end is attached directly to the lifting mechanism. In a **basket** configuration, the sling is passed under the load and both ends are attached to the lifting mechanism.

Example:

*Calculate the lifting capacity of a sling with a working load limit of 1,000 pounds in the following configurations: vertical hitch, choker hitch, and a single sling in a basket hitch having two 90-degree angles.*

In a vertical hitch configuration, the sling's capacity is the WLL of the sling = 1,000 pounds.

In a choker hitch configuration, the tension at the choke reduces the lifting capacity to 75% of the WLL = 750 pounds.

In a basket configuration, each leg of the sling acts as its own leg, resulting in doubling the capacity of a single sling = 2,000 pounds.

# Ventilation and System Design

## Components of Ventilation Systems

**Ventilation systems** consist of an **intake** (if interior to the space, they are called **returns**) that brings air into the system; **ducts** that move air within the system; **a cooling, heating,** or **split** (heating and cooling) **system** that adjusts the air temperature; and **supplies** that allow conditioned air into the occupied spaces. The system for air movement and temperature control is called an HVAC (heating, ventilation, air conditioning) system. HVAC systems also contain a **particulate filter** to remove pollen, dust, and allergens from the air. Thus, air from the room moves into the system through the return, travels via the ducts, passes through a filter, is temperature modified by the heater or air conditioner, continues through ducts, and is pushed into the office through the supplies.

Example:

*Determine the number of air exchanges in an office measuring 15 feet by 15 feet with an 8-foot ceiling that has one HVAC return measured at 60 cfm.*

**Air exchange rate** is how many times all the air in a closed room will be replaced with clean air over a given period of time.

$Q$ = ventilation rate (cubic feet per minute, or cfm), $V$ = room volume (cubic feet)

**Air changes per hour (ACH)** = 60Q / V

$$\text{ACH} = 60 \times 60 \text{ cfm} / 1{,}800 \text{ ft}^3 = 2 \text{ air exchanges per hour}$$

Example:

*Calculate the number of hours it would take a 100 cfm exhaust ventilation system to remove the air in a room measuring 50 feet wide, 30 feet long, and 15 feet high.*

In order to calculate the time to remove the air, the volume of the room (l x h x w) must be calculated and the **exhaust rate** of the fan must be known. The final step is to convert the exhaust rate into the unit of time asked in the problem (in this case, the rate is given in cubic feet per minute, but the answer is in hours).

$t$ = time (hours); $V$ = room volume (cubic feet); $Q$ = ventilation rate (cfm)

$$t = \frac{V}{60Q}$$

$$t = \frac{50' \times 30' \times 15'}{60 \times 100 \text{ cfm}} = 3.75 \text{ hours}$$

## Purpose of Local Exhaust Ventilation Systems

**Local exhaust ventilation (LEV)** systems are designed to remove hazardous atmospheres from the **breathing zone** of an employee. Portable local exhaust ventilation systems use flexible ducting that is positioned in a manner to efficiently remove contaminants before they enter the breathing zone. Systems may be mobile, temporary, or they may be permanently plumbed into a workstation. Consideration must be given to the system exhaust to avoid contaminating other workspaces or offsite locations.

**Ventilation rate** is the volume of air being moved into or out of an area per unit of time, usually expressed as cubic feet per minute. Flow rates can be measured by instruments, such as **anemometers**, at the duct opening and, when multiplied by the face area of the duct, provide the ventilation rate.

Example:

*Calculate the ventilation rate for a portable local exhaust ventilation system for a welding operation using a 6-inch diameter flexible duct and an exhaust rate of 100 fpm.*

$Q$ = ventilation rate (cubic feet per minute); $R$ = exhaust rate (feet per minute, or fpm); $A$ = duct face area (square feet)

$$Q = RA$$

$$\text{Area of a circle} = \pi \times r^2$$

$$Q = 100 \text{ fpm} \times (3.14 \times (0.25 \text{ ft})^2) = 19.6 \text{ cfm}$$

**Exhaust ventilation systems** can be designed to remove contaminants from the breathing zone of workers. Thus, the necessary ventilation rate can be calculated using a pre-determined safety factor to keep the worker's breathing zone concentration below the **action level**. The final rate is dependent on the material being used in the process because the **specific gravity** (weight relative to air) and the exposure level are substance-specific.

Example:

*A cleaning operation uses 4 pints of acetone per hour. Using a safety factor of 5, calculate the dilution airflow requirements of an exhaust ventilation system to keep the acetone at 30 ppm (parts per million). Acetone's molecular weight is 58 amu, and its specific gravity is 0.78.*

$Q$ = ventilation rate (cubic feet per minute, cfm); $W$ = evaporation rate (pints/min); $K$ = safety factor; $M$ = molecular weight; $L$ = desired level

$W$ = 4 pints/hour, convert to minutes = 0.067 pints/min

$$Q = \frac{403 \times specific\ gravity \times W \times K \times 1{,}000{,}000}{M \times L}$$

$$Q = \frac{403 \times 0.78 \times 0.067 \times 5 \times 1{,}000{,}000}{58 \text{ amu} \times 30 \text{ ppm}} = 60{,}519 \text{ cfm}$$

Similar to exposure control, **exhaust ventilation** can be used in the fire prevention process and for emergency responses. The necessary ventilation rate is dependent on the material as the **specific gravity** (weight relative to air) and the **lower explosive limit (LEL)** are material specific.

Example:

*A drum of n-hexane is leaking and evaporating at 1 pint per hour. Calculate the ventilation rate required to keep the LEL below 10%. For n-hexane, MW = 86, specific gravity = 0.66, and LEL = 1.1%.*

$Q$ = ventilation rate (cfm); $W$ = evaporation rate (pints/min); $S$ = safety factor (100% LEL / desired LEL level); $B$ = temperature dependent constant (<250 degrees F, B = 1; >250 F, B = 0.7)

$$Q = \frac{403 \times specific\ gravity \times W \times S \times 100}{MW \times LEL \times B}$$

$$Q = \frac{403 \times 0.66 \times 0.017 \times 10 \times 100}{86 \times 1.1 \times 1} = 47.8 \text{ cfm}$$

## Noise Hazards

Noise is measured in decibels (dB), but OSHA uses a slightly different scale (dBA) that more closely matches the human ear's perception of sound. The most important thing to know about the decibel scale is that it is logarithmic, not linear. This means that an addition of ten decibels indicates that sound intensity (SI) has been multiplied ten. Sound intensity level (SIL) is calculated using the equation,

$$IL(\text{dB}) = 10 \times \log\left(\frac{I}{I_0}\right)$$

where:

- $IL$ is sound level intensity (dBA)
- $I$ is sound level (W)
- $I_0$ is the reference sound level, $10^{-12}$ (W)

Suppose there is a grinding machine that produces a sound intensity level of 60 dBA. The sound intensity can be calculated by:

$$I = I_0 \times 10^{\left(\frac{IL}{10}\right)} = 10^{\ 12} \times 10^{\left(\frac{60}{10}\right)} = 10^{\ 6}\ \mathrm{W}$$

If a second identical machine is turned on, the sound intensity will double, 2×10-6. Plugging this new value into the sound intensity equation yields:

$$IL = 10 \times \log\left(\frac{2 \times 10^{\ 6}}{10^{\ 12}}\right) = 63.01\ \mathrm{dBA}$$

### Determining Adequate Level of Hearing Protection

The OSHA hearing conservation standard establishes a permissible exposure limit to noise at 85 decibels (dBA). Exposures above 85 dBA require employees to wear hearing protection in the form of muffs or earplugs. Hearing protection devices have a Noise Reduction Rating provided by the manufacturer. Theoretically, wearing the device reduces the noise exposure by that number of decibels. In practice, one applies a safety factor. This calculation requires the "A-weighted" sound-level readings from a noise meter (the A-level readings are expressed as "dBA" and represent the exposure as heard by the human ear, with very high and low frequencies screened out). The calculated employee exposure wearing the hearing protection is as follows:

Estimated Exposure (dBA) = TWA (dBA) - (NRR - 7)

If C-level noise readings are available, the Noise Reduction Rating can be subtracted directly from the dBC reading to determine estimated employee exposure.

## Climate and Environmental Conditions

### Climate Conditions

According to NOAA, the **Wet Bulb Globe Temperature (WBGT)** is a measure of the heat stress in direct sunlight, which takes into account temperature, humidity, wind speed, sun angle, and cloud cover (solar radiation). It is measured with a special device that combines several climate measurements into a single temperature reading. This reading is used to calculate the ratio of work to rest workers should use to avoid heat-induced illnesses. WBGT temperature is calculated according to the following equation,

$$WBGT = 0.7T_w + 0.2T_g + 0.1T_d$$

where:

- $T_w$ is natural wet-bulb temperature
- $T_g$ is globe thermometer temperature
- $T_d$ is actual air temperature, or dry-bulb temperature.

## Fall Protection Calculations

### Minimum Safe Distance

The **minimum safe distance** for fall protection is the minimum height required for a **fall arrest system** to deploy and decelerate the fall of a worker. This distance depends on the length of the lanyard, the deployment length of the deceleration device, the height of the worker, and a safety factor. If the calculated minimum safe distance is greater than the height difference between levels, the employee will not decelerate before striking the next level.

Example:

*An employee is wearing a full-body harness and a fall arrest system attached to a d-ring in the middle of their back. The worker is 6 feet tall and the D-ring is between their shoulder blades at a height of 5 feet. The lanyard is 6 feet long and will extend 3 feet during deceleration. Calculate the minimum safe distance for the employee to fall without injury using a safety factor of 2.5 feet.*

*MSD* = minimum safe distance, *L* = length of lanyard from anchor point, *D* = deceleration distance, *H* = height of D-ring, *S* = safety factor

$$MSD = L + D + H + S$$

$$MSD = 6 + 3 + 5 + 2.5 = 16.5 \text{ feet to the next lower level}$$

# General Physics Concepts

## Newton's Laws

### Newton's First Law

Before Newton formulated his laws of mechanics, it was generally assumed that some force had to act on an object continuously in order to make the object move at a constant velocity. Newton, however, determined that unless some other force acted on the object (most notably friction or air resistance), it would continue in the direction it was pushed at the same velocity forever. In this light, a body at rest and a body in motion are not all that different, and **Newton's first law** makes little distinction. It states that a body at rest will tend to remain at rest, while a body in motion will tend to remain in motion. This phenomenon is commonly referred to as **inertia**, the tendency of a body to remain in its present state of motion. In order for the body's state of motion to change, it must be acted on by a non-zero net force. Net force is the vector sum of all forces acting on a body. If this vector sum is zero, then there is no unbalanced force, and the body will remain in its present state of motion. It is important to remember that this law only holds in inertial reference frames.

**Review Video: Newton's First Law of Motion**
Visit mometrix.com/academy and enter code: 590367

### Newton's Second Law

**Newton's second law** states that an object's acceleration is directly proportional to the net force acting on the object, and inversely proportional to the object's mass. It is generally written in equation form **F** = m**a**, where **F** is the net force acting on a body, m is the mass of the body, and **a** is its acceleration. It is important to note from this equation that since the mass is always a positive quantity, the acceleration vector is always pointed in the same direction as the net force vector. Of course, in order to apply this equation correctly, one must clearly identify the body to which it is being applied. Once this is done, we may say that **F** is the vector sum of all forces acting on that body, or the net force. This measure includes only those forces that are external to the body; any internal forces, in which one part of the body exerts force on another, are discounted. Newton's second law somewhat encapsulates his first, because it includes the principle that if no net force is acting on a body, the body will not accelerate. As was the case with his first law, Newton's second law may only be applied in inertial reference frames.

**Review Video: Newton's Second Law of Motion**
Visit mometrix.com/academy and enter code: 737975

### Newton's Third Law

**Newton's third law** of motion is quite simple: for every force, there is an equal and opposite force. When a hammer strikes a nail, the nail hits the hammer just as hard. If we consider two objects, *A* and *B*, then we may express any contact between these two bodies with the equation $F_{AB} = -F_{BA}$. It is important to note in this kind of equation that the order of the subscripts denotes which body is exerting the force. Although the two forces are often referred to as the *action* and *reaction* forces, in physics there is really no such thing. There is no implication of cause and effect in the equation for Newton's third law. At first glance, this law might seem to forbid any movement at all. We must remember, however, that these equal, opposite forces are exerted on different bodies with different masses, so they will not cancel each other out.

**Review Video: Newton's Third Law of Motion**
Visit mometrix.com/academy and enter code: 838401

## Acceleration, Velocity, Momentum

There are two types of velocity that are commonly considered in physics: average velocity and instantaneous velocity, although only the former is in the scope of this review. **Average velocity** is based on two variables: the displacement of the object, or the distance it has traveled, and the time it took to cover the distance. To calculate average velocity, use the following equation, where the subscripts *i* and *f* denote the initial and final values of the position and time:

$$v_{avg} = \frac{(x_f - x_i)}{(t_f - t_i)}$$

In other words, the average velocity is equal to the change in position divided by the change in time. This calculation will indicate the average distance that was covered per unit of time. Average velocity is a vector and will always point in the same direction as the displacement vector (since time is a scalar and always positive).

For example, if a man completes a 3.1-mile race in 18 minutes, his average velocity is:

$$v_{avg} = \frac{(3.1 \text{ miles} - 0 \text{ miles})}{\left(\left(18 \text{ min.} \times \frac{1 \text{ hour}}{60 \text{ min.}}\right) - 0\right)} = 10.33 \text{ mph}$$

**Acceleration** is the change in the velocity of an object. Like velocity, acceleration may be computed as an average or an instantaneous quantity. To calculate average acceleration, use the following equation, where the subscripts i and f denote the initial and final values of the velocity and time:

$$a_{avg} = \frac{(v_f - v_i)}{(t_f - t_i)}$$

The so-called instantaneous acceleration of an object can be found by reducing the time component to an instant, or almost zero. Acceleration is expressed in units of distance divided by time squared, such as feet per second squared.

For example, suppose a vehicle is traveling down the highway at 75 miles per hour, then enters a town and slows down to 40 miles per hour. If it takes the vehicle 10 seconds to slow down, its average acceleration in feet per second squared is:

$$(40 - 75 \text{ mph}) \times \frac{5280 \text{ feet}}{1 \text{ mile}} \times \frac{1 \text{ hour}}{3600 \text{ seconds}} = \text{-51.33 ft/s}$$

$$a_{avg} = \frac{\text{-51.33 ft/s}}{(10 \text{ seconds} - 0 \text{ seconds})} = 5.13 \text{ ft/s}^2$$

In physics, **linear momentum** can be found by multiplying the mass and velocity of a particle:

$$p = mv$$

Momentum has units of foot-pounds per second. Like velocity, momentum is a vector quantity and will always have the same direction as the velocity. Newton's second law describes momentum, stating that the rate of change of momentum is proportional to the force exerted, and is in the direction of the force.

For example, if a 54,000-pound fuel truck is driving at 30 mph, its momentum is:

$$30 \text{ mph} \times \frac{5280 \text{ ft}}{1 \text{ mile}} \times \frac{1 \text{ hour}}{3600 \text{ seconds}} = 44 \text{ ft/s}$$

$$p = 54{,}000 \text{ lb} \times 44 \text{ ft/s} = 2.77 \times 10^6 \text{ ft} \cdot \text{lb/s}$$

## Friction

**Friction** is the resistance to motion of one object moving relative to another. Imagine a book resting on a table. As it sits there, the force of its weight ($W$) is equal and opposite to the normal force ($N$). If, however, a force ($F$) were to be exerted on one side of the book, a frictional force ($f$) would arise, equal and opposite to the pushing force. This kind of frictional force is known as **static frictional force**. As the force on the book is increased, however, it will eventually accelerate in the direction it is being pushed. At this point, the frictional force opposing the pushing force will be known as **kinetic frictional force**. For the most part, kinetic frictional force is lower than static frictional force, and so the amount of force needed to maintain the movement of the book will be less than that needed to initiate movement. Static frictional force has a maximum value, however, which is expressed as the following equation, where $\mu_s$ is the coefficient of static friction, and $N$ is the magnitude of the normal force:

$$f_{s_{max}} = \mu_s N$$

If the magnitude of F should exceed the maximum value of static friction, the body will begin to move. Once the body has begun to slide, the frictional force will generally decrease. The value to which the frictional force will diminish is expressed as the following equation, where $\mu_k$ is the coefficient of kinetic friction:

$$f_k = \mu_k N$$

For example, consider a shipping crate resting on a 30-degree slope. If the crate weighs 100 lb and the coefficient of static friction between the crate and the ramp is 0.3, the maximum static friction force must be:

$$N = 100 \times \cos(30°) = 86.6 \text{ lb}$$

$$f_{s_{max}} = 0.3 \times 86.6 = 26 \text{ lb}$$

### Kinetic and Potential Energy

The **kinetic energy** of an object is the quantity of its motion related to the amount of work performed on the object. Kinetic energy can be defined by the following equation, in which $m$ is the mass of an object and $v$ is the magnitude of its velocity:

$$KE = \frac{1}{2} mv^2$$

Kinetic energy cannot be negative, since it depends on the square of velocity. Units for kinetic energy are the same as those for work: joules or foot-pounds.

**Potential energy** is the amount of energy that can be ascribed to a body or bodies based on configuration. Gravitational potential energy is the energy associated with the separation of bodies that are attracted to one another gravitationally. Any time an object is lifted, its gravitational potential energy is increased. Gravitational potential energy can be found by the equation, where $m$ is the mass of an object, $g$ is the gravitational acceleration, and $h$ is its height above a reference point, usually the ground:

$$PE = mgh$$

Another type of potential energy is elastic potential energy, which is associated with the compression or expansion of an elastic, or spring like, object.

Forces that change the state of a system by changing kinetic energy into potential energy, or vice versa, are called **conservative forces**. This name arises because these forces conserve the total amount of kinetic and potential energy. One example of a conservative force is gravity. Consider the path of a ball thrown straight up into the air. Right when it is thrown, all the energy is kinetic. At the peak of the throw, all the energy is potential. Since there is the same amount of energy in the system at all times, the kinetic energy when the ball is thrown is equal to the potential energy when it is highest in the air.

For example, if a high diver jumps off a diving board and enters the water at a speed of 50 mph, the height of the diving board can be calculated by equating his kinetic energy upon entering the water with his potential energy right before jumping.

$$50 \text{ mph} \times \frac{5280 \text{ ft}}{1 \text{ mile}} \times \frac{1 \text{ hour}}{3600 \text{ sec}} = 73.33 \text{ ft/s}$$

$$h = \frac{\frac{1}{2} v^2}{g} = \frac{\frac{1}{2} (73.33)^2}{32.17 \text{ ft/s}^2} = 83.6 \text{ ft}$$

# Financial Principles

## Time Value of Money

When money is invested in a safe banking type institution, it can accumulate or accrue **interest**. The amount of interest earned is called the **accrued amount**. The interest amount is based on the amount of the investment, the length of time it is invested, and the interest percentage rate. If the money is invested over several time cycles then the interest is calculated differently. At the end of each time cycle the interest is calculated on the increased investment amount which is known as **compounded interest**. The effective interest rate is the interest rate between compounding cycles. If the effective interest rate is calculated over a year it is known as the effective annual interest rate.

## Cash Flow and Cash Flow Diagrams

The analysis of money going in and out of an entity is **cash flow**. If the rent is due on Thursday and you are paid on Friday, you have a cash flow problem. All cash flow analysis is dependent upon the business entity of interest. A cash flow out from one business entity is a cash flow in for another entity. Paying the rent is a cash flow out for the renter but is an inflow of cash for the landlord. A **cash flow diagram** is a chart with the horizontal axis of time with money coming in as an up arrow and money going out as a down arrow. At any point in time, the sum of cash in and out can be represented by individual arrows or a single arrow with the sum. Money cash flow can be a single payment, a uniform series of equal values of money at regular time intervals, or gradient series of increasing or decreasing values of money at regular time intervals.

## Benefit Cost Analysis

One of the five common economic comparisons is the **benefit cost analysis**. Of the five economic comparison techniques, the benefit cost analysis is easily the most complicated to perform and is also most subjective in nature. In simple terms, the benefit cost analysis looks at where benefits will occur for different users and total cost to everyone. Benefit cost analysis is not normally applied to commercial projects unless they are extremely large and is normally applied to government projects. The sum of the benefits divided by the sum of the costs should be greater than one for an acceptable project. When comparing multiple projects, the highest ratio will determine the best project. The exact sum of benefits and costs are sometimes difficult to accurately determine—a benefit to one group may be a cost to another group.

## Break Even Analysis

One of the five common economic comparisons is **break even analysis**. In the simplest terms, break even analysis looks at the shortest time or minimum number of units until the project pays for itself. This analysis is sometimes known as determining the payback period. To use break even analysis, the projects must have costs and generate revenue so this is usually limited to commercial ventures and not government infrastructure projects. If a project ends before the break even or pay back occurs, then the project will be a net loss for the company. At any time after the break even occurs, the company will expect a new profit.

## Rate of Return Cost Analysis

One of the five common economic comparisons is the **rate of return cost analysis**,simply known as **RoR**. The rate of return analysis looks for the highest interest rate of competing cash flow projection scenarios. A simpler definition is how much interest would be earned if that amount of money was placed in a bank, and coincidentally that is also a litmus test for whether a project should be undertaken: Would the money have been better off sitting in a bank instead of risked on this venture? This minimum acceptable interest rate is known as the **minimum attractive rate of**

**return (MARR)** and is established by the company. Some companies use different MARR values for different projects or project lengths.

Suppose Rachel has invested $12,000 in restoring an antique car and $7,000 in Ace Shipping Company. After four years, the antique car sells for $18,000. She sells her shares in Ace Shipping for $9,500 after a year. After calculating the return on investment for both investments and adjusting for time duration, they can be compared.

$$ROI_{car} = \frac{18{,}000 - 12{,}000}{12{,}000} = 0.5$$

$$ROI_{Ace} = \frac{9{,}500 - 7{,}000}{7{,}000} = 0.357$$

Note that to get a more accurate picture of the viability of the investments, the time duration has to be taken into account. To calculate annual ROI, divide ROI by the duration of the investment.

$$Annual\ ROI_{car} = \frac{0.5}{4} = 0.125$$

$$Annual\ ROI_{Ace} = \frac{0.357}{1} = 0.357$$

## Present Worth and Annual Cost Analysis

Two of the five common economic comparisons are present worth and annual cost analysis. These two comparisons are very similar despite one being opposite signs or values. In simple terms, **present worth analysis** looks for the maximum present worth of competing scenarios. **Annual cost analysis** simply looks for the minimum Equivalent Uniform Analysis Cost (EUAC) and is sometimes referred to as annual return method or the capital recovery method. Both of these comparisons use standard discount factors to calculate the present worth or the annual cost of the respective scenarios. Both of these analyses require the projects of interest to be mutually exclusive. Both of these types of analysis are simple to apply to commercial or government projects, although present worth is rarely used for government analysis.

## Net Present Value

**Net present value (NPV)** is based on the principle that money now is worth more than money later, known as the time value of money. This is because money can be used to make more money, whether that money is supporting a business, invested in the stock market, or put it in the bank. NPV is the difference between the present values of cash inflows minus the present values of cash outflows. To calculate it, all cash flows must first be converted from future values to present values. This is accomplished by the following equation and variables:

$$PV = \frac{FV}{\left(1 + \frac{i}{n}\right)^{(nt)}}$$

- $PV$ is the present value of the money
- $FV$ is the future value of the money
- $i$ is the decimal interest rate
- $n$ is the number of times interest is compounded per year
- $t$ is the number of years

Suppose Ethan's good friend asks to borrow $1000 from him today, and repay him $1150 in two years. To determine if it is a good investment, Ethan must first calculate the present value of the sum. Assuming money can be invested elsewhere at a rate of 6% annually, the present value can be calculated:

$$PV = \frac{\$1150}{\left(1 + \frac{0.06}{1}\right)^{(1\times 2)}} = \$1023.50$$

To calculate the net present value of the investment, take the difference between the cash outflow and cash inflow: -$1000 + $1023.50 = $23.50. Thus, assuming his friend can be relied upon to pay him back, it would be a sound investment for Ethan to lend to this friend.

### LIFE CYCLE COST

While capital cost is usually very easy to compare between two different possible purchases, it is only a portion of the total costs that will occur during an asset's lifetime. **Life cycle cost analysis (LCCA)** takes into account the total cost of ownership of the asset, including acquisition costs, operating costs, maintenance costs, disposal costs, and residual value.

For example, consider the life cycle cost of a commercial kitchen mixer. Suppose the purchase price is $8,400, and it uses $30 of electricity every month. Every two years, a technician is paid $200 to service it. After 20 years, the mixer is replaced, and the residual value is $1,000. The life cycle cost of this mixer would then be

$$LCC_{mixer} = \$8{,}400 + \left(\$30 \times \frac{12\text{ mo.}}{1\text{ yr.}} \times 20\text{ yr.}\right) + (\$200 \times 9) - \$1{,}000 = \$16{,}400$$

Note that the mixer is only serviced nine times because there would be no need to service it right before replacement.

## Descriptive Statistics

### MEASURES OF CENTRAL TENDENCY

A **measure of central tendency** is a statistical value that gives a reasonable estimate for the center of a group of data. There are several different ways of describing the measure of central tendency. Each one has a unique way it is calculated, and each one gives a slightly different perspective on the data set. Whenever you give a measure of central tendency, always make sure the units are the same. If the data has different units, such as hours, minutes, and seconds, convert all the data to the same unit, and use the same unit in the measure of central tendency. If no units are given in the data, do not give units for the measure of central tendency.

#### *MEAN*

The **statistical mean** of a group of data is the same as the arithmetic average of that group. To find the mean of a set of data, first convert each value to the same units, if necessary. Then find the sum of all the values, and count the total number of data values, making sure you take into consideration each individual value. If a value appears more than once, count it more than once. Divide the sum of the values by the total number of values and apply the units, if any. Note that the mean does not have to be one of the data values in the set and may not divide evenly.

$$\text{mean} = \frac{\text{sum of the data values}}{\text{quantity of data values}}$$

For instance, the mean of the data set {88, 72, 61, 90, 97, 68, 88, 79, 86, 93, 97, 71, 80, 84, 89} would be the sum of the fifteen numbers divided by 15:

$$\frac{88 + 72 + 61 + 90 + 97 + 68 + 88 + 79 + 86 + 93 + 97 + 71 + 80 + 84 + 88}{15} = \frac{1242}{15} = 82.8$$

While the mean is relatively easy to calculate and averages are understood by most people, the mean can be very misleading if used as the sole measure of central tendency. If the data set has outliers (data values that are unusually high or unusually low compared to the rest of the data values), the mean can be very distorted, especially if the data set has a small number of values. If unusually high values are countered with unusually low values, the mean is not affected as much. For example, if five of twenty students in a class get a 100 on a test, but the other 15 students have an average of 60 on the same test, the class average would appear as 70. Whenever the mean is skewed by outliers, it is always a good idea to include the median as an alternate measure of central tendency.

A **weighted mean**, or weighted average, is a mean that accounts for the varying degree of importance of the various values in a data set; for example, grade point averages sometimes account for tests as a larger percent of a final grade and homework assignments collectively as a smaller percent of the final grade.

$$\text{weighted mean} = \frac{w_1x_1 + w_2x_2 + w_3x_3 \ldots + w_nx_n}{w_1 + w_2 + w_3 + \cdots + w_n}$$

### *MEDIAN*

The **statistical median** is the value in the middle of the set of data. To find the median, list all data values in order from smallest to largest or from largest to smallest. Any value that is repeated in the set must be listed the number of times it appears. If there are an odd number of data values, the median is the value in the middle of the list. If there is an even number of data values, the median is the arithmetic mean of the two middle values.

For example, the median of the data set {88, 72, 61, 90, 97, 68, 88, 79, 86, 93, 97, 71, 80, 84, 88} is 86 since the ordered set is {61, 68, 71, 72, 79, 80, 84, **86**, 88, 88, 88, 90, 93, 97, 97}.

The big disadvantage of using the median as a measure of central tendency is that is relies solely on a value's relative size as compared to the other values in the set. When the individual values in a set of data are evenly dispersed, the median can be an accurate tool. However, if there is a group of rather large values or a group of rather small values that are not offset by a different group of values, the information that can be inferred from the median may not be accurate because the distribution of values is skewed.

### *MODE*

The **statistical mode** is the data value that occurs the greatest number of times in the data set. It is possible to have exactly one mode, more than one mode, or no mode. To find the mode of a set of data, arrange the data like you do to find the median (all values in order, listing all multiples of data values). Count the number of times each value appears in the data set. If all values appear an equal number of times, there is no mode. If one value appears more than any other value, that value is the mode. If two or more values appear the same number of times, but there are other values that appear fewer times and no values that appear more times, all of those values are the modes.

For example, the mode of the data set {**88**, 72, 61, 90, 97, 68, **88**, 79, 86, 93, 97, 71, 80, 84, **88**} is 88.

The main disadvantage of the mode is that the values of the other data in the set have no bearing on the mode. The mode may be the largest value, the smallest value, or a value anywhere in between in the set. The mode only tells which value or values, if any, occurred the greatest number of times. It does not give any suggestions about the remaining values in the set.

**Review Video: Mean, Median, and Mode**
Visit mometrix.com/academy and enter code: 286207

## Measures of Dispersion

A **measure of dispersion** is a single value that helps to interpret the measure of central tendency by providing more information about how the data values in the set are distributed about the measure of central tendency. The measure of dispersion helps to eliminate or reduce the disadvantages of using the mean, median, or mode as a single measure of central tendency and gives a more accurate picture of the dataset as a whole. To have a measure of dispersion, you must know or calculate the range, standard deviation, or variance of the data set.

### *Range*

The **range** of a set of data is the difference between the greatest and lowest values of the data in the set. To calculate the range, you must first make sure the units for all data values are the same, and then identify the greatest and lowest values. If there are multiple data values that are equal for the highest or lowest, just use one of the values in the formula. Write the answer with the same units as the data values you used to do the calculations.

### *Standard Deviation*

**Standard deviation** is a measure of dispersion that compares all the data values in the set to the mean of the set to give a more accurate picture. To find the standard deviation of a sample, use the following formula:

$$s = \sqrt{\frac{\sum_{i=1}^{n}(x_i - \bar{x})^2}{n - 1}}$$

Note that $s$ is the standard deviation of a sample, $x$ represents the individual values in the data set, $\bar{x}$ is the mean of the data values in the set, and $n$ is the number of data values in the set. The higher the value of the standard deviation is, the greater the variance of the data values from the mean. The units associated with the standard deviation are the same as the units of the data values.

**Review Video: Standard Deviation**
Visit mometrix.com/academy and enter code: 419469

### *Variance*

The **variance** of a sample, or just variance, is the square of the standard deviation of that sample. While the mean of a set of data gives the average of the set and gives information about where a specific data value lies in relation to the average, the variance of the sample gives information about the degree to which the data values are spread out and tell you how close an individual value is to the average compared to the other values. The units associated with variance are the same as the units of the data values squared.

### *Outliers*

An **outlier** is an extremely high or extremely low value in the data set. It may be the result of measurement error, in which case, the outlier is not a valid member of the data set. However, it may also be a valid member of the distribution. Unless a measurement error is identified, the experimenter cannot know for certain if an outlier is or is not a member of the distribution. There are arbitrary methods that can be employed to designate an extreme value as an outlier. One method designates an outlier (or possible outlier) to be any value less than $Q_1 - 1.5(IQR)$ or any value greater than $Q_3 + 1.5(IQR)$.

## Probability

**Probability** is the likelihood of a certain outcome occurring for a given event. An **event** is any situation that produces a result. It could be something as simple as flipping a coin or as complex as launching a rocket. Determining the probability of an outcome for an event can be equally simple or complex. As such, there are specific terms used in the study of probability that need to be understood:

- **Compound event**: an event that involves two or more independent events (rolling a pair of dice and randomly selecting a playing card)
- **Desired outcome** (or **success**): an outcome that meets a particular set of criteria (a roll of 1 or 2 if we are looking for numbers less than 3)
- **Independent events**: two or more events whose outcomes do not affect one another (two coins tossed at the same time)
- **Dependent events**: two or more events whose outcomes affect one another (two cards drawn consecutively from the same deck)
- **Certain outcome**: the probability of a particular outcome is 100% or 1
- **Impossible outcome**: the probability of a particular outcome is 0% or 0
- **Mutually exclusive outcomes**: two or more outcomes whose criteria cannot all be satisfied in a single event (a coin coming up heads and tails on the same toss)
- **Random variable**: refers to all possible outcomes of a single event which may be discrete or continuous

**Review Video: Intro to Probability**
Visit mometrix.com/academy and enter code: 212374

### *Theoretical and Experimental Probability*

**Theoretical probability** can usually be determined without actually performing the event. The likelihood of an outcome occurring, or the probability of an outcome occurring, is given by the formula:

$$P(A) = \frac{\text{Number of acceptable outcomes}}{\text{Number of possible outcomes}}$$

Note that $P(A)$ is the probability of an outcome $A$ occurring, and each outcome is just as likely to occur as any other outcome. If each outcome has the same probability of occurring as every other possible outcome, the outcomes are said to be equally likely to occur. The total number of acceptable outcomes must be less than or equal to the total number of possible outcomes. If the two are equal, then the outcome is certain to occur and the probability is 1. If the number of acceptable outcomes is zero, then the outcome is impossible and the probability is 0. For example, if there are 20 marbles in a bag and 5 are red, then the theoretical probability of randomly selecting a red marble is 5 out of 20, ($\frac{5}{20} = \frac{1}{4}$, 0.25, or 25%).

If the theoretical probability is unknown or too complicated to calculate, it can be estimated by an experimental probability. **Experimental probability**, also called empirical probability, is an estimate of the likelihood of a certain outcome based on repeated experiments or collected data. In other words, while theoretical probability is based on what *should* happen, experimental probability is based on what *has* happened. Experimental probability is calculated in the same way as theoretical, except that actual outcomes are used instead of possible outcomes. The more experiments performed or datapoints gathered, the better the estimate should be.

Theoretical and experimental probability do not always line up with one another. Theoretical probability says that out of 20 coin-tosses, 10 should be heads. However, if we were actually to toss 20 coins, we might record just 5 heads. This doesn't mean that our theoretical probability is incorrect; it just means that this particular experiment had results that were different from what was predicted. A practical application of empirical probability is the insurance industry. There are no set functions that define lifespan, health, or safety. Insurance companies look at factors from hundreds of thousands of individuals to find patterns that they then use to set the formulas for insurance premiums.

**Review Video: Empirical Probability**
Visit mometrix.com/academy and enter code: 513468

### ADDITION RULE

The **addition rule** for probability is used for finding the probability of a compound event. Use the formula $P(A \text{ or } B) = P(A) + P(B) - P(A \text{ and } B)$, where $P(A \text{ and } B)$ is the probability of both events occurring to find the probability of a compound event. The probability of both events occurring at the same time must be subtracted to eliminate any overlap in the first two probabilities.

### COMPLEMENT OF AN EVENT

Sometimes it may be easier to calculate the possibility of something not happening, or the **complement of an event**. Represented by the symbol $\bar{A}$, the complement of $A$ is the probability that event $A$ does not happen. When you know the probability of event $A$ occurring, you can use the formula $P(\bar{A}) = 1 - P(A)$, where $P(\bar{A})$ is the probability of event $A$ not occurring, and $P(A)$ is the probability of event $A$ occurring.

### MULTIPLICATION RULE

The **multiplication rule** can be used to find the probability of two independent events occurring using the formula $P(A \text{ and } B) = P(A) \times P(B)$, where $P(A \text{ and } B)$ or $P(A \cap B)$ the probability of two independent events occurring, $P(A)$ is the probability of the first event occurring, and $P(B)$ is the probability of the second event occurring.

The multiplication rule can also be used to find the probability of two dependent events occurring using the formula $P(A \cap B) = P(A) \times P(B|A)$, where $P(A \cap B)$ is the probability of two dependent events occurring and $P(B|A)$ is the probability of the second event occurring after the first event has already occurred. Before using the multiplication rule, you MUST first determine whether the two events are dependent or independent.

Use a **combination of the multiplication** rule and the rule of complements to find the probability that at least one outcome of the element will occur. This is given by the general formula $P(\text{at least one event occurring}) = 1 - P(\text{no outcomes occurring})$. For example, to find the probability that at least one even number will show when a pair of dice is rolled, find the probability that two odd numbers will be rolled (no even numbers) and subtract from one. You can always use a tree diagram or make a chart to list the possible outcomes when the sample space is small, such as in the dice-rolling example, but in most cases it will be much faster to use the multiplication and complement formulas.

**Review Video: Multiplication Rule**
Visit mometrix.com/academy and enter code: 782598

### Permutations and Combinations

When trying to calculate the probability of an event using the $\frac{\text{desired outcomes}}{\text{total outcomes}}$ formula, you may frequently find that there are too many outcomes to individually count them. **Permutation** and **combination formulas** offer a shortcut to counting outcomes. A permutation is an arrangement of a specific number of a set of objects in a specific order. The number of **permutations** of *r* items given a set of *n* items can be calculated as ${}_nP_r = \frac{n!}{(n-r)!}$. Combinations are similar to permutations, except there are no restrictions regarding the order of the elements. While ABC is considered a different permutation than BCA, ABC and BCA are considered the same combination. The number of **combinations** of *r* items given a set of *n* items can be calculated as ${}_nC_r = \frac{n!}{r!(n-r)!}$ or ${}_nC_r = \frac{{}_nP_r}{r!}$.

Suppose you want to calculate how many different 5-card hands can be drawn from a deck of 52 cards. This is a combination since the order of the cards in a hand does not matter. There are 52 cards available, and 5 to be selected. Thus, the number of different hands is ${}_{52}C_5 = \frac{52!}{5!\times 47!} =$ 2,598,960.

**Review Video: Probability - Permutation and Combination**
Visit mometrix.com/academy and enter code: 907664

## Lagging Indicators

**Lagging indicators** in occupational health and safety are those metrics that are gathered after an event such as a workplace injury has occurred. They are a useful indicator of the effects of incidents and they are helpful, but they do not provide a proactive opportunity to prevent such incidents. Examples of lagging indicators are the number of lost workdays, the number of days an employee is on restricted duty, the cost incurred for medical visits, and the number of recordable injuries. While it is essential to track lagging indicators and target improved performance over time, they do not provide a snapshot of future performance. Lagging indicators are often used to assess actual regulatory compliance and are essential for reporting purposes.

### Calculating Incidence Rates

The **Total Case Incident Rate (TCIR)** is a health and safety metric that calculates the total number of OSHA recordable injury cases in a year and is weighted by the number of total hours worked by employees at the organization during the year to allow comparison between companies in similar industries. The formula to calculate the TCIR is as follows:

$$TCIR = \frac{Number\ of\ recordable\ injuries\ in\ calendar\ year\ \times\ 200{,}000}{Total\ hours\ worked}$$

The **Days Away, Restricted Duty, or Transfer (DART)** is a measure of the number of injury cases that involved days off work, on restricted duty, or transferred to another job. Note that the calculation uses the number of cases, not the total number of days. The calculation is as follows:

$$DART = \frac{Number\ of\ cases\ with\ days\ away, job\ restriction, or\ transfer\ \times\ 200{,}000}{Total\ hours\ worked}$$

Ideally, the DART is lower than the TCIR. The 200,000 hours figure refers to the number of hours worked in a year by a company with 100 full-time employees.

### Direct Costs of Incidents

The **direct costs of an incident** are actual monetary costs attributable to the incident. In the case of an injury, the direct costs are the medical bills for the treatment of the injured worker, the money paid to a worker as worker's compensation payments during lost work time, the cost of medications, and the cost of transportation to and from the clinic to attend doctors' appointments. These costs can be readily identified by collecting the invoices from these various services and totaling them. However, in the case of an injury, the direct costs are usually borne by the insurance company and are not readily apparent to the organization.

## Leading Indicators

A **leading indicator** is an objective measure that is used to assess actions taken proactively to improve organizational performance. This is a useful measure in evaluating the impact of an occupational health and safety management system because it measures what the organization is doing to prevent injuries and improve effectiveness in a proactive manner instead of reacting to incidents. Examples of leading indicators include the number of training courses given, the number of safety meetings held, the number of behavioral safety observations completed, the number of area safety inspections completed, and the number of near miss root cause analyses completed. These leading indicators can be used to assess overall proactive performance, and thorough implementation of the leading indicator activities can strengthen the occupational health and safety program.

### Near Miss Reporting

A **near miss** is an incident that comes very close to being an occupational injury but does not result in injury. Examples include having something fall off a highly stacked pallet of material and nearly hit a worker standing nearby, or two forklifts backing up toward each other and nearly crashing into each other, or an employee using a box cutter that slips and cuts his glove but misses cutting his hand. Diligent monitoring of near misses and responding to them as if they were injury incidents by completing **root cause analyses** and developing **action plans** to prevent recurrences can put into place the systems, procedures, and practices that create a safe work environment that responds to incidents before they occur.

### Inspection Frequency and Response

Routinely scheduled inspections are an integral part of an effective occupational health and safety system. The **frequency of inspections** must be aligned with the degree of risk posed by the operation, in conjunction with regulatory requirements. Inspections that are conducted too infrequently are a sign of a lax occupational health and safety management system that potentially allows noncompliance or nonconformance to exist without correction between inspections. Moreover, the timeliness and attention paid to correcting issues identified in inspections is an indicator of the effectiveness of the health and safety system. Companies that recognize the importance of timely corrective action will realize the benefits of maintaining a safe work environment that promptly **responds** to issues identified.

# Safety Management Systems

## Hierarchy of Hazard Controls

### Basic Safety Through Design

The hierarchy of controls refers to the preferred methods of controlling health and safety hazards. In order of most preferred first, these include the following:

1. **Elimination** is completely eliminating the hazard through process changes.
2. **Substitution** is substituting a lesser hazard, for example, changing from an organic solvent parts washer to an aqueous parts washer.
3. **Engineering controls** are physical modifications to a work station that serve to reduce or eliminate hazards. An example of engineering controls is to install duct work and exhaust ventilation to remove fumes from the breathing zone of the worker.
4. **Administrative control** refers to worker management as a means of controlling the hazards. An example of administrative controls is job rotation to limit an employee's exposure to repetitive motion.
5. **Personal protective equipment (PPE)** is garments or auxiliary equipment used to protect workers.

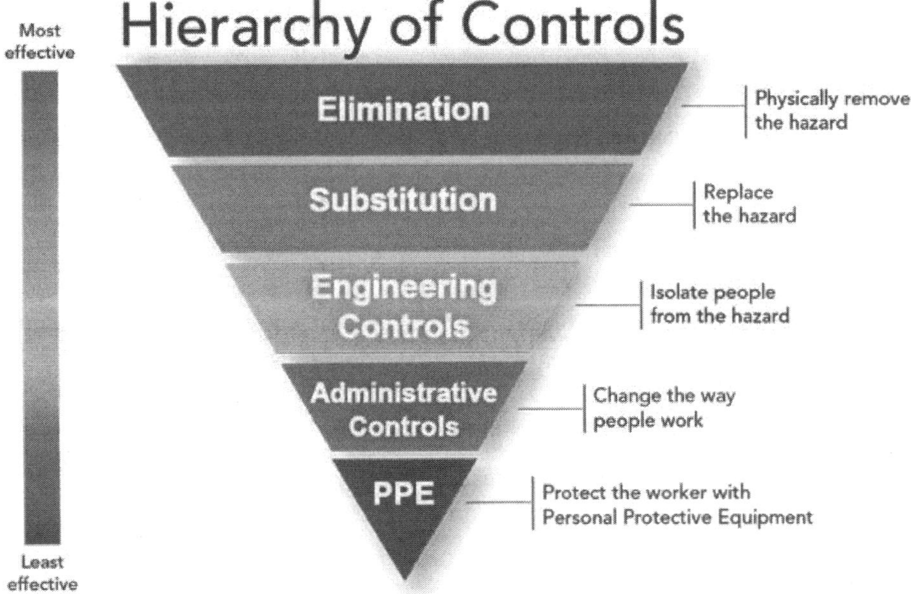


### *Elimination of Hazards and Substitution to Mitigate Hazards*

Elimination of hazards refers to making process changes that completely eliminate the hazard rather than developing a work-around or protective device. An example would be changing a process to eliminate solvent use. Another example of elimination of hazards would be to change the way parts are delivered to an assembly line that eliminates the need to lift heavy boxes. Substitution is another mechanism to mitigate hazards. Examples of substitution include substituting chemicals in a process that are of lower toxicity than the original chemical or substituting a tool that requires awkward, forceful grasping with one that uses a more ergonomically favorable grip.

### *Engineering Controls*

Engineering or physical controls to mitigate occupational hazards are changes in the way the process is designed or the physical controls on the process that make it unlikely or impossible to be injured by the hazard. Examples of engineering controls include:

- Installing ventilation systems to remove hazardous vapors from the worker's breathing zone, eliminating chemical or hazardous dust exposure
- Installing permanent access platforms with proper guardrails to provide elevated machinery access that will eliminate the hazard of using an aerial lift or ladder to access at heights
- Installing a switch on an electrical testing device or press brake that requires two hands to activate it, eliminating the possibility of inserting one's hands into the point of operation while it is operational
- Providing machine guarding to protect from pinch points and gears
- Constructing barriers to prevent entry into confined spaces

### *Administrative Controls & PPE*

Work practice controls or administrative controls seek to control risk by policies and procedures rather than physical barriers. Examples of work practice controls are as follows: implementing a policy that any lifting of objects more than fifty pounds requires two people or instructing an employee operating a grinder to always wear a face shield during the grinding. Face shields are considered PPE (personal protective equiment); examples of other PPE include respirators, gloves, Tyvek suits, welding hoods, and steel-toed boots, and it is. often uncomfortable to wear.Clearly, work practice controls and PPE are potentially not as effective as the physical controls as they rely on employees following instructions and policies, whereas physical controls do not present the option to circumvent the control and be exposed to the risk.

## Risk Transfer

**Risk** can have different meanings in different industries. In the financial sector, it refers to the probability of losing money in an investment. In the hospital setting, risk evaluates the potential of an error that can negatively impact a patient's safety. In an occupational setting, risk refers to the probability of an employee getting injured while performing a task as well as how severe the injury would be. Risk can also evaluate the fiscal loss due to accidents, both to property and to employees.

Quantitative calculations for risk typically require numeric values for **probability**, **severity**, and **frequency** to arrive at a final statement of risk. Expressed as a formula, $R = p \times f \times s$. Values for probability, frequency, and severity must be determined in an objective fashion so that the result of the calculation provides meaningful guidance for management. For example, values must be established such that the resultant value for a cut requiring stitches and a fatality have widely varying values. The last element is to determine ranks (e.g., High/Medium/Low, Danger/Caution/Warning) so that, when evaluated side-by-side, an action plan that is both economically feasible and effective at protecting employee health and safety can be created.

### Classes of Risk Assessment

**Risk**, the probability of a negative outcome for a situation or process, can be identified by informal or formal methods. The desired outcome of any **risk assessment** method is to identify, evaluate, and estimate the level of harm that may arise from an activity and to provide guidance on preventing the negative outcomes from happening. Additionally, once the level of risk is determined, the amount of perceived risk is compared to benchmarks or criteria to determine if the task should proceed or if other actions need to be taken.

**Informal methods** of risk assessment typically rely on the experience of those performing the job. The extent of the analysis can be an individual working safely due to their personal knowledge of the process they are performing. In other settings, it could simply consist of reminders from a supervisor during a "tailgate" briefing based on their experience. The reliability of such a method is dependent on the individual experiences of those involved.

Numerous **formal risk assessment** methodologies exist, such as HAZOP, FMEA, and FTA. Some of these methods can be used in a **predictive** manner, while others are designed for post-incident investigation. These methods typically rely on groups of stakeholders, with each bringing their own knowledge and experience. Methods can be **subjective** or **objective** and some can be supplemented to provide **quantitative** results. Some formal methods will also result in a ranking or prioritization that can give management guidance on how to effectively deploy resources.

### Methods of Managing Risk

**Risk transfer** is when the degree of potential loss is known or unknown and is no longer managed by the primary entity. Risk can be transferred by hiring subcontractors to conduct the work, purchasing insurance, or by including contractual language such as indemnification.

**Risk control** is when the degree of potential loss is known and measures are put in place to keep the risk at an established threshold. Control methods can include contractual language, such as establishing parameters for a project or by environmental, physical, or chemical hazard control methods, such as engineering, administrative, and personal protective equipment methods.

**Risk acceptance** is when the degree of potential loss is known and is below the predetermined acceptable threshold established by management. Risk can never be completely eliminated—the goal is to reduce it to the lowest level possible while still considering economic, personnel, and industry standards.

## Management of Change

### Management of Change (MOC) Systems

A **Management of Change (MOC)** system is a documented process to alter work flows or standard operating procedures. Proper use of an MOC system provides every department an opportunity to review and comment on proposed changes and provides a verifiable and auditable trail of documentation of process changes and approvals. The most important elements of the documented MOC process are the origination, the changes to any written documents, the complete scope of affected departments, and approvals of the change. An example is a process change that requires input from the production manager, the quality manager, and the environmental manager. The MOC process is started, and each department manager in turn can review the change and recommend alterations. Ancillary documents or training programs that are affected by the change can then be considered and documented, with these documents attached to verify that they were completed.

# Hazard and Risk Analysis Methods

## Preliminary Hazard Analysis (PHA)

**Preliminary hazard analysis (PHA)** is a method to identify, describe, and rank major hazards of a process. It is typically applied in the early stages of process development, but it has also been adapted for broader applications. A task or portion of the process is evaluated for hazards by identifying the number of employees exposed, the probability of occurrence, and severity of the injury or loss. The output is typically a code or numerical value that allows for hazards to be ranked by impact. PHA has an advantage in that it can be done in a relatively short period of time if the team is experienced in the process.

## Sub-System Hazard Analysis (SSHA)

The **sub-system hazard analysis (SSHA)** method examines subsystems within a process to identify how normal performance, degradation, failure, unintended function, or inadvertent function (proper function but at the wrong time or place) can create hazardous conditions.

Typically done in the design phase of a process, this method is used to address these potential outcomes prior to implementation. Remediation can include redesign to eliminate or minimize the hazard, incorporation of safety devices, or identification of procedures to address the hazard.

In this method, a process or task is broken down into components or sub-systems and related hazards are identified. Each hazard is classified by its **severity** and **likelihood**. Hazards are ranked by their **overall risk,** which is the severity multiplied by likelihood. The design of the sub-system is then evaluated to determine if the hazard can be eliminated, controls or warnings installed, or whether a procedure can be developed to eliminate or minimize the hazard. These controls are then incorporated into the final design of the system.

## Hazard And Operability (HAZOP)

A **hazard and operability (HAZOP)** risk assessment study is a systematic brainstorming process to identify hazards or process failures before they occur. The tool is a **bottom-up** approach wherein subject matter experts are relied upon to provide management with potential outcomes of any deviation. This system is best suited for identifying the impact of human performance on the system. The system has a difficult time evaluating the interaction of different process steps and does not provide management with prioritization. This system relies on an established list of **guide words** to assist the team in identifying potential deviations (e.g., *less, more, before, after, early, late,* etc.).

## Failure Modes Effects Analysis (FMEA)

**Failure modes effects analysis (FMEA)** is a step-by-step, bottom-up evaluation of all possible failures in a system and what effect each would have on the process. A system or process is divided into functions and each function is evaluated for how all possible failures could happen (mode). A failure can be an error or a defect in the final product. FMEA uses a **cross-functional team** to identify and prioritize a failure based on the impact of its consequence, the frequency, and how easily it can be detected. Consequences are evaluated for their impact on the system, subsystems, products, services, and customer experience. The goal of FMEA is to reduce or eliminate failures, starting with the most impactful. This process can be used during the design phase to prevent failures and can also be used once the process is implemented to control failures. FMEA can also be implemented as a continual improvement tool during the life cycle of the process.

## Fault Tree Analysis (FTA)

**Fault tree analysis (FTA)** is a diagrammatic, top-down tool used to identify contributing factors to a failure. The process starts with the failure or negative consequence listed at the top of a diagram. Each entry underneath the consequence is an **event** that leads to the ultimate failure. Events are related by **gates**, with the most common two gates being "and" and "or." This tool is used to identify which basic, minor events may have been overlooked that contributed to a failure to prevent recurrence. If probabilities can be associated with the contributing events, the system can provide a quantitative result and provide direction for resource allocation. The strength of this method lies in its ability to identify combinations of failures that led to the incident.

## Fishbone Diagrams

A **fishbone diagram** (also known as a **cause/effect diagram** or an **Ishikawa diagram**) is a visual technique designed to identify all contributing factors to a failure or negative event. Originally developed as a quality control tool, it can also be applied to determining the **root cause** of a system failure. A failure or negative consequence is identified and placed on one end of a horizontal line. Next, general contributing factors are identified (e.g., people, equipment, systems, materials, etc.) and written at the end of diagonal lines attached to the central line, thus resembling the bones of a fish. Potential causes of a failure for each factor are brainstormed and recoded as branches of the factor line. Likely causes can then be identified from the potential causes and can be addressed to prevent similar failures.

## What-If/Checklist Analysis

A **what-if/checklist analysis** combines a "what-if" analysis with a checklist process to produce a failure evaluation tool that is more robust than either of the two would be on their own.

**What-if** is a brainstorming technique that is used to identify events and their potential outcomes that could impact a process. A **team leader** guides the group through the process to keep the team within the confines of the process being evaluated. The phrase "what if…" is used to identify potential negative events. Once events have been identified, the team assesses each one for the likely source of errors and whether the result has an acceptable level of risk. For those events deemed unacceptable, **corrective actions** are identified and implemented before the event can occur. This process is limited in that only events that are considered can be evaluated and has a high level of subjectivity.

A **checklist analysis** relies on published standards, codes, or industry practices to determine whether a process meets all the criteria. Responses can be "yes," "no," or "not applicable." This method relies on a walk-through method to verify the existence of necessary controls or processes.

The **what-if/checklist** combination uses the brainstorming process to identify controls necessary to address the failures anticipated by the group.

## Change Analysis

Change within an organization, be it a process or policy, can result in altering the existing risk level in an organization. Thus, any proposed change should be analyzed for its impact on the process or organization and whether the resultant risk level is still acceptable to management.

Aspects to be evaluated should include the difference in the organization both before and after the change is implemented, the financial impact of the change, any safety impacts of the change, and who, both inside and outside of the organization, will be impacted by the change and how. The assessment should also identify the needed training, personnel, equipment, or program modifications, as well as the associated costs necessary to reach the new operational state.

### Energy Trace And Barrier Analysis (ETBA)

**Energy trace and barrier analysis (ETBA)** is a qualitative method that identifies potential hazards by tracing **energy flow** through a system or process, evaluating any point where energy enters a system, how the energy interacts with the system, and where the energy exits the system. In this model, a **mishap** is identified by an undesired transfer of energy to a target. A **target** can be a person, process, or property that receives the energy. If the energy transferred has an unwanted result, a **barrier** or control must be identified. A barrier must either contain or direct the hazardous energy to avoid the target or reduce the impact. Barriers can include physical (engineering controls) and procedural (administrative controls) means. ETBA is often a component of a management oversight risk tree (MORT) risk assessment.

### Systematic Cause Analysis Technique (SCAT)

**Systematic cause analysis technique (SCAT)** is a post-incident technique that is used to quickly identify the root cause of accidents and near misses. The intent is to determine the **system failures** that need to be corrected to prevent similar losses, damage, or injuries in the future. The foundational theory of SCAT is that all accidents have the same basic causes and that all causes are mainly due to **management system** inadequacy.

Utilizing a chart, the incident is analyzed sequentially by way of a domino-effect back to the root cause. Starting with the incident, the team first classifies the type of event and then identifies the **immediate cause** (sub-standard acts or conditions that allowed the event to occur). Continuing along the chart, the team next identifies **basic causes** (personal or system factors) which ultimately lead to the control areas that resulted in the incident, such as inadequate programs, standards, or compliance that management can address. The chart utilizes **standardized event and cause descriptions** so that the tool is broadly applicable to most incidents or near misses.

## Process Safety Management

### Basic Concepts of Process Safety Management

OSHA's Process Safety Management regulation (29 CFR 1910.119) has several required subparts that must be completed and documented, as follows:

**Process Hazard Analysis:** The facility must define an appropriate process hazard analysis technique that is suitable for the process at hand and must engage an individual trained in the PHA technique to assist in evaluating all hazardous processes. Examples of appropriate PHA techniques to be used are *what-if*, *failure mode effects analysis*, or *fault tree analysis*.

**Operating Procedures:** All processes subject to PSM must have written and evaluated operating procedures. These must be communicated to all personnel involved in the process to ensure proper operating procedures in order to prevent fires, explosions, releases, etc.

**Training**: All employees that work with and around the process must be trained in the operating procedures and the emergency response procedures associated with the process. This training must cover the results of the process hazard analysis and must prepare employees to react to catastrophic failure of the process.

**Contractors**: All contractors that will work on-site where PSM-applicable processes are conducted must receive training in the process hazards and emergency response procedures. All contractors must adhere to all site-specific safety procedures.

**Pre-Startup Safety Reviews:** A standard procedure and checklist must be developed. There must also be a formal pre-startup safety review conducted before each PSM process is restarted after a period of inactivity. The purpose of this is to review that all equipment repairs have been completed, that all systems are returned to the 'ready' state, that all employees involved in the process have received the proper training, and that all emergency systems are operational.

**Mechanical Integrity**: A PSM regulation that requires all pressure vessels, tanks, piping, relief valves, emergency shutdown equipment, controls, and pumps undergo regular inspection and testing according to generally accepted engineering principles or according to manufacturer recommendations.

**Hot Work Permit**: A PSM regulation that requires a formal hot work permit be issued for any hot work conducted on a PSM-covered process. This includes any welding or torch cutting. The fire prevention and detection provisions of the hot work permit must be in place before the work is conducted, and the employees must be trained in its use.

**Management of Change**: A PSM regulation that contains specific provisions requiring use of a documented Management of Change procedure. This requires review and approval of any change to the process by all departments affected by any proposed change, including engineering, maintenance, operations, health and safety, and quality.

**Emergency Planning and Response**: A PSM regulation that requires documented planning for emergencies covering the entire plant's operations. Local officials must be informed of the plan in order to coordinate response. Drills must be conducted to ensure employees are aware of their duties in an emergency situation. The plan must include a release of hazardous chemicals response.

## Fleet Safety Principles

**Fleet safety** is comprised of the policies and procedures implemented by management to protect employees and vehicles in a commercial fleet. A fleet safety program should address the following elements:

1. **Identify** all drivers: Evaluate all jobs and determine everyone who will be driving company vehicles as part of their work duties.
2. **Express** management's commitment to fleet safety.
3. Insert a robust **hiring process** for drivers, including background checks.
4. **Train** all drivers on safe driving habits and on any specialized equipment, such as forklifts.
5. Institute a method of continual or periodic **monitoring** driving habits.
6. **Manage accidents** immediately by having procedures in place for responding to and investigating all incidents and near misses.
7. Have written policies and procedures.
8. Institute a vehicle **inspection and maintenance** program.

Safe driving behavior starts before an employee gets behind the wheel. **Training** on defensive driving behavior, both initially and on a recurring basis, provide the employee with management's expectations before they drive a company vehicle. **Testing** employees after they have been trained and periodically during their employment is one method to **evaluate** their knowledge of safe driving behavior.

**Continuous monitoring** of driver behavior is an essential element of any fleet safety program. Ride-along evaluations, public hotline numbers, accident investigations, and onboard computer monitoring systems (**telematic systems**) can provide feedback on driver behavior and adherence to policies. Management can review the data generated from these methods to evaluate the continued application of safe driving behavior. Deficiencies can be identified and addressed, preferably before an employee-involved accident.

### Defensive Driving

**Defensive driving** is when a driver uses strategies to minimize risk in order to avoid accidents. The goal of defensive driving is to predictively identify potential hazards and determine a way to avoid them. Once the hazard is identified and the avoidance strategy is determined, the driver then acts decisively and immediately to avoid the hazard.

Defensive driving strategies include avoiding distracted driving, yielding the right of way, using appropriate following distances, avoiding emotional driving, and driving within the speed limit. Other methods include pre-driving checks, avoiding substances and medications that interfere with driving, using indicator lights, obeying all traffic laws, and regular vehicle maintenance.

### Distracted Driving

Driving is a process wherein a person must process multiple streams of information simultaneously. The National Highway Traffic Safety Administration (NHTSA) defines **distracted driving** as any activity that diverts the driver's attention away from the primary task of driving. Whenever a person attempts to perform another task in addition to driving, such as eating or communicating on a mobile device, they are being distracted. Some studies have shown that drivers distracted by texting perform equivalent to an individual with a blood alcohol level of 0.08.

**Distracted driving** is any time when a driver does not apply all of their attention to the driving task. Distractions can be **mental** (daydreaming), **physical** (adjusting the AC), or **visual** (looking at a text message). Distractions can lead to accidents resulting in employee injuries and financial losses. In today's connected world, drivers often receive directions, updates, or changes in real time when they are behind the wheel.

Organizations can reduce losses from distracted driving through **training** and **policies**. Initial and recurring training on defensive driving strategies can reduce the chance of accidents. Policies that prohibit employees from answering calls or texts while driving, setting GPS before starting the vehicle, and scheduling stops to communicate with dispatch can reduce the distractions for the driver.

## Hazard Communication and Globally Harmonized System

### The Globally Harmonized System of Classification and Labeling of Chemicals (GHS)

Hazard communication refers to the Occupational Safety and Health Administration (OSHA) Hazard Communication Standard found in 29 CFR 1910.1200. The Hazard Communication Standard governs the requirements to notify workers of chemical hazards faced at work and to provide information on protection from hazards. GHS refers to an international standard developed by the United Nations to guide hazardous chemical labeling, warning systems, and safety data sheets. The

GHS was developed to standardize hazard warning terminology, pictograms, and safety data sheets worldwide so that international commerce could be improved and language barriers overcome. The OSHA Hazard Communication Standard has recently been updated to include the requirements of the GHS. As of 2015, all workplaces in the United States are required to have safety data sheets available on site that conform to the GHS system and to use these in their notification and training programs.

### *SDS (Safety Data Sheets)*

**Safety Data Sheets** (SDS, formerly Material Safety Data Sheets, MSDS) provide information on the physical and chemical properties of a substance as well as potential health and environmental concerns. OSHA requires that all chemicals be labeled appropriately and that SDS be readily available in the workplace. The hazard communication standard also requires employees to be trained, and for the employer to maintain records of the training given. The format for SDS includes sixteen sections. The required sections are as follows:

- **I:** Identification
- **II:** Hazard Identification
- **III:** Composition/Information on Ingredients
- **IV:** First Aid Measures
- **V:** Firefighting Measures
- **VI:** Accidental Release Measures
- **VII:** Handling/Storage Requirements
- **VIII:** Physical/Chemical Properties
- **IX:** Exposure Controls/Personal Protection
- **X:** Stability/Reactivity
- **XI:** Toxicological Information
- **XII:** Ecological Information
- **XIII:** Disposal Considerations
- **XIV:** Transportation Information
- **XV:** Regulatory Information
- **XVI:** Other Information

SDS provide a number of indicators for possible health threats of a particular chemical. They are required to provide all known information regarding **carcinogenicity** of a substance (known or potential cancer-causing risks). Carcinogenic risks are published in the National Toxicology Program report (NTP), the International Agency for Research on Cancer (IACR), and Occupation Safety and Health Administration (OSHA). Toxicity levels are indicated by numbers called the $LD_{50}$ and the $LC_{50}$. $LD_{50}$ refers to the dose at which 50% of the test subjects were killed. $LC_{50}$ is the lethal concentration at which 50% of test subjects were killed. Dosages are typically normalized to include the mass of the possible toxin divided by the mass of the test subject. $LD_{50}$ values may also include descriptors that indicate the mode of administration of the dose (intravenously or orally) and the timeframe for death after administration. Limits for exposure to a particular chemical are also provided. These can be measured as the OSHA permissible exposure limit (PEL) and/or the Threshold Limit Values (TLV), which are published by the American Conference of Governmental Industrial Hygienists (ACGIH).

SDS often recommend the usage of chemical protective clothing (CPC). Protective eye goggles with splash guards and air vents should be used when handling chemicals. Face shields should be used when working with large quantities of a substance and are most effective when used in conjunction with safety goggles. If the mode of possible hazard is through contact and/or absorption on skin, appropriate gloves should be worn. Gloves are chosen based upon their permeability to and reactivity with the chemical in use. Personal respiratory equipment may be indicated if fume hoods do not provide adequate ventilation of fumes or airborne particulates. Body protection depends on the level of protection needed and ranges from rubberized aprons to full suits that are evaluated for their permeability and leak protection. Closed-toed protective shoes should always be used when working with chemicals.

### Requirements for Labels

The term *label* under the GHS of Classification and Labeling of Chemicals refers to the label on the container. Under GHS, it's required to contain certain elements; these requirements apply whether the label is affixed by the manufacturer or whether the chemical is placed into a smaller, secondary container in the workplace. The label must include the identification of the chemical, the manufacturer's name and contact information, the applicable GHS pictograms, the applicable signal words (either *danger* or *warning*, as applicable), and precautionary statements (measures to reduce risk from exposure to the chemical).

### Pictograms

The pictograms used in the GHS system are simple pictures used to convey hazards posed by the chemical. They are meant to be universally understandable by people with diverse language and reading fluencies. They are as follows:

| | | |
|---|---|---|
| *Health Hazard* | *Flammable* | *Sensitizer/ Irritant* |
| *Gas Under Pressure* | *Oxidizer* | *Corrosive* |
| *Reactive* | *Environmental Hazard* | *Poison* |

### Signal Words

Under the GHS hazard communication and safety data sheet system, the term **signal word** is used to describe one word that summarizes the degree of danger posed by the substances. There are only two signal words: *danger* and *warning*. The word **danger** is used for more hazardous substances that present immediate hazards such as flammability, reactivity, poison, and so on. The word **warning** is used for lesser hazards such as irritants, environmental hazards, and less toxic substances. The signal word is used on the label to provide a quick and easily understandable indication of the degree of hazard posed by the substance.

# Control of Hazardous Energy

## Hazardous Energy

**Hazardous energy** is energy that is stored in a machine or device that, if suddenly released, could activate the machine in such a way that it could injure an employee. Stored energy can be of many kinds—mechanical energy (e.g., coiled springs, compressed air) is the most obvious, but energy can also be stored in chemical systems, in steam systems, and as electrical energy. Controlling hazardous energy requires systematic development of a lockout/tagout program that identifies the potential types of stored energy in machines and identifies specifically for each piece of equipment how one releases the energy and physically locks the machine, so it cannot be reactivated until the service or maintenance is completed and the all-clear signal has been given. Best practice is to post lockout procedures for each piece of equipment at the equipment and to use photos to document lockout points. Ideally, each person has his or her own lock, and each person working on the machine attaches a lock to control the residual hazardous energy.

## Lockout/Tagout

Lockout/tagout refers to the process of isolating hazardous energy during maintenance activities to prevent employee injury. **Lockout** refers to physically placing a lock on the power source (to isolate electrical energy) or other means of starting the source of hazardous energy. **Tagout** refers to placing a tag on the switch to indicate that the energy source is isolated and should not be turned back on without following proper procedures. Tagout systems should not be used unless accompanied by the more robust and undefeatable lockout system, although tagout is a best practice for notifying who has placed the equipment in lockout.

### *Training Requirements*

The Occupational Safety and Health Administration (OSHA) lockout/tagout regulation lists specific training requirements for employees both initially and on an annual basis. The training must cover the types of hazardous energy that can/should be controlled (not just electrical energy), what are authorized and affected employees, the specific lockout procedures for equipment they will be locking out, the difference between lockout and tagout, why tagout alone is not an approved control of hazardous energy, and the process to commence safe start-up of equipment after lockout.

### *Authorized and Affected Employees*

An **authorized employee** under the lockout/tagout regulations is an employee who has been thoroughly trained in the reasons for lockout and the methods to lock out equipment and has been issued a lock to use. The lock should be personalized by color coding, and/or by the use of personalized tags to notify others who is responsible for a particular lockout. An **affected employee** is one that has a general awareness of what lockout/tagout is and works near machinery that will be locked out from time to time. However, these employees are not responsible themselves for performing the lockout or for following the steps to safe start-up of equipment after lockout.

# Excavation, Trenching, and Shoring

## Hazards and Controls Associated with Excavations

### *Training Requirements*

As part of a comprehensive injury prevention plan and hazard communication plan, workers who work in an excavation site must be trained on the hazards of an excavation and how they are protected from injury. They should be trained in site-specific emergency procedures. If wearing a harness, the employee must be trained in how to use the harness and how to inspect it to ensure it is working optimally.

### Safety Considerations When Planning Projects

A trenching or excavation project poses many safety hazards that must be carefully considered through a site-specific pre-job planning process; potential cave-ins are the greatest risk. Considerations must be given to the type of soil to be excavated, and cave-in prevention measures will be taken according to the type of soil, location of underground and overhead utility lines, the weather forecast, and the potential for a hazardous atmosphere in the trench or excavation. Consideration must be made for the types of personal protective equipment (PPE) the employees will need. Everyone should wear a high-visibility vest, and if entering excavations of a deep and confined space, employees must wear a harness and lifeline. Provisions should be made for daily inspections for excavation integrity; inspections should also be done when conditions have changed in the excavation (e.g., due to weather).

### Soil Types

The type of soil to be excavated into is important in determining the proper safety measures that must be taken. A qualified soil classification specialist must perform the determination and make the recommendations. The unconfined compressive strength must be evaluated, either in the field or in the laboratory. The unconfined compressive strength is the load at which the soil will fail. The basic soil types are as follows:

- Stable rock: this is natural solid material that can be excavated and remain intact while work is performed in the excavation.
- Type A soil: this is soil that has an unconfined compressive strength of 1.5 tons per square foot or greater. These soils are described as clay, silty clay, sandy clay, or clay loam.
- Type B soil: this is soil that has an unconfined compressive strength of 0.5 to 1.5 tons per square foot. It may be described as crushed rock, angular gravel, silt loam, or sandy loam.
- Type C soil: this is soil that has an unconfined compressive strength of less than 0.5 tons per square foot. This type of soil may have water seeping from it or may be a layered system that reaches into the trench or excavation.

### Safety Requirements

The risk of a cave-in is the greatest risk at an excavation site. Any excavation of greater than five feet deep must have a protective system in place to prevent cave-ins (barricades, sloping side, benching, etc.). If the excavation is greater than twenty feet deep, this protective system must be designed by a registered professional engineer. There are several types of cave-in protection available, such as shoring the sides, sloping the sides to reduce the vertical edge, benching the sides, and shielding workers from the sides. A qualified individual should be consulted when choosing cave-in protection, as site conditions such as soil type, moisture level, and the amount of activity around the excavation must be taken into consideration. Access and egress to the excavation area and the excavation itself must be controlled with barricades and work practice controls. A ladder or ramp must be provided as a means of egress if the depth of the excavation is four feet or greater. The route to the means of egress cannot be more than 25 feet for any employee who may be working in the excavation. The spoil pile (the soil removed from the pit) must be set back from the edge of the excavation at least two feet. This prevents material falling on workers and makes an even walking surface at the edge of the excavation.

### *Conducting the Required Daily Inspection of an Ongoing Excavation Site*

Daily inspections of excavation sites are required as a minimum but inspections can be made at any time a change in work, weather, or environmental conditions makes more frequent inspections desirable. The safety inspector must be alert to all hazardous conditions affecting worker safety but there are certain commonalities of concern:

- Examine for failure of protective systems, hazardous atmospheres, water accumulation and the ground signs which may indicate a potential collapse of excavation walls.
- Means of exit or egress should be inspected. Stairways, ladders, ramps or other safe means of evacuation from trenches are required in ditches or trenches that are 4 feet or more in depth. A worker should not have to travel more than 25 feet to reach a means of safe exit.
- Stability of adjoining walls, buildings, or other nearby structures should be inspected for settling, leaning, or other signs of tipping.

# Confined Spaces

## Common Hazards and Controls Associated with Working in Confined Spaces

A **confined space** is an area with limited entry and exit access that is not designed for regular employee occupancy but that is routinely entered for maintenance or other activities. The definition includes spaces that even arms are placed into, not just spaces that can accommodate the entire body. Confined spaces are dangerous because they cannot be exited easily in an emergency, they may have oxygen-deficient atmospheres, and there may be dust or vapors present that can pose a hazard to employees entering them. For this reason, Occupational Safety and Health Administration (OSHA) requires assessments and inventories of potential confined spaces to determine appropriate entry procedures.

### *Permit-Required and Non-Permit-Required Confined Spaces*

There is a significant difference between a permit-required and non-permit required confined space. Confined spaces are areas not designed for continuous employee occupancy, and which have limited means of egress. They may also have the potential for a hazardous atmosphere, either oxygen deficiency, presence of chemical vapors, or extreme temperatures.

Entry into a confined space using a permit system is required when there is a potential for oxygen deficiency, explosive atmosphere, and/or chemical vapor exposures. The permit provides a mechanism to track entries and to document that the proper pre-entry procedures have been followed, such as measuring oxygen levels and measuring chemical vapors. Employees must also have an attendant outside the confined space at all times and emergency equipment on hand in case of emergency.

Permits issued for this purpose must:

- Identify the space to be entered.
- Identify the type and nature of the work to be performed and provide substantial justification for issuing a permit.
- Be date stamped with the date of authorization and the number of hours or days in which confined-space work has been authorized.
- Identify the person or persons who are authorized to enter the confined space. This section of the permit should specify the type of tracking and monitoring system used to control entrance and egress.

### Working in Permit-Required Confined Spaces

A confined space has the following characteristics:

- An area sufficient in size as to accommodate a worker of normal size to enter and perform assigned work with necessary tools and uniform.
- A confined space has limited entry and/or egress points which are so constructed as to limit the free passage of employees or rescuers into the area. Holding tanks, grain silos, manure pits, and entry passages to sewage tunnels are confined spaces requiring special methods of access and preparatory measures taken to ensure health and safety under poor atmospheric conditions.
- A confined space is one in which continuous employee occupancy for work purposes cannot be expected to last for an entire 8-hour period of time as would be the case under normal working conditions. OSHA limits the amount of time a worker may be exposed to confined spaces with limited or extremely hazardous atmospheres.

### Confined Space Programs

A confined space program must contain an inventory of all confined spaces at a site, a formal documented assessment of the potential hazards posed by the space (e.g., Is there a danger of oxygen deficiency? Are there potentially hazardous vapors or fumes present? Is there a risk of high or low temperature environment?). A confined space entry permit must be developed and required to be used for all permit-required confined spaces. All confined spaces must be labeled as such, and the label should identify whether the space is permit required or not. The employees that will enter the confined space must receive appropriate training in the entry procedures and what appropriate emergency procedures are.

To fully implement a confined space safety program, one must be able to evaluate whether a hazardous atmosphere exists inside the confined space. The first assessment that must be made is to determine whether there is an oxygen-deficient atmosphere. For this, an oxygen level meter is needed to confirm that the oxygen content of the air inside the confined space is at least 19.5 percent. Second, if there is any possibility that flammable dust or vapors exist, the air must be analyzed for either dust or organic vapors. Organic vapors can be analyzed using a handheld organic vapor analyzer, and the results can be used to establish whether respiratory protection is necessary. The confined space entry plan and testing plan should ideally be overseen by an industrial hygienist to ensure that no potential hazards are overlooked.

### Controls for Working in Confined Spaces

Confined spaces include such work areas as tank cars, boilers, silos, underground tunnels, and railroad boxcars. All these spaces have limited entrances and exits and require specific controls to ensure worker safety. Hazards that workers in confined spaces face include toxicity, potential oxygen deficiency, and fire or explosion from flammable or combustible gases or dust. To protect workers, the following actions should be taken:

- Always evaluate a confined space for hazards before workers enter.
- Ensure that the confined space has adequate ventilation.
- Include equipment for suppressing fires and removing smoke and fumes.
- Train workers on safety procedures they need to follow when working in a confined space.
- Institute a buddy system for confined spaces so two workers are always present.

# Physical Security

## Physical Security Programs

Physical security is important in an industrial environment; it is unfortunately rather common for there to be instances of workplace violence that may have been prevented by a more robust physical security program. **Physical security programs** should include controlled and locked access points, the use of photo identification badges that are required to be worn in a visible location, and requiring badge entry at all entrances. Employees should be educated about the importance of physical security and not providing access to those who are not able to show a current badge for entry. Upon separation of an employee, badges should be confiscated immediately and deactivated.

## Workplace Procedures for Keeping Employees Safe from Terrorism

Maintaining a secure workplace is one key to keeping employees safe from terrorism. This includes the following: restricting and screening visitors; enforcing parking restrictions; and preventing access to the building through the roof, garages, windows, loading docks, and ventilation systems. Requiring employees and visitors to wear a badge helps security personnel quickly identify unauthorized visitors. Visitors should always sign in and out of the building. Similar procedures should be in place for delivery personnel. In addition to securing the building itself, an anti-terrorism plan also needs to consider the grounds. Clear visibility around the building makes it harder for unauthorized people to approach the building in secret. The grounds should be kept clear of clutter and debris, and trash cans should be either secured to the building or located away from the building.

# Fall Protection

For effective fall protection, OSHA recommends that companies adhere to the following practices:

- The company should have a written **fall protection plan** as part of its overall health and safety plan. The plan should include company rules for how and when to use fall protection equipment.
- The company should follow standard **fall protection requirements** when fall protection equipment must be used, usually when an employee in a general industry is four feet above the floor, when an employee of a construction company is six feet above the ground, or when an employee is on scaffolding 10 feet above the ground.
- The company should provide correct **fall protection equipment** and ensure that it is not only used, but is used properly.
- The company should **inspect, maintain, repair, and replace** fall protection equipment regularly.
- The company should provide supervisors and workers with **training** on how to recognize fall-related hazards and how and when to use fall protection equipment.

A **fall protection system** can limit or prevent falls. A fall protection system can include safety belts, safety harnesses, lanyards, hardware, grabbing devices, lifelines, fall arrestors, climbing safety systems, and safety nets. Most of these elements stop a fall that has already started and must meet specific standards.

- Safety belts are worn around the waist while harnesses fit around the chest and shoulders and occasionally the upper legs.
- Safety harnesses lessen the number and severity of injuries when they arrest a fall because the force is distributed over a larger part of the body.
- Lanyards and lifelines connect safety harnesses to an anchoring point while grabbing devices connect lanyards to a lifeline. Lanyards absorb energy, so they reduce the impact load on a person when the fall is arrested.

To prevent people from falling, the following actions should be taken:

- Reduce slipping and tripping hazards.
- Install barriers such as guardrails and covers over holes. OSHA requires that guardrails be at least 42 inches high.
- Install warning devices such as barricades and flags.
- Install handholds for people to use when they are moving up or down ladders or stairs.
- Design doors and walls in multi-story buildings so people cannot fall through them.
- Use railings and shrubs to prevent people from climbing on retaining walls.

In certain situations, such as at construction sites, you may also need to include fall-limiting devices to reduce the possibility of injury if someone does fall. Examples of fall-limiting devices include harnesses, safety nets, and catch platforms.

### *Types of Fall Protection Systems*

When determining what type of fall protection to employ, it is important to consider the task the worker will be performing while using the system. For tasks that do not require much side-to-side moving, a vertical lifeline may be best. If the job includes multiple workers, a horizontal lifeline system may be best. To calculate the clearance required to use a vertical lifeline system, add the lanyard length and maximum elongation distance to the height of the worker's back D-ring. Then add a margin of safety: three feet is common. Suppose a 5'6" worker is attached to a 10' lanyard that has an elongation distance of 3'6". His back D-ring is mounted between his shoulder blades at a height of 4'6". The fall clearance to safely use this lanyard system would be 10' + 3'6" +4'6" + 3' = 21 feet.

## Machine Guarding

**Machine guarding** involves examining machines for places or operations that can injure hands or other body parts during normal operation. This includes assessing potential pinch points, rotating shafts that might pull arms or fingers into equipment, exposed chains that might pull hands or digits into machinery, or conveyor belts that may entangle employees. Successful machine guarding involves fabricating guards that shield the employee from contact, whether intentional or inadvertent, from getting caught by or pulled into moving machinery. Entanglement in moving machinery can result in cuts, bruises, and more serious injuries such as amputations. Occupational Safety and Health Administration (OSHA) regulations for general machine safety requirements are found in 29 CFR 1910.212.

Machine guards can serve multiple purposes:

- To keep people or their clothing from coming into contact with hazardous parts of a machine.
- To prevent flying debris from striking people.
- To muffle noise.
- To capture and enclose dust.
- To contain and exhaust contaminants.

To be effective, **guards** must be a permanent part of the equipment and must be durable enough to withstand the use environment. They must also not create additional hazards or interfere with the normal functions of the machine. Guards may include openings for inserting materials into a machine and for allowing access for inspections and maintenance. Such openings must be small enough so people cannot reach into hazardous parts of the machine.

The **point of operation** is the location where the machine performs work, such as cutting, punching, or assembling. Point-of-operation guards and devices protect users at this point. Examples of point-of-operation guards include the following:

- **Enclosure guards**, which keep body parts or clothing from contacting the point of operation.
- **Interlocked guards**, which keep a machine from operating when a section is open.
- **Ring guards**, which enclose a rotating cutter.
- Devices to **keep a machine from operating** when an operator's fingers or hands are in the point of operation.

# Powered Industrial Vehicles

## Hazards and Controls for Powered Vehicles

Powered vehicles for materials handling include forklifts, trucks, cranes, etc. Hazards associated with these vehicles include the following:

- Visibility problems because operators cannot always see how well the load is positioned or whether other people or equipment are in the area
- Falling loads, overloading
- Heating and fire from hot engines and exhaust
- Tipping

To reduce the dangers from powered equipment:

- Choose vehicles with a rollover protection system (ROPS) such as a rollover bar, cab, or seatbelts.
- Choose vehicles with a falling object protection system (FOPS) to protect operators from falling objects.
- Inspect, maintain, and repair powered equipment regularly.
- Train operators on how to safely use their equipment.
- Ensure good ventilation in areas where exhaust fumes could create a hazard.
- Ensure that pathways are clear of obstructions.
- Use mirrors to improve the operator's visibility.
- Use hand signals to direct the operator when visibility is limited.

## Forklifts

### Forklift-Attachable Devices

Devices can be purchased that are cages meant for lifting workers to heights using a standard forklift. These must meet specifications with regard to securely fastening to the forks of the forklift, they must be equipped with guard rails of an approved height, the access gate must swing inward instead of outward, and they must undergo regular inspections. Under no circumstances should homemade work platforms be used because they must be engineered for strength and load limits. In addition, OSHA regulations do specify that if one is using such a cage as a man lift, one should obtain a letter from the forklift manufacturer specifying what the load limits are using the cage and that the capacity decal should be changed accordingly [29 CFR 1910.178(a)(4)].

### Daily Inspection Checklist Elements for Forklifts

Daily forklift inspections must be conducted by each driver before driving the forklift. Inspection elements include the following: check that horns and alerts are operational; check the parking brake works; check the mast operation for smooth operation and no broken chain links; check the forks for signs of cracks or wear that would weaken the forks; check the tires; check the fluid levels in the forklift, and check for leaks; ensure the seat belt is present and operational; and if there is a propane tank, check for leaks and rust.

### Forklift Traffic

A well-designed traffic pattern plan for forklift traffic can greatly increase the safety of the workplace. "Rules of the road" should be established that are enforceable for all forklift drivers and pedestrians. Similar to public roadways, there should be designated lanes of travel for forklifts. Pedestrian walkways should be designated and separate from forklift lanes. Intersections should be posted with forklift stop signs. Speed limits should be established and enforced (maximum of eight miles per hour). High traffic areas such as receiving docks should restrict pedestrian access.

### Pedestrian Safety Around Powered Industrial Trucks

Although pedestrians always have the right of way, it is important for pedestrians to observe best management practices when walking in areas with forklift traffic. At all intersections, forklifts are instructed to stop and sound their horn; pedestrians should stop at all intersections and look for forklifts. Pedestrians should be aware that forklifts may be backing out of inventory rows. Pedestrians should stop and wait for an acknowledgment to pass through the path of a traveling forklift to ensure that the driver sees them and will stop for them. Never walk under raised forklift forks.

### Forklift Driver Training

The Occupational Safety and Health Administration (OSHA) standard 1910.178 states that forklift driver training covers three areas: formal instruction, practical training, and evaluation.

The **formal instruction** can be accomplished either online or in a classroom setting. Instruction must include vehicle safety checks, operating instructions (including warnings and precautions for the model being used), differences between a vehicle and an industrial truck, controls and instrumentation, engine operation, steering, maneuvering, visibility restrictions, use of forks, lifting capacity, vehicle stability, inspections, safe loading, use on ramps or docks, and interaction with pedestrians.

**Practical training** must take place with the actual vehicle or vehicles the operator is being trained on. Practical training can include demonstrations, hands-on instructions, and operation under supervision of a trainer.

**Evaluation** of the driver must occur in the vehicle the operator is to be certified to operate. If an operator is to use multiple vehicles, they must be evaluated on each vehicle. Evaluation involves an assessment of the operator's knowledge and abilities by a trained evaluator who observes the individual operating the vehicle. Evaluation should include proper operation of the lifting devices, driving with and without a load, and proper pre-use inspection.

**Retraining** must occur whenever an operator must use a new vehicle, whenever the work conditions or locations change, or whenever there is evidence that retraining would be appropriate, such as observed unsafe driving. OSHA does not designate a refresher training frequency.

### *Load Limit of Forklifts*

The forklift generally has two front wheels and one back wheel that pivots around when turning the unit. This three-point triangle formed by the three wheels is the "stability triangle." One must be mindful of the center of gravity in relation to this stability triangle in determining the load limit of the forklift. Manufacturers establish the load limit for various loads relative to the load's center. For example, a 48-inch pallet has a load center of 24 inches. Lifting loads in the air also affects the center of gravity. The load limit therefore depends on three factors: the load center of the object being lifted or transported, the height the load will be lifted, and the counterbalanced weight of the forklift itself.

All forklifts are equipped with a capacity plate affixed by the manufacturer. This plate lists the load limit of the forklift for several common load centers (such as 24 inches and 36 inches). This will be the amount of weight the forklift can safely carry and move, given a certain load center. This load limit assumes that the forklift will be operated at a reasonable speed, especially around corners. Turning corners quickly can quickly shift the load center outside of the stability triangle, causing the forklift to turn over and potentially crushing an employee. Any changes to the forklift that affect the stability triangle or maximum mast height will affect the load limit and the manufacturer must be consulted to determine the new load limit.

### *Battery Charging Stations*

Forklift batteries contain strong acid. Therefore, it is important to observe proper training and precautions when recharging batteries. Battery charging stations should be located outdoors if at all possible. OSHA requires that an eyewash station be available in the battery charging area. Proper PPE must be available to the employee that will be handling the batteries. Gloves must be worn to plug in and unplug the batteries; extra precautions must be taken if a person will be checking the water level in the battery and adding water. Additional PPE to wear when servicing batteries includes acid-resistant gloves, safety glasses, and a face shield. Water should only be added to the batteries after charging and once the battery has a full charge. Only deionized water can be used to fill the batteries. The level should be checked at least once per week and water added to the fill line if it is low. If there is any acid spilled on the outside of the battery, it should be cleaned up using appropriate precautions while wearing proper PPE.

## Crane Inspections

The Occupational Safety and Health Administration (OSHA) Standard 1910.179 requires two recurring inspections for cranes: frequent and periodic.

**Frequent inspections** must occur daily to monthly, depending on crane usage. Inspection, which may also occur by way of observation during use, shall address all functional operating mechanisms, deterioration or leakage in any part of the hydraulic system, hooks, hoist chains, operating mechanisms, and ropes. Hook and chain inspection must be documented.

**Periodic inspections** shall occur either monthly or annually. In addition to all items in the frequent inspection, the periodic inspection must also examine all members for cracks or damage, all bolts and rivets, sheaves and drums for wear or cracks, all moving or locking mechanisms, brake system, winding mechanism, engine, chain drive, and electrical system.

## Scaffolding

Hazards associated with scaffolds include the following:

- Unsecured or loose planks
- Overloading and structural failure
- Tipping over
- Falls

To improve safety when using scaffolds, the following actions should be taken:

- All scaffolds must be assembled by a competent person capable of supervising the placement, disassembly, and moving of scaffolding.
- The competent person must have knowledge of guardrail specifications for tubular welded frame scaffolds and for the manner in which they are to be braced.
- Mobile scaffolds must be tightly planked with scaffold grade planking. Planking which extends beyond scaffold supports must meet additional OSHA specifications.
- The base of any scaffolding must be set upon a sound and stable base. The positioning of upright supports must be plumb and the joints securely locked.
- Safe access by means of a secure ladder or permanent stairway must be provided. Ladders must be affixed to the scaffold frame. The scaffold frame is to be anchored into solid and stable side structures at points along its heights.
- Scaffolding and planking must be able to support at least four times the maximum intended load.
- Scaffolding should be inspected before use, and all planks, bolts, ropes, outrigger beams, bracing, and clamps should be checked.

There is good reason for the OSHA requirement that scaffolds be able to support far more than their intended load:

- In addition to the workers using the scaffold, there is the added weight of tools and equipment to consider.
- The effect of the elements like snow and wind can have an impact on the carrying capacity of scaffolding.
- Planking may be weaker than the specifications would indicate, particularly if the lumber is of lower quality and contains knots or fissures.

### *Pre-Job Scaffolding Inspections*

Scaffolding must be inspected after it's erected, before use, and periodically thereafter (daily). Platforms must be at least 18 inches wide and must be secured so that they don't wobble. The scaffold should not block any exits and must be accessible by a ladder or ramp. It should not be erected near any power lines. There must be diagonal cross bracing to support the platforms, and protection must be provided overhead to protect against falling objects. Employees must be required to wear fall protection equipment if they will be working 10 feet or more above the next accessible level.

# Ergonomics

## Fitness for Duty

A **fitness for duty examination** is a medical examination to determine if an employee is physically or psychologically able to execute the essential functions of a job. Depending on the reason for the examination, the results may determine if the individual should be assigned to a particular job, whether an employee is ready to return to work after an absence, or even if they are capable of working in that job.

Employers are legally allowed to request the examination if there is a reasonable concern about the ability of the employee. There are three occasions where an employer has a right to request such an examination: before employment, when an employee returns to work after a serious injury, and when there are observed job performance issues.

- Employers can submit an employee to a **pre-employment physical** to determine their ability to execute the essential job functions. Typical examinations consist of vision and hearing tests and may include functional tests and a drug test.
- Employees who are returning to work after a serious injury can also be submitted to a fitness for duty examination. The employer may seek assurances that the employee is truly able to return to full duty or whether they require additional treatment and rehabilitation. The goal of this type of examination is to make sure the employee does not get injured upon return.
- The instance that has the most legal jeopardy is when there are job performance issues that cause an employer to seek a fitness for duty examination. An employee who is found unconscious may need to be examined to determine whether there are underlying health conditions that could introduce hazards in the workplace. Other examples include when the demeanor of an employee changes over time, such as an employee who has sustained a head injury is noticed to have become more temperamental and argumentative. Criteria for submitting employees to performance-related examinations must be objective, as claims of discrimination related to violating protections offered by the Americans with Disabilities Act can put the company in a position to be sued. It is recommended to seek legal advice before subjecting employees to this type of examination.

## Stressors

**Environmental stressors** are those factors in the physical environment that can adversely impact worker productivity, safety, health, and mental wellness. The most commonly encountered environmental stressors are temperature, noise, and light.

The ability of the employer to mitigate these hazards depends on the employee's work environment. In modern office environments, environmental stressors can be mitigated or even eliminated by office design, equipment selection, HVAC units, and even interior decorations. In industrial or outdoor environments, the ability to manage the hazards is typically less controlled and may require the employer to rely on more extensive controls, including personal protective equipment, to lessen the impact on the employee.

## Temperature

Employees can be exposed to heat stress and cold stress, both of which can impact their productivity and have negative health consequences.

**Heat stress** is when an employee's body temperature rises due to exposure to heat sources, high work rate, and protective clothing. If the body is unable to manage the increase in thermal load, the employee can experience negative physiological effects, termed **hyperthermia**. Heat stress symptoms can vary from mild (heat rash or muscle cramps) to health emergencies (heat stroke). If not treated as a medical emergency, heat stroke can result in brain damage or even death.

**Cold stress** is when an employee's body temperature decreases due to exposure to temperatures lower than room temperature. If the body is unable to keep its core temperature within the normal range, the employee can experience negative health effects, termed **hypothermia**. Cold stress can be brought on in cold temperatures (as high as 40 °F), when an employee gets wet, and in windy conditions. Cold stress symptoms can start as shivering, be realized as tingling or discoloration of extremities (frostbite), and if left untreated, progress to loss of consciousness and even death.

### *Mitigation Strategies for Temperature Stress*

Temperature stress can be mitigated by way of engineering controls, administrative controls, and personal protective equipment.

**Engineering controls** that can address heat stress include the use of air conditioners, fans, or shade structures. Cold stress can be addressed using heaters and wind screens.

**Administrative controls** for temperature stress include rotating workers out of the environment to rest and recover, scheduling tasks for a different part of the day to avoid the stressor, and regularly scheduled breaks. Buddy-systems or periodic supervisor checks can be used to monitor employees for signs and symptoms of temperature stress. Lastly, training staff on recognizing temperature stress and how to mitigate the hazard is critical in lowering the chances of a temperature-related injury.

Modern fabrics and advances in clothing design have allowed for a wide selection of both hot and cold weather **personal protective equipment**. Cooling vests, microfiber fabrics, and lightweight clothing can help employees keep cool in hot environments. Advances in cold weather gear, gloves, and footwear can protect employees from injuries caused by cold stress.

## Lighting

Vision is one of the primary senses humans use to safely navigate the world around them. Thus, improper lighting can have a profound impact on worker performance and safety.

Improper lighting can negatively impact worker performance of visual tasks. Lighting should be designed for the task, with high-detail work requiring more illumination than low-detail tasks. Illumination should be of the proper strength and provide appropriate contrast for the employee to do their job. For example, without proper lighting, a quality control specialist may not see defects in a final product, or a fine motor skill may not be done correctly because the employee is struggling to see.

Improper lighting, either too much or too little, can cause physical discomforts in employees. Common health effects include eye strain and headaches. When there is improper lighting, employees may squint or lean forward, both of which are **ergonomic stressors** and can lead to cumulative trauma injuries.

### Mitigation Strategies for Lighting Stress

Proper illumination of the workspace is critical not only for employees to complete their tasks, but also to avoid the physical effects of improper illumination. Headaches, eye strain, and neck pain are common health effects attributed to light being reflected off **luminous displays,** such as computer displays and LED monitors. Thus, employers should evaluate how to reduce light reflecting off these displays, referred to as **glare**. Examples of available methods include:

- Adjustable **blinds** allow workers to change the amount of light entering their workspace. When they are placed over a window, blinds allow the worker to reduce the amount of natural light reflecting off the display.
- **Shades** can be used to block unwanted light from the user or the work surface. Shades can be placed over the windows or near the workspace.
- **Dimmer switches** can be used to adjust the amount of light being produced by a given source.
- **Anti-glare devices** can be placed on computer monitors to reduce the amount of light reflecting off the surface. Either as after-market add-ons or integrated into the monitor, these devices are intended to reduce the light that reflects off the screen and into the user's eyes.

### Ambient Lighting

**Ambient** or **general lighting** is the lighting that is meant to illuminate broad areas. It can be applied to both indoor and outdoor locations. Indoors, it is generally provided by overhead light fixtures. Outdoors, it can be flood lights, streetlights, or other fixtures designed to illuminate large areas.

Improper general lighting can increase the risk of employee injuries. Whether the light is too dim or if there are too many shadows, ambient lighting is critical to employee safety in that it must provide enough light for employees to identify potential hazards. **Slip, trip, and fall hazards** become more dangerous as an employee's ability to detect them diminishes with decreasing illumination or increased shadows.

Improper general illumination can be corrected by replacing bulbs, increasing the wattage of bulbs in current fixtures, or by adding additional light fixtures.

### Task Lighting

**Task lighting** is the use of a light source that can be focused on a specific area to make the completion of visual tasks easier. In contrast to general illumination provided by overhead lights, task lighting allows the user to control the amount of illumination on their work surface to reach the desired level of contrast necessary for the task. Task lighting is best suited for high detail work or work that requires high contrast.

Improper illumination for high detail work can lead to eye strain and headaches for employees. Modern task lights incorporate LED bulbs that are easier on the eyes than incandescent bulbs. Ergonomically designed task lights are articulated to allow the user to adjust the light intensity and location based on the need.

## Indoor Air Quality

The Occupational Safety and Health Administration (OSHA) defines **indoor air quality (IAQ)** as the quality of the air within a building and its impact on the health and well-being of the inhabitants. Although it can also refer to the indoor air temperature and its effects on employees, IAQ is most often associated with air contaminants within a building. Sources of indoor air contaminants include office machines, personal hygiene products, office furniture, sources outside the building, and mold. The causes of poor IAQ include poor ventilation, humidity (either high or low), and external activities that generate hazardous contaminants that are brought into the building by the HVAC system.

Employees exposed to poor indoor air quality might experience symptoms that include headaches, fatigue, issues with concentration, and irritation to the eyes, nose, or throat. They may complain of persistent odors, notice recurring residues on their workspaces, or have other non-specific issues when in the building environment. Indoor air quality should be considered as a source when the effects tend to improve whenever an employee leaves the building, such as a sore throat that improves over the weekend and then worsens during the week.

## NOISE

**Sound** is the variations in air pressure created by objects vibrating that are received by the ear drums and converted into neural signals. **Noise** is a subjective term defined as unwanted or irritating sounds—what is pleasant to one listener may be unpleasant to another.

**Occupational noise** can create hazards for an employee. Noise can interfere with the ability to communicate and the ability to hear warning or alarm signals. Prolonged exposure to noise has been found to increase psychological stress and can result in a threshold shift. A **threshold shift** is when the **baseline** level of what an employee can hear prior to noise exposure rises over time, indicating a loss in hearing ability. The impact of noise on an employee exposed to high levels of noise is monitored by way of **audiometric tests**—one prior to noise exposure and annually thereafter to identify any potential threshold shifts and related hearing loss.

### *MITIGATION STRATEGIES FOR NOISE*

**Noise** is any unwanted sound that can result in psychological or physical stress of an employee. Whenever employees are exposed to an 8-hour time-weighted average noise level of 85 decibels or higher, an employer must implement a **hearing conservation program.** An employer can control noise using the **hierarchy of hazard controls**: elimination, substitution, engineering controls, administrative controls, or personal protective equipment.

Once the source is identified, the employer should first determine if it can be **eliminated** from the workplace. Removing or relocating unnecessary noise sources, such as an air conditioning compressor, can reduce the overall level of noise.

If the source cannot be removed, the employer should next determine if a less noisy unit can be **substituted** for the current unit. Older units tend to be noisier than new units due to wear and technological advances.

In order for noise to be hazardous, the employee must be receiving **sound power** from the source. Power decreases with increasing distance. Thus, **engineering controls** can either interrupt the path of the sound or increase the distance between source and receiver. Enclosing the employee or the unit can reduce the noise exposure by interrupting the sound wave path. Placing noisy machines or the noisy part of the machine further away from employees also reduces the net sound power they experience. The installation of dampening pads under the machine or installing sound dampening materials around the machine can also reduce the overall noise.

Routine maintenance and repair can ensure that machines are functioning smoothly and reduce the noise they produce. This can be an **administrative control** used to reduce the noise level. Another method is to reduce the amount of time employees are exposed to noise, such as by job or task rotation, to decrease the effect of noise on their hearing.

The last method to reduce noise exposure is to issue hearing **protection devices**. Ear plugs, ear caps, and earmuffs are all designed to be worn by the employee to reduce the amount of noise that enters the ear.

### *Hearing Conservation Programs*

The Occupational Safety and Health Administration (OSHA) Standard 29 CFR 1910.95 requires a hearing conservation program to be instituted whenever employee exposure to noise exceeds a **time-weighted average (TWA)** of 85 dB when measured on the A scale. The time-weighted average is arrived at for an 8-hour day. This means that an employee may occasionally exceed the 85 dBA limit for short periods of time, as long as the average exposure calculated over an 8-hour time frame does not exceed the action level.

When the TWA exceeds 85 dBA, the employer must implement a **hearing conservation program.** This program must contain a means for measuring the noise to determine employee exposure, a means for notifying employees of hazardous noise, an audiometric testing program to evaluate employees' hearing over time, the use of hearing protection or other means to reduce the noise exposure, recurring evaluation of the effectiveness of the hearing protection devices, a written program, and training.

### *Hearing Protection*

Hearing protection **attenuation** is the amount of protection, in terms of decibels (dB), that a particular device provides. For example, if a pair of ear plugs has an attenuation rating of 20 dB and are used to protect from a source generating 85 dB of noise, the employee experiences 65 dB of noise. Thus, a hearing protection device is selected by the amount of noise it can reduce, considering that too much attenuation can prevent an employee from hearing alarm indicators or other warnings. There are three main types of **hearing protection devices:**

**Foam ear plugs** are an inexpensive, disposable type of hearing protection. Foam plugs are designed to be inserted into the ear canal and expand to fit the individual. Additionally, they do not typically interfere with other protective equipment. However, they can be ineffective if not installed correctly and, if soiled, can introduce dirt into the ear canal.

**Ear caps** are similar to foam ear plugs in their design but are usually attached to a band and are reusable. Where ear plugs are easily lost, either singly or in pairs, canal caps can be worn around the neck when not in use. Their effectiveness is dependent on the design of the tips and how deep they fit into the ear canal.

**Earmuffs** differ from plugs and caps in that they are designed to cover the entire outer ear. They are reusable, can be used by multiple employees, and require proper cleaning and maintenance. Earmuffs are also easier to use effectively than plugs or caps. As they are designed to fit over the ear, there is more interpersonal variability in the shape of the head and ears that can impact the effectiveness of the device. Also, because the headbands can interfere with other protective equipment, they are less effective when safety glasses are required, and they are heavier and more cumbersome than plugs or caps.

### Noise Reduction Rating (NRR)

The **noise reduction rating (NRR)** is a value assigned to a hearing protection device that estimates the noise attenuation achieved by the device. The Environmental Protection Agency (EPA) regulates hearing protection devices and the labeling which includes the NRR.

The NRR is determined in a laboratory, under controlled conditions, and with an individual familiar with hearing protection using a specific noise scale. Thus, the Occupational Safety and Health Administration (OSHA) suggests derating the listed protection as outlined in 29 CFR 1910.95, Appendix B. The OSHA standard is described using the A-weighted slow scale. However, not all noise meters are capable of that measurement. Therefore, adjustments must be made to accommodate for the different weightings. Per OSHA, this is achieved by subtracting 7 dB from the rating. Additionally, conservative estimates recommend dividing the NRR by 2 to account for improper wearing of the ear protection device, improper sizing, movement of the body during tasks that cause movement to the protective device, and wear of the device that occurs in a real-world situation. Thus, the formula to determine the actual noise reduction = measured noise value – (NRR – 7 dB) / 2.

Example:

*Calculate the NRR of a moldable foam ear plug with a rating of 30 dB in the vicinity of a grinding machine generating 92 dB of noise.*

If moldable foam ear plugs have an NRR of 30 dB, this is adjusted to 23 (30 - 7) and divided by 2 = 11.5 dB of attenuation. The final noise experienced by the employee is estimated as 92 dB – 11.5 dB = 81.5 dB, which has reduced the perceived noise below the OSHA action level of 85 dB and is acceptable for this application.

### Sound Power

The unit used to quantify noise is the **decibel**. Decibel (dB) is a logarithmic unit that expresses the ratio of the **sound power** of a source ($I$), in Watts, to a fixed reference power ($I_0$) where $L = 10\log(I/I_0)$. The reference power is the established lowest sound that a person can detect and is established as $1\text{x}10^{-12}$ Watt. (Note: sound can also be expressed in terms of **pressure** using Pascals, with the reference pressure ($P_0$) being $2\text{x}10^{-5}$ Pa and the formula modified to $L = 20\ \log(P/P_0)$.

As the scale is logarithmic, the power produced by multiple sources cannot be combined using simple addition. Thus, the first step is to convert the noise produced by each source to sound power in Watts. Then, the values are added in the formula and converted back into dB for the final noise exposure determination: $L_f = 10\log\frac{I_1+I_2+I_3}{I_0}$.

Example:

*Calculate the total noise exposure for an employee working with two fans, each generating 65 decibels of noise.*

$L = 10\log\frac{I}{I_0}$ where L = 65 dB. Thus $65 = 10\log\left(\frac{I}{1\times10^{-12}\text{ W}}\right)$; $I = 3.16\times10^{-6}\text{ W}$

$$L_f = 10\log\frac{3.16\times10^{-6}\text{ W} + 3.16\times10^{-6}\text{ W}}{1\times10^{-12}\text{ W}} = 68\text{ dB}$$

## Sources of Stress

**Stress** can be defined as an individual's perceived threats and their psychological and physiological response to those threats. In the context of a workplace, stress can be described as a person's response to the demands placed on them. The main sources of stress in the modern workplace can be placed into four main categories:

- **Organizational factors** that contribute to stress are those facets related to the company and its culture that place increased pressure on an individual. Poor vertical communication can lead to an employee not knowing the direction the company is heading or even what they are working towards. Discrimination, pay inequality, and lack of promotional opportunities can also contribute to a feeling of helplessness within the organization. Conflicting goals from various levels in the organization can cause stress when an employee does not know whose directions they should be following. Finally, a lack of control over their job and being excluded from decision-making can further add stress to an employee by making them feel inadequate or unappreciated.
- **Individual factors** are another source of stress. Some people have a predisposition that can lead to stress, such as being overly rigid, impatient, or if they tend to put a lot of pressure on themselves. Other individual factors include expectations from family members, such as a spouse demanding they ask for a promotion or raise, as well as expectations from both supervisors and subordinates. When an individual feels they have failed to meet those expectations, the inadequacy can result in a stress response.
- The individual's job can also induce stress into their lives. **Job factors** include jobs that are too complex for the individual to complete, which can create a feeling of hopelessness. Jobs that are too monotonous can also feel hopeless by being boring, resulting in a feeling of defeat. Unsafe jobs or unsafe environments can put a person in a constant state of "fight-or-flight," resulting in a fear for their own well-being. This ever-present feeling of fear can be exhausting, leading to mental stress in an employee.
- Finally, the pressures of society, referred to as **extra-organizational factors**, can also create stress in the employees. In today's information society, employees are constantly bombarded by news about the economy, the government, and society. Additionally, personal economic worries, family obligations, and personal issues may be on the mind of an employee. Such pressures can distract them from focusing on their work and lead to injuries or build on the other factors and contribute to their overall stress and poor mental health, which can cause burnout, breakdowns, or cause them to lash out at others.

### *Workplace Stress*

**Workplace stress** can be defined as the employee's perceived difference between the demands of the job and their ability to cope with the demand. Stress can lead to employee turnover, workers' compensation claims, and injuries.

Workplace stress is individualized and can have several different sources. A job that is overly complex may cause an individual to feel inadequate, while one that is too simple may become monotonous. Employees can experience stress when they feel they do not have adequate control over their jobs, such as a supervisor or electronic monitoring system constantly looking over their shoulder, taking away their sense of autonomy. Workers who are in constant fear of losing their job experience higher levels of stress, not knowing what their future at the company may be. Employees who feel isolated at work can suffer from a lack of belonging and feel like an outsider, both within the company and within their peer group, which can negatively impact their mental health. Finally, the lack of a safe environment can result in an employee constantly being concerned over their physical well-being instead of focusing on completing their job.

# Risk Factors

## Ergonomic Risk Factors

**Ergonomic risk factors** are those aspects of the job that negatively impact the body and can result in injury over the long-term. These **cumulative trauma injuries** are typically slow in onset and very difficult to recover from without medical intervention. The primary categories for physical ergonomic risk factors are **repetition, force, posture,** and **vibration**.

**Repetition** is when the body executes the same motion using the same muscles and joints. Repetitive motion can be defined as any motion having a **cycle time** of less than 30 seconds or one that is repeated 1,000 times during a shift. The impact is that the body has inadequate time to properly recover, which can result in ligament or tendon damage, including swelling, fraying, or tears.

**Force** refers to the exertion of physical effort in accomplishing a task. Force can include **lifting, pushing,** and **pulling**. Force can be injurious when the weight being moved exceeds the body's capabilities and muscular or joint injuries occur. Small forces can also be harmful if the motion becomes repetitive. Force can result in strains to the muscles, sprains to ligaments or tendons, and joint damage.

**Posture** refers to the general body position throughout the work task. **Awkward posture** refers to tasks where the body position is out of neutral alignment. This includes bending, twisting, raising arms above the shoulders, and reaching beyond the center of mass. Posture also can refer to tasks that involve prolonged **static tasks** where the body is in one position for an extended period of time. Sitting and standing are prime examples of a static posture—both of which can be harmful in large doses.

**Vibration** is the body's repeated exposure to a repetitive force, such as using an impact hammer or driving in a vehicle with bad shocks. The body is constantly being compressed by an external force that can damage the blood vessels and nerves. This constant compression can result in tissue damage for the affected body part.

### *Ergonomic Risk Factors in Office Environments*

Modern office environments can expose employees to several physical **ergonomic risk factors**. Awkward postures, repetitive motion, contact pressure, and poor lighting can all result in cumulative trauma injuries.

- Poorly designed workstations and improper equipment can cause joints and bodies to deviate from neutral positions, creating an **awkward posture** and the potential for injury. Inadequate seating can lead to poor posture, while improper workstation setup can cause joints to be bent awkwardly. These positions can disrupt the proper blood flow or put pressure on veins and nerves that, if left unchecked, can result in injury.
- The dependency on computer workstations has led to an increase in cumulative trauma wrist injuries from the **repetitive motion** associated with keyboard and mouse use. Also, employees who constantly reach for the phone or office supplies can experience shoulder and elbow injuries.
- Whenever hands, arms, or wrists are rested against hard surfaces, the resultant **contact pressure** can cause cumulative trauma injuries. The contact can impact proper blood flow and nerve conduction, resulting in tissue damage.
- Poor office lighting coupled with the illumination of computer monitors can cause eye strain and associated headaches.

### Ergonomic Risk Factors in Industrial Environments

Industrial settings are extremely variable regarding the hazards they present to workers. Additionally, the **ergonomic risk factors** that an employee would experience are job- and task-dependent. However, repetitive motion, lifting, awkward position, and vibration are common ergonomic risk factors found in industry.

- **Repetitive motion** refers to repeating the same motion with the same muscle or groups of muscles without adequate rest or recovery. This motion can lead to a variety of musculoskeletal injuries, including pulled muscles and damage to ligaments and tendons.
- Injuries from **lifting** are common in industrial settings. Whether it be moving a load that is too heavy or using an improper lifting technique, injuries can occur to muscles and joints whenever a person must move a load from one level to another.
- Working in an **awkward position** is another risk factor for industrial injuries. Reaching, stretching, twisting, bending, and kneeling are all positions that can expose the body to injury. The strain on joints and muscles from non-neutral body positions can cause injury, both immediately and over time.
- Nerves and blood vessels that are continually compressed due to **vibration** can suffer damage over time. Hand tools, machinery, and driving can cause vibration injuries with constant exposure.

### Repetitive Motion Injuries

**Repetitive motion** is a musculoskeletal injury caused by repeated similar motions without proper rest and recovery. These types of injuries can also be referred to as **cumulative trauma injuries**. Examples include carpal tunnel syndrome, cubital tunnel syndrome, bursitis, tendonitis, tenosynovitis, and trigger finger.

Repetitive motion can be described as any motion that occurs more than twice per minute (<30 second cycle time) or more than 1,000 times per work shift. Without proper rest, fatigue and damage can occur to muscles, ligaments, and tendons. If the body is not allowed enough recovery time between cycles, inflammation and tenderness can result.

### Mitigation Strategies for Vibration Exposure

There are two main types of **vibration exposures** for an employee: **hand-arm vibration (HAV)** and **whole-body vibration (WBV).** Chronic exposure to HAV can result in loss of dexterity, weakness in grip, and cumulative trauma injuries, such as carpal tunnel and cubital tunnel syndromes. Whole-body vibration can result in low back pain and headaches. In both instances, injuries result from the constant compression of nerves and blood vessels, which can permanently interrupt their proper functioning.

Mitigating vibration hazards depends on the source of the stressor. Proper selection of hand tools can reduce the HAV exposure. The use of vibration-dampening gloves can also minimize the impact on hands and arms. Whole-body vibration is typically associated with vehicles. Thus, proper maintenance and repair of vehicles, proper tire selection, and proper tire inflation can reduce the potential for injury. For both HAV and WBV exposures, it is critical to reduce the amount of time the employee is exposed to the vibration source. Additionally, training employees on the hazards and controls for managing vibration hazards is a key component to any successful mitigation program.

## Work Design

Broadly speaking, **ergonomics** (also referred to as **human factors**) refers to designing and evaluating systems as it relates to the capabilities of the people who interact with them. Ergonomics looks at designing equipment, machines, and environments that leverage the strengths of humans while compensating for their deficiencies. Human factor theory is instrumental in the modern design of control panels, tools, and alarm notification systems.

The Occupational Safety and Health Administration (OSHA) defines ergonomics as the science of designing work tasks to fit the worker, not fitting the worker into the task. The concept of "one-size-fits-all" runs counter to modern ergonomic principles.

### Principles of Physical Stress

**Physical stress** can be defined as demands placed on the body and how it responds to prolonged exposure to that stress. When evaluating the impact of a task or job on the body, the following eight variables of physical stressors should be evaluated:

- **Sitting vs. standing**: In general, sitting is less impactful on the body than standing. However, prolonged sitting can impact circulation, digestion, and posture. These impacts can result in negative health effects. Prolonged standing can also have negative health impacts, such as varicose veins, lower back pain, and foot injuries.
- **Stationary vs. mobile**: Physical stress increases for stationary jobs when the employee does not take a break from their static position; physical stress for a mobile job increases if the worker must move heavy loads.
- **Demand for physical power**: Physical stress increases as the weight of the load increases. Similarly, a small load moved many times can expose the employee to **repetitive motion injuries**.
- **Horizontal work area**: Bending or reaching places stress on the muscles and joints of the back, arms, and shoulders. Optimized work areas reduce the total horizontal area a worker must manage for the job or task.
- **Vertical work area**: Lifting, bending, or reaching can negatively impact the muscles and joints of the legs, back, and shoulders. The preferred work zone should be below the shoulders and above the waist to minimize awkward positions.
- **Repetitive motion**: Repeated motions with the same muscle group or groups performed in short periods or for the duration of the work shift can cause physical stress on employees. The chance for injuries to muscles, tendons, and joints increases as the frequency of the motion increases.
- **Amount of surface contact**: Prolonged contact with hard surfaces can result in damage to nerves and capillaries. The amount of contact, pressure of contact, and contact surface all contribute to the opportunity for injury.
- **Negative environmental stressors**: Other environmental stressors, such as temperature, noise, and vibration, must also be considered for their impact on the physical well-being of the employee.

## Material Handling

### Manual Materials Handling

**Manual materials handling** is the human activity related to moving an object. That motion may be along a horizontal surface (e.g., pushing, pulling), carrying, or lifting/lowering. If not done properly, if done repeatedly without rest, or if the load exceeds what the body is able to move, then an injury can result. The following situations can result in a manual materials-handling injury:

- Lifting a load from the ground
- Twisting while moving a load
- Lifting the load above the shoulders
- Heavy lifting without assistance
- Repetitive lifting without appropriate rest and recovery

## Common Injuries

**Materials handling** is the movement of a load from one location to another. Improper lifting techniques, lifting loads that are too heavy, and awkward postures while lifting (such as reaching or twisting) can result in injuries during materials handling. Injuries can be muscle strains, soft tissue sprains, or even soft tissue tears. Body parts that can be injured include backs, arms, shoulders, knees, legs, and ankles. Loads that are dropped on an individual can also cause fractures, cuts, or contusions.

Injuries from manually moving loads can include sprains, strains, and tears of muscles and other soft tissue. In order to reduce the chance of being injured, an employee should perform the following tasks before any lift:

- **Examine** the load for any potential hazards, such as slivers, jagged edges, pinch points, or container flaws.
- **Plan** the route of the lift by removing any slip, trip, or fall hazards and ensure the final resting place is ready to receive the load.
- **Evaluate** the load to determine if assistance is needed for heavy loads.
- **Locate** proper grip locations and determine if any gripping devices present are in good condition.
- Make sure they have a **firm grip** on the container and can move the load in their "power zone" (located between the hips and the shoulders, at waist level) without blocking their view.
- Avoid moving materials up or down stairs, using ramps or elevators when possible.
- When possible, use carts, dollies, or other mechanical devices for the load.

## NIOSH Lifting Equation

A **lift** is defined as moving materials by way of grasping with the hands without mechanical assistance. With manual lifting of loads being a continual source of worker injuries, the National Institute for Occupational Safety and Health (NIOSH) has developed an equation to assist professionals in assessing the hazard associated with a manual lift.

The **lifting equation** takes into consideration the distance the load is carried from the body, the height the load is lifted to and from, the height of the load as carried, the frequency of the lift, the impact of the grip, and the amount of torso twisting involved. When all of these are considered, the output of the equation is the maximum weight of a load that would be considered safe. Thus, the resultant value, **recommended weight limit (RWL)**, can be compared to the actual load to be lifted to determine if other control methods, such as a buddy-lift or mechanical lift device, should be implemented. Once the RWL is calculated, the load weight is divided by the RWL with the resultant value, the **lifting index (LI)**, determining the relative risk of the lift. An LI value greater than 1 indicates a higher risk of injury associated with the lift.

The **lifting equation** developed by the National Institute of Occupational Safety and Health (NIOSH) calculates the recommended maximum weight for a manual lifting event that can be executed over an 8-hour time frame. If the actual load exceeds the recommended weight limit (RWL), then the lift requires assistance by way of another individual or a mechanical device. The formula is:

$RWL = LC \times HM \times VM \times DM \times AM \times FM \times CM$, where the multipliers are calculated as follows:

*LC* = load constant (51 lb)

*HM* = horizontal distance (H) of the hands on the load as measured to the center of the ankles, in inches, divided into 10: HM = 10 / H. If less than 10 inches, use 10 inches.

*VM* = starting vertical distance of the hands (V) on the load to the ground, in inches, corrected for optimum height as: VM = 1 - (0.0075|V-30|)

*DM* = the vertical distance (D) the hands move from the start to the end of the lift, in inches, corrected as: DM = 0.82 + (1.8 / D) using a minimum D of 10 inches

*AM* = the angle of the load (between 0 and 135 degrees) relative to the midpoint (belly button) of the worker, corrected as AM = 1 - (0.0032A); A = 0 if greater than 135 degrees

*FM* = the frequency of the lift calculated as lifts per 15 minutes and the duration of the lift; value is obtained from a table

*CM* = the coupling constant which represents how good a grip the employee has on the load, which is impacted by the shape and construction of the container as well as the quality of any available handles or handholds; evaluated from a table using ratings of *good*, *fair*, and *poor*

Once the RWL is calculated, the actual load weight is divided by the RWL to yield the **lifting index (LI)**, which can be used to determine the relative risk of the lift. An LI value greater than 1 indicates a higher risk of injury for the lift.

<u>Example:</u>

*Calculate the recommended weight limit and the lifting index for moving 30-pound bags of fertilizer having the following variables: horizontal distance of hands from body: 12 inches; vertical height of hands from ground during lift: 33 inches; vertical distance of the pallet to the shelf: 24 inches; angle of torso twist: 15 degrees; two lifts per minute for 1.5 hours (FM = 0.84); and a poor coupling constant (CM = 0.90).*

The NIOSH lifting equation is $RWL = LC \times HM \times VM \times DM \times AM \times FM \times CM$

For this example:

$$RWL = 51 \times \frac{10}{12} \times (1 - (0.0075|33 - 30|)) \times (0.82 + \frac{1.8}{24}) \times (1 - (0.0032 \times 15)) \times 0.84 \times 0.90$$

$$RWL = 51 \times 0.83 \times 0.98 \times 0.90 \times 0.95 \times 0.84 \times 0.90$$

$$RWL = 26.81 \text{ pounds}$$

This means that 26.8 pounds is the maximum recommended safe load for this type of lift.

$$LI = \frac{30}{26.81} = 1.1$$

This means there is an increased risk for this lift. The employer should evaluate ways to adjust the variables, such as reducing the lift frequency, reducing how long the lift is executed during the day, modifying torso rotation, or changing $t$, the vertical displacement of the load to reduce the risk of injury.

## Work Practice Controls

### Work Hardening

**Work hardening** is a process used to return an injured employee to their pre-injury ability, both physically and psychologically. Using a multi-disciplinary team, the process involves a physical therapist, occupational therapist, psychologist, and vocational specialist. The process uses simulated work conditions, movements, and activities to restore the employee's function. The goal is to make sure the employee is ready to return to work and does not reinjure themselves, leading to additional missed work.

### Work Conditioning

**Work conditioning** is a process used to return an injured employee as close to their original physical ability as possible. The intent is to help injured employees regain strength, flexibility, power, endurance, and motor control to prevent reinjury after returning to work. Work conditioning is for those employees who do not require the behavioral, pain management, or vocational aspects of **work hardening**.

### Job Rotation

**Job rotation** is the process of moving workers between different jobs or different workstations at prescribed intervals. Job rotation reduces the chance of cumulative trauma injuries by changing the physical demands on the worker, decreasing the risk of repetitive motion injuries, and changing the muscle groups used during the shift. Job rotation can improve the mental focus of an employee by reducing boredom and also expanding their skill sets. This process does not eliminate ergonomic risk factors—it simply reduces the employee's exposure. Before any job rotation is implemented, an expert should evaluate the potential impact on the employee of the cumulative risk factors for all the jobs or tasks in the rotation.

## Early Symptom Intervention

**Early symptom intervention** is a proactive strategy used to identify **ergonomic risk factors** before they result in injuries. **Cumulative trauma injuries** develop over time and are difficult to recover from. The earlier an ergonomic risk factor is identified and corrected, the less likely it is to result in a cumulative trauma injury and the more likely an employee is to recover.

The five steps of an early intervention process include:

- **Employee awareness**: training and educating employees on ergonomic risk factors and on the early warning signs of **musculoskeletal disorders (MSDs)** can empower employees to prevent and identify the onset of MSDs.
- **Early reporting**: employees should report any potential discomfort before it becomes an injury. The sooner a risk factor is reported, the sooner it can be corrected.
- **Rapid response**: safety professionals should respond to any report of a potential MSD as quickly as possible. MSD injuries are very costly as they often require surgery. However, when caught and addressed early, physical therapy can be effective in returning an employee back to work quickly.
- **Assessment**: a thorough ergonomic assessment should be conducted for any employee reporting the onset of a potential MSD. The safety professional or trained individual can identify all potential risk factors, even those that are not yet impacting the employee, and recommend corrective measures in a holistic approach.
- **Follow up**: the safety professional should conduct a follow up with the employee to make sure the mitigation strategies are being properly implemented. Closing the loop on the process will make sure that all efforts to stop MSDs before they happen are successful.

# Fire Prevention and Protection

## Chemical

**Flash point** is the minimum temperature where enough vapor exists above a material to ignite when exposed to an ignition source.

**Lower flammable/explosive limit** is the minimum concentration (expressed as a percentage) of flammable vapor in air that is capable of propagating a flame when exposed to an ignition source. Below this concentration, there is not enough fuel for the fuel/air mixture to ignite—the mixture is "too lean."

**Upper flammable/explosive limit** is the maximum concentration (expressed as a percentage) of a flammable vapor in air that is capable of propagating a flame when exposed to an ignition source. Above this concentration, there is too much fuel and not enough air for the mixture to burn—the mixture is "too rich." The area between the lower and upper flammable/explosive limit is called the **flammable range**. The difference between a flammable range and explosive range is determined by whether or not the fuel is contained within an enclosed space or container.

**Auto-ignition temperature** is that minimum temperature where a chemical will ignite without the presence of an ignition source. The energy in the environment is at a level high enough for combustion.

### Control Measures for Chemical Fires

Control measures for any hazard should follow the hierarchy of controls—**elimination, substitution, engineering controls, administrative controls,** and **personal protective equipment (PPE)**. In the case of preventing chemical fires, PPE will not be applicable.

**Elimination**: determine if the chemical is necessary or can be removed from the process. Eliminating a redundant cleaning step or unnecessary heating can remove the hazard.

**Substitution**: replacing the flammable chemical with a combustible or non-flammable substitute can address the fire hazard. If feasible, water-based solutions would be preferred to flammable mixtures.

**Engineering controls**: exhaust ventilation can be used to remove flammable vapors and combustible dusts from the environment. Containing or removing ignition sources, such as enclosing pilot lights or grounding equipment susceptible to static charge buildup, can reduce the chance of a chemical fire. Proper storage of flammable and combustible liquids, including the use of safety cans and fire-resistant storage cabinets and refrigerators for chemicals with low flash points, can prevent fuels from catching fire. Proper **separation** and **segregation** of incompatible materials can prevent chemical reactions from initiating a fire. Finally, intrinsically safe lighting in chemical storage areas and grounding of equipment that builds static charges can further eliminate sources of ignition.

**Administrative controls**: policies limiting the amount of flammable chemicals in an area or process can reduce the chance of fire. Adherence to standard operating procedures can assist in reducing the chance of fire due to operator error. Proper signage prohibiting open flames can remind employees to avoid ignition sources in hazardous atmospheres. Finally, proper training of staff on chemical hazards, proper chemical handling, and how to respond to releases can further assist in preventing chemical fires.

### Vapor Pressure and Flammability

**Vapor pressure** is the force exerted by the vapor of a material. It is caused by the evaporation or sublimation of the material under normal conditions. The amount of material evaporating is dependent on temperature, with higher temperatures causing higher amounts of vapor above the material.

It is only the vapor of a material that burns, not the liquid or solid itself. Therefore, materials that have higher vapor pressures evaporate at lower temperatures. This means that at any temperature, the material will have a significant concentration of vapor above the material available to burn. The vapor will mix with available air to create **flammable mixtures**. Thus, materials with high vapor pressures have decreased lower flammable/explosive limits, higher upper flammable/explosive limits, and lower ignition temperatures.

### Pyrophoric and Water-Reactive Chemicals

**Pyrophoric** chemicals are those chemicals that spontaneously combust when exposed to air. To prevent combustion, these chemicals can be stored underwater. Examples of pyrophoric chemicals include metal hydrides, finely divided metal powders, and specialized chemical reagents.

**Water reactive** chemicals react, sometimes violently, with water. The degree of reaction can vary from forming a gas to a sustained flame to an explosion. These chemicals must be stored away from any source of water and may be stored under a heavy oil, such as kerosene. In certain climates, these chemicals can react with the humidity in the ambient air. Examples of water reactive chemicals include sodium metal, potassium metal, aluminum chloride, lithium metal, and phosphorus pentachloride.

# Electrical

## GFCI

A **Ground Fault Circuit Interrupter (GFCI)** protects against the most common type of electrical shock, a ground fault. A **ground fault** occurs when an electrical current finds an alternate 'path of least resistance' to the ground (or earth) than the ground wire. A person receives a shock when this path of least resistance is through their body. GFCIs are commonly used and required in wet areas such as bathrooms or kitchens, since the presence of water increases the chance that electrical current will experience a ground fault. Water is very conductive and provides an easy path for electrical current. The GFCI works by comparing the current that exits the unit to the current returning to it; if a significant difference is detected, it immediately cuts off the electricity flow through the circuit and protects from the risk of electrical shock.

### Grounding and Bonding

Chemical fires can be initiated by **static discharge**. **Static electricity** is an electric charge that is at rest. A **static charge** can be formed whenever two dissimilar materials make contact and are then separated and neither of the materials can dissipate the charge. In chemical processes, this condition can arise by the friction of fluids or solids moving through pipes or agitation in their containers. This motion results in a charge being unequally distributed, resulting in a difference in potential. When the potential difference between two materials or containers becomes large enough and they are brought into contact with each other, the current moves between the materials or containers in the form of a discharge. In the presence of flammable liquids or dusts, a fire or explosion can result.

**Bonding** is a method of equilibrating the potential of the two containers so that no differential exists. Electrons move freely through a conductor so that the charge on both containers is equal. This is typically accomplished by way of a metal strap or wire that is attached to both containers. Bonding does not remove the charge from the containers but makes the charge equal, thereby preventing a discharge.

**Grounding** is the process of providing a path to earth that removes the charge from the container. The path for the charge must include a wire or rod that is in contact with bare earth to allow the charge to flow from the container. Grounding can be used in conjunction with bonding.

### Arc Flash Hazards

The arc flash hazard level is determined by calculating the expected energy of an arc flash at various distances from the source. It is an engineering calculation that takes into account the fault current of the panel or connection involved and determines the energy felt at various distances away from the work. The energy is calculated in units of calories per square centimeter. The distance used is generally three feet (an arm's length) for the workers who will be doing the work. The equation can also be used to determine the exclusion boundary around the work; this is the distance at which the incident energy is less than 4 cal/cm$^2$, and a bystander can observe the work clad in regular work clothes. These are engineering calculations that must be performed by a qualified engineer.

The **Arc flash level of PPE** is presented in National Fire Protection Association (NFPA) 70E, Standard of Electrical Safety in the Workplace. The level of protection required to protect a worker from an arc flash hazard is determined by engineering calculations that estimate the amount of incident energy potentially released from an arc flash, measured in calories per square centimeter. There are four levels, numbered from one to four (category zero can be considered normal industrial protection—safety glasses, hard hat, gloves, and steel-toed boots). The categories are as follows:

- **Category 1**: up to 4 cal/cm$^2$—flame-resistant long-sleeved shirt, pants, and coveralls, plus face shield
- **Category 2**: up to 8 cal/cm$^2$—cotton underwear, plus flame-resistant long-sleeved shirt and pants, and face shield
- **Category 3**: up to 25 cal/cm$^2$—all of Category 2 plus Level 3 arc flash suit
- **Category 4**: up to 40 cal/cm$^2$—all of Category 2 plus Level 4 arc flash suit

## Hot Work

**Hot work** refers to work with hot metal such as brazing, welding, soldering, cutting with a torch, and drilling or grinding that potentially create a fire hazard. Employees engaged in hot work must be trained in the hazards posed by the work and how to mitigate them. A hot work program must include assessment of industrial hygiene hazards (exposure to metal dusts and fumes), assessment of noise hazards, assessment of proper personal protective equipment (PPE; eye protection, proper gloves, and respiratory protection if required) and must include an assessment of fire hazards posed by the hot work.

## HOT WORK PERMIT SYSTEMS

A hot work permit ensures that safety precautions have been taken for welding or torch cutting activities. The permit is designed as a job aid to check that the work area has been prepared for flying sparks by removing **flammable debris** in a radius around the work area. The work permit should prompt a check that the **fire sprinkler protection system** is in place and functional, and that fire extinguishers of the correct type are staged and ready. The permit should include a provision to test the work environment to ensure there is no **explosive atmosphere**. The permit should document that the employees have received the required training and have the proper PPE available. The permit should include a provision to have a **fire watch** in place for at least thirty minutes after the hot work has been completed, and for the area to be periodically monitored for at least six hours after the work is completed.

## SUPERVISOR'S DUTIES FOR HOT WORK

Supervisors are responsible for planning the work and ensuring that the hot work permit system is implemented. The use of the hot work permit checklist is a means of ensuring the proper safety precautions are taken and planning is completed prior to the hot work beginning. The supervisor is responsible for ensuring employees have the proper PPE on hand. Supervisors are responsible for providing the proper manpower and personnel to use a designated fire watch employee if necessary. The supervisor is also responsible for ensuring that employees have received the required safety and operational training to conduct the hot work.

## FIRE WATCH

Proper planning for hot work or welding includes having a person to act as "fire watch." This is necessary for any activities that have a fire risk. The fire watch person should be trained in the duties and should understand the requirements of the **hot work permit**. The person should be stationed in the area and remain alert for sparks or embers emitted during the work. The person must be prepared to use a fire extinguisher and to alert other workers and authorities in the event of an emergency. Fire watch duties must extend after the hot work is finished until there is absolutely no chance that any embers remain that could cause a fire. If the fire watch must leave the work area at any time during work, work must be stopped until he or she returns.

# Fire Science

## FIRE TETRAHEDRON

**Fire** is a rapid and self-sustaining chemical reaction involving oxygen, heat, and fuel. This can be visualized with the **fire triangle** or, if the chemical chain reaction is included, the **fire tetrahedron.** If any one of the four elements of the tetrahedron is removed, the fire cannot continue. Thus, fires can be extinguished by removing the oxygen, removing the fuel, cooling the fire down, or blocking the chemical reaction with an inert agent.

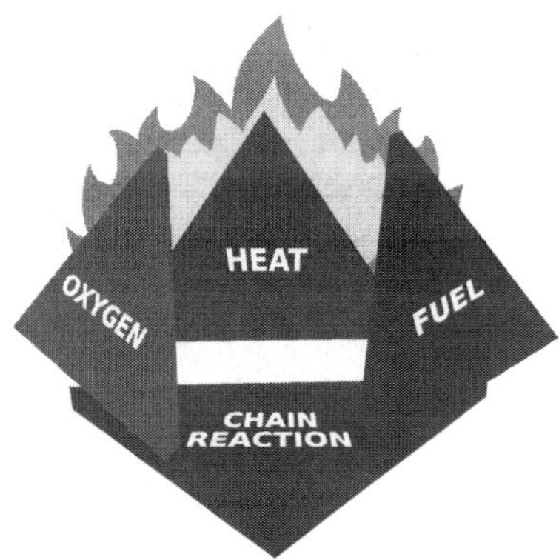


In the US, there are five **classifications** of fire, defined by the combustible they burn:

**Class A**: ordinary combustibles such as wood, paper, cloth, trash, and plastics

**Class B**: flammable liquids (or gases) such as gasoline, petroleum oil, and paint

**Class C**: energized electrical equipment

**Class D**: combustible metals such as potassium, sodium, aluminum, and magnesium

**Class K**: cooking oils and fats

Water and foam extinguishers are good for class A fires only. Carbon dioxide, clean agent, or halogenated extinguishers can be used on class B and C fires. Dry powder extinguishers are designed for class D fires. Wet chemical extinguishers are used on class K fires.

## Upper and Lower Explosive Limits

The main difference between flammable liquids and gases is that **flammable gases** are ready to burn, but **flammable liquids** must be vaporized to burn. Vapor can only burn if the concentration in air is between the **lower flammability limit (LFL)** and **upper flammability limit (UFL)**. If the concentration is lower than the LFL, the mixture of gas and atmosphere is "too lean." If the concentration is higher than the UFL, it is "too rich." For example, gasoline has a flammable range of 1% to 8%, meaning it can only burn when the concentration of gasoline vapor in the air is between 1 and 8 percent.

The flammable range of a mixture of gases in air can be calculated by using **Le Chatelier's mixing rule** for combustible volume fractions:

$$\mathrm{LFL_{mix}} = \frac{1}{\sum \frac{f_n}{\mathrm{LFL_n}}}$$

Where:

$LFL_{mix}$ = lower flammability limit of the mixture

$f_n$ = fractional concentration of component $n$

$LFL_n$ = lower flammability limit of component $n$

Note that the formula is the same for UFL, simply substituting $UFL_{mix}$ for $LFL_{mix}$ and $UFL_n$ for $LFL_n$. For example, consider a gas mixture of 40% carbon monoxide, 10% octane, and 50% ammonia. Assuming the flammable ranges for these gases are 12-75%, 1-7%, and 15-28%, respectively, the upper flammability limit of the mixture can be calculated as such:

$$UFL_{mix} = \frac{1}{\sum \frac{f_n}{UFL_n}} = \frac{1}{\frac{0.4}{0.75} + \frac{0.1}{0.07} + \frac{0.50}{0.28}} = 0.267, \text{or } 26.7\%$$

# Combustible dust

## Dust Explosions

Dust explosions occur when fine particles of a material disperse in the air and then ignite. The dust can become airborne during a normal working procedure or when dust that has settled in a room is disturbed. Such explosions can occur in a series with an initial explosion disturbing settled dust, causing it to become airborne and ignite. In addition, oxidizing agents in the air can make a dust explosion even more severe. Most organic dusts are combustible in the air, as are some inorganic and metallic dusts. The *severity* of the explosion depends on numerous factors:

- Type of dust.
- Size of the dust particles (Smaller particles ignite more easily).
- Concentration of particles in the air (Higher concentrations of particles are more flammable).
- Presence of oxygen (More oxygen pressure increases the likelihood of an explosion).
- Presence of impurities (Inert materials mixed in with the dust reduces its combustibility).
- Moisture content (Moisture increases the ignition temperature, making combustion less likely).
- Air turbulence (Combustion occurs more readily and explosions are more severe when air turbulence mixes the dust and air together).

The **combustible dust explosion pentagon** is similar to the fire triangle in that both require fuel, an oxidizer, and an ignition source to occur. In addition to these, a dust explosion must have dispersion and confinement of dust particles. These elements are created when dust particles are suspended in air in an enclosed space. If any of the five elements are not present, a dust explosion cannot occur.

# Detection systems

**Smoke detectors** detect particulate matter in the air associated with smoke. There are two types: **ionization detectors** and **photoelectric detectors.** An ionization detector uses a small radioactive source and detector in a chamber. The source creates a charge that crosses a small chamber to complete the circuit. Smoke particles interrupt the current, thereby triggering an alarm. A photoelectric detector uses a light sensor system. A light source is directed away from the detector in the unit. When smoke particles enter the unit, the light is scattered and strike the sensor, initiating the alarm.

**Heat detector**: in environments where particulate matter may be present and a smoke detector would initiate false alarms, a heat detector may be a better choice. In these types of detectors, two thermistors are used, with one sealed from the environment and another exposed to the air temperature. A change in current between the exposed thermistor and the reference thermistor will cause a current to flow, thereby initiating the alarm.

**Flame detector**: these units will respond when they detect specific frequencies of light (ultraviolet, visible, or infrared) associated with combustion.

# Suppression Systems, Fire Extinguishers, Sprinkler Types

## Classes of Fire Extinguishers

The National Fire Protection Association's Standard 10 identifies five (5) different classes of portable fire extinguishers: **A, B, C, D,** and **K**. Selection of the appropriate extinguisher is based on the fuel type(s) present that would contribute to a fire and the amount of combustible material present (fuel load). Combination extinguishers, such as A/B, B/C, or A/B/C, can be used in environments where multiple fuel types exist.

**Class A**: primary fuel is ordinary combustibles, such as wood or paper, or paper-based materials, such as cardboard; extinguishing material may be water or a dry chemical-extinguishing material.

**Class B**: the main fuel source for this class would be petrochemical products, such as flammable liquids, combustible liquids, solvents, alcohols, and flammable gases; extinguishing material can be dry chemical, foam, or carbon dioxide.

**Class C**: fires that involve energized electrical equipment; extinguishing material is typically dry chemical or carbon dioxide.

**Class D**: fires involving flammable metals that burn at very high temperatures, such as magnesium titanium, sodium, and lithium; extinguishing material is dry chemical, typically sodium chloride or graphite.

**Class K**: kitchen fires involving grease and fat; extinguishing material is typically an alkaline mist, such as those containing potassium citrate, potassium acetate, or potassium carbonate.

## Extinguishers for Electrical Fires

A dedicated **Class C** extinguisher is recommended for use on fires that involve energized electrical equipment. This also refers to fires involving portable equipment that is still plugged in. The extinguishing medium must be non-conductive to prevent an electrocution hazard to the individual using the extinguisher.

However, these types of fires can cause surrounding materials to ignite. Thus, a dedicated Class C extinguisher may not be appropriate for the surrounding materials. If a dedicated Class C extinguisher is necessary for delicate electronic equipment, then a supplemental Class A or Combination A/B should also be available in the area. Another option is to select a Class A/B/C extinguisher for the area to address all available fuel types.

## Fire Extinguisher Inspections

In Standard 10, the National Fire Protection Association (NFPA) establishes the requirements for portable extinguisher inspections. A **portable extinguisher** is any device that is hand-carried or on wheels that contains an extinguishing agent under pressure. The goal of an inspection is to ensure the extinguisher is in the proper location and has not been actuated, damaged, or tampered with and is ready in an emergency. NFPA has established two types of inspections which must be recorded on a tag affixed to the extinguisher: **monthly** and **annual**.

The monthly extinguisher inspection serves to check that the unit is ready if needed and also that units are in their proper locations. The monthly visual inspection is recorded on the tag by way of initials and date of the individual conducting the inspection. The inspector must check the following:

- Area around extinguisher is clear, with a clearance of no less than 24 inches.
- Pressure gauge is in the operable range.
- Extinguisher contains agent, which is verified by lifting the unit.
- Tamper seal and pin are in place and intact.
- Unit is not visibly damaged.

A record of the inspection is made by replacing and marking the tag on the unit. The annual inspection shall address all the elements of a monthly inspection and also the following (note: inspection frequency may vary based on the construction and type of extinguisher):

- Operating instructions are present and visible.
- Hydrostatic test has not expired (6-year interval for most extinguishers).
- Pin removes from handle when pulled.
- All boots, foot rings, and attachments are in good condition and are removed.
- Internal inspection.

## Carbon Dioxide Suppression Systems

**Carbon dioxide-based extinguishing systems** can be used when water may create additional hazards, such as the presence of water-reactive chemicals causing burning liquids to flow, or when water may damage sensitive equipment. Such systems can be found on ships, in certain metal processing industries, and in computer rooms. Carbon dioxide is an **inert gas** that removes the oxygen from the system to inhibit combustion. The gas is non-flammable, provides its own pressurization in the system, is non-reactive with other materials, works in three dimensions, and does not leave a residue after discharge.

However, there are issues to consider with carbon dioxide systems. Carbon dioxide systems are designed to achieve an airborne concentration of approximately 34%, which is lethal. Additionally, the agent is designed to reduce the **oxygen level** in the room, creating an IDLH environment. The National Fire Protection Association (NFPA) Standard 12 outlines the requirements for carbon dioxide systems. Wherever carbon dioxide systems are installed, **warning signs** must be visible informing employees to leave the area when the **alarm** sounds and not to re-enter until properly ventilated. Additional warnings must be posted in the gas storage area in the event the storage tanks leak. The system must also be outfitted with **audible and visual alarms** that actuate prior to system discharge to provide occupants time to evacuate. These alarms must be distinct from other alarm systems in the building and must be at least 90 dB. Audible alarms can be silenced after all entrances have been secured, while visual alarms must continue to function until the atmosphere is safe for re-entry.

## Water-Based Sprinkler Systems

### *Inspections for Water-Based Sprinkler Systems*

The National Fire Protection Association (NFPA) Standard 25 denotes the required inspection regimen for a **water-based automatic fire suppression system**. The major components of the system must be inspected on a recurring basis. The frequency of some inspections is dependent on the system components and, in some locations, can vary in winter months to avoid freeze damage. These inspections must be recorded to demonstrate compliance at the frequency listed below:

- **Sprinklers** are to be inspected from the floor level annually. Sprinklers should be inspected for leakage, corrosion, damage, loss of fluid in heat detection element, and paint.
- **Standpipe and hose systems** shall be visually inspected annually, ensuring that the hydraulic design information sign is present and legible.
- Wet standpipe gauges shall be visually inspected quarterly, while dry standpipe gauges shall be inspected weekly.
- **Private fire hydrants** have components that must be inspected quarterly, semi-annually, and annually.
- **Pump systems**, if present, shall be visually inspected weekly for damage, leaks, and proper pressure.
- **Water storage tanks**, if present, have components that must be inspected daily, weekly, monthly, quarterly, annually, and at 3-5-year intervals, depending on the system.
- **Valve systems** must be inspected weekly, monthly, quarterly, or annually, depending on the system components.
- **Specialized systems**, such as water spray, mist, and foam-water systems have additional inspection requirements.

### *Sprinkler Requirements for Storage Racks*

Warehouses are designed to compactly store large amounts of materials. The storage capacity in any floor space is vastly increased with the use of **storage racks**. However, storage racks may contain a high **fuel load** of flammable or combustible materials stacked several feet high. This increases the fuel load for each square foot of storage space in the warehouse. For materials that are classified as **high-pile** (12 feet high or more), the National Fire Protection Administration (NFPA) Standard 13 describes the sprinkler system requirements. Fire and loss risk increase because high-piled materials can act like flues, increasing the rate of smoke generation and flame spread.

Factors that are considered in system design include the type and amount of materials to be stored, density of the stored materials, the rack design, the height of the racks, aisle width, the slope of the roof, and the height of the roof. At a minimum, NFPA 13 requires sprinklers to be installed 18-54 inches above the storage rack, depending on the rack design and construction. The use of in-rack sprinklers with heads in between two levels of storage can also increase coverage and decrease losses in the event of a fire. Because of this, any sprinkler system for high-piled storage must be designed by an engineer.

### *Fire Sprinkler Repair Requirements*

The National Fire Protection Association (NFPA) Standard 25 outlines the inspection, maintenance, and testing requirements for water-based fire protection systems, including automatic sprinkler systems. The standard requires an annual inspection of spare sprinklers. Spare sprinklers must be immediately available in the event of damage or actuation of the system in order to return the system to a state of readiness as soon as possible. Spare sprinklers of each type used in the system must be kept on hand along with a wrench for each type. (A pipe wrench or crescent wrench cannot be used to substitute for manufacturer-recommended tools.) Replacement sprinklers must be the same style, orifice size, temperature rating, spacing requirements, deflector type, and system design ratings.

No less than six (6) new replacement sprinklers must be kept on the premises at all times. At least two (2) sprinklers of each type must be maintained. All sprinklers must be stored in a cabinet where the temperature will not exceed 100 °F.

# Segregation and Separation

## Segregation of Hazardous Materials for Storage

Hazardous materials must be properly segregated for storage. The materials should be classified according to hazard class. The US Department of Transportation hazard classification system provides a suitable guide for hazard classification. Strong acids must be segregated from storage near strong bases, because when the two mix a violent exothermic reaction can occur. Similarly, oxidizing materials must be stored away from flammable materials because oxidizers promote fire. Flammable or combustible materials must be stored away from any sources of heat or ignition (including a hot environment). Alkali metals must be stored under oil to prevent air contact and must be stored away from any flammable materials. Attention must be paid to possible chemical reactions; a good source of information for chemical incompatibility is the Safety Data Sheet.

## Storing Compressed Gas Cylinders

Commonly used hazardous materials that are supplied and stored in gas cylinders include oxygen, argon, acetylene, and helium. Care must be taken when storing and handling them to prevent release of the compressed gas or fires and explosions. The cylinders should be stored upright in a well-ventilated area and must be chained in place to prevent them toppling over. The caps that cover the valves should be tightly secured to prevent the valves being opened inadvertently. If cylinders are stored outside, they must be protected from ice, rain, and high temperatures and be stored on a fireproof surface. If stored inside, they must also be on a fireproof surface. Oxygen must always be stored segregated from fuel gases (such as acetylene) and separated by a distance of at least twenty feet or by a fire-resistant wall of at least five feet in height.

## Storage and Handling of Flammable Materials

Flammable liquids must be stored in approved flammable containers; for example, flammable liquids will generally be supplied in glass bottles or metal drums, not in plastic containers. If a secondary container is to be used (e.g., to transport a small quantity of gasoline), the container must be approved to hold flammable liquids. Flammable liquids must be stored in approved flammable liquid storage cabinets or in segregated rooms that have separate ventilation and whose walls meet fire resistance ratings. Aisles must be maintained at 3 feet in width, and egress routes must be kept clear in areas where flammable liquids are stored.

When storing flammable or combustible materials indoors, the following actions should be taken: Store only small amounts in occupied areas or buildings; larger amounts need to be stored in separate facilities. Follow National Fire Protection Association (NFPA) standards when designing storerooms for flammable and combustible materials, including standards for ventilation, static electricity grounding systems, explosion-proof light switches and fixtures, self-closing doors with raised sills, signage, and floor contours. Follow NFPA standards for storage cabinets designed to hold small quantities of flammable and combustible items. When transferring flammables from one container to another, ensure that the containers are touching each other or are connected to a grounding rod or line. Store flammable liquids in closed containers. When dispensing flammable liquids from drums, use gravity or suction pumps rather than pressurizing the drum. Use safety cans to move flammable liquids from their storage area to their point of use. Use plunger cans if you need to wet cleaning cloths with a flammable liquid. Store cloths that have been contaminated by flammable liquids in a small self-closing container that you empty regularly.

# Housekeeping

**Housecleaning** refers to the process of cleaning an area: sweeping, wiping surfaces, throwing away trash, etc. **Housekeeping** means putting things away where they belong. Every tool, piece of equipment, and material should have a designated storage area. Hazardous materials should have special storage areas designed specifically for them.

**Effective housekeeping** is important from both environmental and safety standpoints. Poor housekeeping can increase the volume of waste generated by causing spills and by accumulating out-of-date materials that must be discarded. From a safety standpoint, poor housekeeping can create slip, trip, and fall hazards; can block emergency exits; and can block emergency equipment such as fire extinguishers. Setting **housekeeping policies** and enforcing them, along with employee training and an inspection program, are the key elements of an effective housekeeping program. Effective housekeeping begins with only necessary materials in the work area, with everything having a designated location, and with clear communication of these guidelines (all elements of a 5S program). Employees should be trained to clean up as they go along throughout their shift and should set aside time at the end of shift to clean up completely. All tools should be replaced into storage lockers and containers returned to storage locations. Surfaces should be kept clean. Effective housekeeping promotes a safe workplace and increases job satisfaction because it is more pleasant to work in an orderly environment.

### *Controlling Hazardous Chemicals*

Part of housekeeping is removing dust and cleaning up spills. **Hazardous dust** needs to be regularly vacuumed from surfaces so that it will not become airborne. A vacuum that traps the contaminants must be used. Materials can become airborne when they are loaded, unloaded, and transferred to other containers. Transferring within a closed transfer or exhaust system can protect workers from being exposed to airborne dust and vapors. For **liquids**, it is also helpful to use drip pans or containers to collect overfill spills and leaks. Leak detection programs can include both automatic sensors and regular visual inspections of valves and pipes. The sensors can trigger alarms or even shut down a process. Repairing leaks quickly minimizes any potential exposures. Workers and supervisors who use hazardous chemicals need to receive training on what hazards they face and how to protect themselves. This training will help them stay safe and is also required by OSHA standards and by law in some states.

Housekeeping is important in controlling fire hazards, especially storage and handling of rags and wipes soaked in flammable materials. If one accumulates rags and wipes soaked with solvents or similar materials, they should be stored in metal canisters rated for flammable rag storage and emptied daily into suitable containers. If rags and wipes soaked with flammable solvents are stored in piles outside of the metal canister, they can build up heat and create conditions favorable to spontaneous combustion. It is also important to store flammable liquids in an orderly manner in cabinets or rooms rated for flammable chemicals.

# Emergency Response Management (ERM)

## Emergency, Crisis, Disaster Response Planning

### Fire Evacuation Drills

The National Fire Prevention Association (NFPA) Standard 1 establishes the provisions for **evacuation drills**. Drills must:

- Be held with a **sufficient frequency** to familiarize occupants with the process (typically at least annually)
- Be managed in an **orderly and organized** fashion to convey individual responsibilities during a true emergency and not purely focused on speed of egress
- Not be held always at the same time and manner to better **resemble an actual event**
- Identify a **relocation area** to allow for all occupants to be accounted for
- Be **documented** by way of a record noting the date, time, and type of drill

### Components of Emergency Response Plan Preparation

An **emergency** is any sudden and unexpected event that has the potential to harm life or the environment. Emergencies may be a result of natural or man-made causes. Companies that store or use hazardous materials must prepare an **emergency response plan** to reduce any potential harm that may be caused by a release. The ability to quickly respond and stabilize an emergency requires planning, practicing, evaluating, and adjusting.

- **Planning**: creating an emergency response plan in advance of an emergency is critical in managing the event. Planning allows for establishing **roles and responsibilities,** as well as allowing the company to procure necessary materials before they are needed. The overall goal of planning is to reduce the time between event and mitigation to reduce losses.
- **Practicing**: response team members must learn to use equipment, ask questions about their role, and troubleshoot the response plan elements before an actual emergency occurs. **Practicing and training** is the most effective method for team members to learn to work together without the stress of a real emergency.
- **Evaluating**: the effectiveness of a plan must be continually evaluated. Practicing an emergency response allows the team to identify **areas for improvement** before an emergency occurs. Robust plans are also evaluated after an emergency response. Evaluation should include identifying aspects that worked well, areas that can be improved, and things that failed to work as designed.
- **Adjusting**: the plan should be adjusted whenever improvements are identified. Response activities that worked well can be expanded to other aspects of the response. Areas that need correction can be adjusted and then practiced again to determine if the performance goals were achieved.

### Emergency Planning and Community Right to Know Act

The Environmental Protection Agency (EPA) is assigned responsibility for enforcing the **Emergency Planning and Community Right to Know Act (EPCRA)**. This Act was created to help communities plan for chemical emergencies that could originate from companies in or around their area that store or handle toxic chemicals. The intent of the EPCRA is to increase community knowledge and access to information regarding chemicals at facilities, their uses, and provisions to manage releases. EPCRA addresses four main elements:

- **Planning**: facilities that store large amounts of toxic or hazardous chemicals are required to cooperate with local agencies in preparing **emergency release response plans**.
- **Notification**: facilities must immediately report any release of hazardous substances that exceed a designated reportable quantity (RQ).
- **Information**: in order to inform the community, facilities must provide local response agencies with the safety data sheets (SDS) of those materials on-site and also an inventory form delineating those chemicals.
- **Toxic release inventory**: facilities must annually submit a report of the release of specified chemicals that exceed certain thresholds.

## Emergency Action Plans Vs. Emergency Response Plans

Emergency planning is a critical element for any organization to reduce losses to people, property, and the environment. A robust plan prepares for emergencies and outlines proper response activities to allow the business to respond quickly and effectively. There are two basic types of plans: an emergency action plan (EAP) and an emergency response plan (ERP).

The Occupational Safety and Health Administration (OSHA) in 29 CFR 1910.38 requires that businesses develop an **emergency action plan (EAP).** An EAP is for companies who will only respond to emergencies in a **defensive** fashion—meaning only evacuation and communication with first responders will take place. An EAP is a general guidance document that can be used for a variety of emergencies, from fire to mass violence incidents. The goal of the EAP is to ensure employee safety, not to address the emergency. The EAP must be in writing for employers having more than ten (10) employees and must include the following elements:

- Procedures for emergency reporting.
- Procedures for evacuation.
- The process for maintaining critical operations.
- Procedures to account for employees after an evacuation.
- Procedures for employees providing rescue or medical aid.
- Procedures for those responsible for the plan.

For facilities who will act as their own **first responders** for chemical emergencies, OSHA requires an **emergency response plan (ERP)** by way of 29 CFR 1910.120. The ERP establishes emergency response procedures, assigns roles and responsibilities, identifies necessary equipment, defines training requirements, and requires measures to prevent the spread of the chemical release to the surrounding environment. Within the ERP framework, employers can determine the level of response they will have their employees engage in before transitioning to external assistance.

## Emergency Action Plans

The Occupational Safety and Health Administration (OSHA) requires that employees have plans in place to provide for the safe evacuation of employees during emergencies. This **emergency action plan (EAP)** is required in 29 CFR 1901.38, which outlines the necessary parts of the Plan. An EAP can be thought of as a collection of situation-specific plans, written for each foreseeable emergency (e.g., fire, flood, tornado, earthquake, etc.). Each of these specific plans should have three main components: procedures, coordination, and assignments.

**Procedures**: Each individual plan within the EAP should have specific, step-by-step procedures describing the **actions** employees should take, beginning when the emergency occurs and ending when they are released to return home. Procedures should include notification systems, response actions, assembly areas for counting employees, and criteria for releasing employees.

**Coordination**: Each action plan should include how the company will coordinate with responding agencies. This may differ for the various emergency events, or it may be a single local agency for all situations. Coordination should include identifying points of contact for each agency and a means to communicate with the agency in the event normal communication (i.e., cell phones) are not functioning.

**Assignments and responsibilities**: The EAP should clearly assign individuals who will be responsible for managing the actions outlined in the plan. From individuals responsible for ensuring the building is evacuated to identifying who will give the "all clear" to return, each role needs to be clearly assigned to an individual or position.

## Emergency Evacuation Plans

An effective **emergency evacuation plan** requires both pre-planning and training all staff on the plan. If employees do not know how to evacuate in an emergency, the risk of injury and loss of life increases dramatically. Information that staff should be informed of includes:

- Location of primary and secondary **evacuation routes,** including signage.
- Location of fire alarm pull stations.
- Primary and secondary **assembly areas** to report to after the building has been evacuated to account for all staff.
- Designating who is responsible for evacuating visitors.

In addition to staff responsibilities, the emergency coordinator must also account for:

- Employees and visitors with mobility, hearing, or sight impairments.
- Identifying medical aid for staff, including meeting with area hospitals to ensure they can address specific hazards at the facility, including chemical exposures and burns.

## Post-Emergency Trauma Response Teams

In addition to the loss of property and physical injuries after an emergency, companies should also be prepared to manage psychological injuries to their employees. Emergency situations may place people in highly stressful situations or expose them to sounds, images, or other experiences that may be disturbing. If left untreated, psychological trauma can result in post-traumatic stress disorder, which can have long-lasting effects on employees. Employers can assist employees through the post-emergency period using trauma response teams.

A **trauma response team (TRT)** is one or more persons who are psychologists or have specialized training in helping people who have been exposed to extremely stressful situations. Providing employees access to this support service as soon as possible after an emergency can help employees navigate the emotions related to the emergency. The TRT can work with employees individually or in group settings and, if necessary, can refer employees to additional mental health support services.

## Disaster Recovery Plan Team Members

Although employers may put a lot of effort into emergency planning, equal effort must be put into recovery planning. **Recovery planning** is all the activities necessary to return the business to its pre-emergency functionality as quickly as possible. Recovering too slowly can have long-lasting impacts on the survival of a company. The plan should outline when and how the company will begin its efforts to move from response to recovery. A disaster recovery plan should have assignments for the following team members: recovery coordinator, recovery teams, damage assessment team, salvage team, logistics coordinator, and technology coordinator.

The **recovery coordinator** is the individual with the ultimate responsibility and authority over recovery operations. They must have the authority to make decisions, delegate responsibilities, and approve resource allocation.

**Recovery teams** are task-specific groups assigned by the recovery coordinator. Depending on the facility, teams can include facility management, security, human resources, environmental protection, and technical work groups.

The **damage assessment team** is responsible for an inventory of all plant systems, equipment, goods, and stores that require repair or replacement. The damage assessment team must include representatives from the facilities or maintenance department who are familiar with all the facility's systems and may include external contractors, such as engineers or utility company representatives. The team should document all damage with photographs for insurance purposes.

**Salvage teams** are responsible for securing systems, equipment, goods, and stores that can be used during recovery and after normal operations have resumed. The salvage team should be able to report on the usability of items after they have been assessed by knowledgeable persons.

**Logistics and supply line coordinators** are responsible for reestablishing all vendor contacts and contracts after the emergency has subsided. Receiving necessary raw materials or goods and securing shipping of finished goods are critical in getting the business back up and running. If prior contacts and contracts are no longer feasible, then new suppliers and shippers must be procured.

**Communication and technology coordinators** are responsible for addressing the phone, data, and online services after the emergency. If systems cannot be brought online at once, they are responsible for prioritizing systems and coordinating with service providers to reestablish external communications.

## Incident Command System

The Federal Emergency Management Agency (FEMA) has implemented the **Incident Command System (ICS)** as a means of coordinating multi-agency responses to an emergency event. The intent is to use standardized assignments, language, and responsibilities to efficiently and effectively leverage the unique capabilities of multiple agencies that respond simultaneously to a large-scale emergency event. The ICS model eliminates redundancy, reduces overlap, and consolidates control to effectively manage emergency response actions. The ICS is designed to be scalable in that it can be used for small incidents with minimal staffing or for large multi-agency incidents.

### *Command Staff Positions*

All command staff report to the **incident commander,** who is not part of the command staff but directs its efforts. The command staff consists of the public information officer, safety officer, and liaison officer.

- The **public information officer** (PIO) communicates with the media and holds press briefings. The PIO should be the only individual providing updates to the public through the media or online platforms to maintain consistent messaging.
- The **safety officer** is responsible for the overall safety of the responders. They review the response plan to identify any hazardous situations. They also receive and review updates on changing hazards as well as conduct safety briefings for staff.
- The **liaison officer** acts as the point contact for all responding agencies. They maintain a list of all primary agency contacts and a knowledge of each agency's capabilities to provide the IC input for response activities.

Promulgated by the Federal Emergency Management Agency, the **Incident Command System (ICS)** is a command and control system for emergency responses. The incident commander establishes the objectives of an emergency response and relies on specific functional groups to execute and support the **incident action plan (IAP)**. The ICS is divided into five functional areas, or sections: operations, planning, logistics, finance/administration, and intelligence. The intent of the division is to assign specific responsibilities to avoid redundancy. All functional area section chiefs report directly to the incident commander.

**Operations**: responsible for conducting the tactical operations for an incident and directing resources to execute the incident action plan.

**Planning**: Responsible for developing and updating the incident action plan to achieve the objectives established by the incident commander. This section is also responsible for assessing resource utilization and coordinating additional resources with the logistics section.

**Logistics**: Plans, acquires, and provides the resources needed by operations and other sections. In addition to tools and equipment, logistics also addresses personnel needs, such as hygiene, food, and rest areas.

**Finance/administration**: Monitors costs and makes funds available for logistics. This functional area is also responsible for tracking and recording all activities to apply for applicable reimbursements after the emergency has abated.

**Intelligence**: An optional functional area that can be formed in specific responses, such as mass attacks. This functional area conducts investigations, manages evidence related to unlawful events, conducts missing persons investigations, and works to prevent additional attacks.

### Role of the Incident Commander

The **incident commander** has overall responsibility for the incident and ultimately oversees the **Incident Command System**. All of the support sections relay information to and receive directions from the incident commander.

The incident commander is responsible for establishing the overall objectives for the response. They determine and approve the **incident action plan** and coordinate command staff and section chief activities. They establish the incident command post, which is the singular location for all information to funnel into for decision-making and prioritization. Lastly, it is the incident commander who determines when the Incident Command System can be deactivated.

## ICS General Staff

The Incident Command System (ICS) is overseen by the **incident commander,** who is directly supported by the general staff. The **general staff** is made up of the chiefs for each of the functional areas: operations, logistics, planning, and finance/administration. These positions report directly to the incident commander and can be filled by qualified persons from any agency or jurisdiction. If external personnel are not assigned as chiefs, interagency coordination can be facilitated by appointing agency representatives as deputy chiefs.

General staff can pass information horizontally or vertically within the system. However, all directions can only take place through their respective chains of command. For small scale events, positional responsibilities can be combined within a single individual as long as they are capable of executing all responsibilities effectively.

## ICS Command Staff

The Incident Command System (ICS) is overseen by the **incident commander,** who is directly supported by the general staff. The **general staff** is made up of the chiefs for each of the functional areas: operations, logistics, planning, and finance/administration. The command staff provide additional support to the incident commander but do not fall into any other functional area. The command staff consists of the public information officer, safety officer, and liaison officer. Some responses may require additional expertise added to the command staff, such as legal counsel and a medical advisor.

**Legal counsel** may be added to advise the incident commander of issues pertaining to evacuations, emergency proclamations, and the media's right to access. In responses with large numbers of injuries or fatalities, a **medical advisor** may be necessary. This individual would direct the work of trained medical staff, coordinate transportation of the injured to hospitals, and coordinate with the coroner or medical examiner to manage the deceased and their families.

## Comparison of ICS to Other Systems

The **Incident Command System** is the **field-level** emergency response structure. Based on a standardized structure, roles, and responsibilities, its primary purpose is to address an emergency incident.

The **Standardized Emergency Management System (SEMS)** is designed to be leveraged when an emergency exceeds the capabilities or resources of a local agency. SEMS is organized into five levels: **field, local, operational area, regional,** and **state.** As the resources of the local agency are exhausted or as the incident grows to impact multiple jurisdictions, SEMS coordinates resources between local and regional governments all the way up to the state level. Under SEMS, each level of government operates a coordinated emergency operations center, using the ICS terminology, to coordinate activities and resource allocation.

The **National Incident Management System (NIMS)** is the emergency response structure promulgated by the Federal Emergency Management Agency (FEMA). It requires agencies that will work together in emergency responses to adhere to similar basic principles, terminology, and structure. Where ICS is used at the field level, NIMS uses the same structure at the state operations center for statewide or regional responses.

### Training for Command Staff in NIMS

The Federal Emergency Management Agency (FEMA) establishes and offers training on the elements of the **Incident Command System**, which is the basic response structure for emergencies. After Hurricane Katrina, FEMA established the NIMS Training Program. Federal, state, local, and private entities have the responsibility to identify personnel to be trained on the NIMS curriculum.

**Command staff** should complete, at a minimum, **IS-700 NIMS**: an introduction (which addresses the goals and objectives of the NIMS) and **IS-100 NIMS** Incident Command System (an introduction to the roles and terminology used in ICS). Additional, specialized training, including role-specific training, is available through FEMA.

## Workplace Violence

### Reducing Workplace Violence

Managers can incorporate several strategies into the workplace to prevent or reduce **workplace violence** and provide a secure workplace.

- The workplace should be well-lit with no areas that are secluded or isolated.
- Work flows and traffic patterns should be easily observed so employees are never left in a vulnerable position. Employees should have freedom and control within their own area of the workplace but limited access to other areas.
- Surveillance cameras can allow for further monitoring of the workplace.
- Employers can also control access to the workplace. Fencing and locks can restrict trespassers from entering the work area. Security procedures that require visitors to check in reduce the risk of violence from outsiders.

#### *Establishing a Workplace Violence Protection Program*

A workplace violence protection program should establish a zero-tolerance policy toward threats and intimidation in the workplace. The policy must be communicated to all employees, managers, and supervisors.

- Personnel must be encouraged to promptly report observed or experienced incidents of violence or threats of violence in the workplace.
- Anonymous reporting procedures can be established and implemented in the form of a "complaint box."
- Written incident reports should be maintained detailing time, date, and nature of the threat incident. Part of the written report should be geared toward risk assessment and the likelihood of future occurrences.
- Liaison with law enforcement and social service agencies should be made so that appropriate referrals can be made when necessary.
- Training teams should be established to address, advise, and counsel employee groups with a view toward maintaining a civil and non-threatening work atmosphere.

# Industrial Hygiene and Occupational Health

## Sources of Biological Hazards

### Pathogens

A **pathogen** is a biological organism that causes a disease in humans. Pathogens require a host for nutrients and protection from the environment. The pathogen utilizes the body's resources to thrive and replicate. A pathogen may come from the environment (such as a fungal spore), an animal (rabies), or from another person (hepatitis A).

The primary mode of causing harm to employees is through infections. Viruses, bacteria, and fungi can cause infections, particularly in immunocompromised individuals. Bacteria, once established, can release toxic byproducts which can harm the host. Parasites can divert nutrients from the host, eventually causing starvation and death. Insects can spread viral and bacterial infections, which can lead to sickness and, in some cases, death.

Pathogens fall into one of four classes: viruses, bacteria, fungi, and parasites.

- **Viruses** consist of a piece of genetic code protected by a protein coating. They require a living host in order to replicate. The virus attaches itself to a cell and hijacks the replication process, forcing the cell to replicate the virus. The cell reaches a point where it bursts, releasing viruses to invade nearby cells. Viruses cause infections and can be transmitted from one person to another.
- **Bacteria** are single-cell organisms that have a nucleus, but do not have a cell membrane. Bacteria come in a variety of forms, with some being beneficial, if not necessary, for human survival. Bacteria replicate independent of the host and pathogenic bacteria can release toxic agents into the host organism or cause infections.
- **Fungi** are single-cell organisms with a thick membrane that cause disease in humans. Fungal infections can be mild, such as athlete's foot, or severe, such as aspergillosis. Fungi are prevalent throughout the world, with only about 300 being pathogenic.
- **Parasites** rely on the host for nourishment and, if left unchecked, may kill the host by diverting nutrients. Human pathogenic parasites fall into three main groups:
    - **Protozoa**: single-celled organisms that replicate within the body.
    - **Helminths**: worms that can live inside or on the body.
    - **Ectoparasites**: parasites that live on the outside of the body, including ticks and mosquitoes.

The method of protecting an employee from biological pathogens depends on the pathogens that employee may encounter.

Employees working in tropical climates can be vaccinated against known pathogenic hazards. The use of insect repellent can deter disease-carrying mosquitoes and flies. Proper handwashing and sanitation practices can protect against bacterial and parasitic infections. Fungal spores can be addressed by using respiratory protection, such as filtering facepieces or an air-purifying respirator with a HEPA filter attachment.

# Protocol for Bloodborne Pathogen Control

## Bloodborne Pathogens

The Occupational Safety and Health Administration (OSHA) (29 CFR 1910.1030) defines a **bloodborne pathogen** as any pathogenic microorganism that can be found in human blood that causes disease in humans. Although the bloodborne pathogen standard focuses on hepatitis B and HIV, there are numerous bloodborne pathogens, including hepatitis C and hepatitis A.

Any bodily fluid that is visibly contaminated with blood, any unfixed organ from a human, or known contaminated cell cultures that could cause an exposure are referred to as **other potentially infectious material (OPIM).** Exposure by blood or OPIM can occur by way of contact with a mucous membrane or non-intact skin, ingestion of the fluid, or injection into the body (such as a contaminated syringe or other sharp object).

## Controlling Bloodborne Pathogen Hazards

Procedures that can protect workers from **bloodborne pathogens** in the workplace include the following:

- Treating all bodily fluids as if they are contaminated
- Using self-sheathing needles, leakproof specimen containers, and puncture-proof containers for sharp objects
- Providing handwashing stations with antiseptic hand cleaners and requiring workers to wash their hands after removing gloves that could be contaminated
- Prohibiting employees from eating or drinking in areas where bloodborne pathogens could be present
- Providing gloves, goggles, respirators, aprons, and other personal protective equipment
- Regularly decontaminating and cleaning equipment and potentially contaminated areas
- Labeling potential biohazards

A **bloodborne pathogens policy** should be developed before any employees test positive for a disease. Preparing in advance allows the company to spend time determining appropriate actions instead of having to react quickly. A bloodborne pathogens policy needs to include at least three elements: employee rights, testing, and education. It should define the rights of employees who have been diagnosed with a bloodborne pathogen, including reasonable accommodations that will be made. The policy will also include whether employees will be tested for bloodborne diseases. Finally, the policy should include procedures for educating workers on how bloodborne pathogens can be transmitted and prevented.

# Mutagens, Teratogens, and Carcinogens

## Mutagens

A **mutagen** is a chemical substance or radioactive particle that causes mutations in a cell's DNA. This is important in planning for toxic material hazards because mutagenesis is thought to be one mechanism by which toxic substances can cause cancer. A mutagen acts to disrupt the normal pattern of the building blocks of DNA (the genes) that code for proteins necessary for cell life. Normal cells have many redundant repair mechanisms that allow for repair; however, repeated assaults by a mutagen can overwhelm the normal repair mechanisms and allow mistakes in the DNA to persist. Tumors are cells that have malfunctioned and proliferate unimpeded, and eventually take over the organism. Examples of commonly encountered mutagens are polycyclic aromatic hydrocarbons (found in tar and charred meat), benzene (found in gasoline), and ionizing radiation (found in the sun's rays). It must be noted that mutagens are not necessarily carcinogens but are likely to promote carcinogenesis.

## TERATOGENS

A **teratogen** is a chemical substance that causes birth defects when either the mother or father has been exposed to the substance before or during the conception and gestation of the baby. Many teratogens act in the first trimester of pregnancy, when a large amount of cell division and specialization occurs. Teratogens can be chemicals or medicines that are prescribed for common medical conditions. A common teratogen is ethyl alcohol; overexposure to alcohol during pregnancy can cause a cluster of problems in the child known as fetal alcohol syndrome. A teratogen of the 1960s was thalidomide; women who ingested the drug (prescribed for morning sickness) gave birth to babies with stunted limbs and other physical abnormalities. Because of these possible long-lasting effects, it is important to limit a pregnant woman's exposure to chemicals. There are substances that exert teratogenic effects in males, such as polychlorinated biphenyls and DBCP (a pesticide).

## CARCINOGENS

A **carcinogen** is any substance that is known or suspected of causing cancer or increasing the incidence of cancer. **Cancer** is a condition involving uncontrolled cell growth. This can be manifested in the form of **tumors**. The tumors can interrupt normal physiological processes and, if left uncontrolled, can cause death. This condition can be caused by damage to the cell's DNA or disruption in the cellular metabolism. Disruption in cellular metabolism can cause a cell to become less specialized, which can mask it from the immune system's cell termination process.

Carcinogenic substances include radionuclides, certain wavelengths of radiation, and certain chemicals such as benzene, polynuclear aromatic hydrocarbons, and aflatoxins.

### *CARCINOGEN GROUPS*

The **International Agency for Research on Cancer (IARC)** is an intergovernmental agency that is part of the World Health Organization (WHO). The goal of the agency is to promote international collaboration in the fight against cancer. The agency has four major objectives: monitor the global occurrence of cancer, identify causes of cancer, investigate the biological processes behind cancer-related diseases, and develop strategies to control cancer. As part of their mission, the IARC groups substances based on their potential to cause cancer in humans using a numbered scale from 1-4, with Group 1 being the most hazardous.

- **Group 4**: Substances designated at Group 4 are probably not carcinogenic in humans. Scientific evidence shows either a lack of cancer-causing results in humans and animals or an inadequate evidence of cancer-causing effects.
- **Group 3**: Substances in this group are considered not classifiable as causing cancer in humans. The substances either have inadequate information in humans and animals, or have caused cancer in animals but present no evidence that it may do so in humans. Substances in this group are considered to need more research.
- **Group 2B**: Substances in Group 2B are designated as possible human carcinogens. The substance has limited data on its effects on humans but has sufficient animal data. Additionally, substances in this group may have suggestions of being human carcinogens based on other data.

- **Group 2A**: Substances in this group are probably human carcinogens. A substance may be classified as Group 2A if it has similar data results as Group 2B but belongs to a class of substances designated as Group 2A or Group 1.
- **Group 1**: Substances in this group are known human carcinogens with sufficient human or animal data and strong indications of cancer-causing mechanisms.

# Chemical Hazards

## Hazard Control Hierarchy

The **National Institute of Safety and Health (NIOSH)** has developed a **hierarchy of controls** as a recommended approach to mitigating any hazard, including chemical hazards. The hierarchy establishes the order of strategies to be used to address hazards based on their effectiveness. Hazard controls should be assessed in the following order:

1. Elimination
2. Substitution
3. Engineering controls
4. Administrative controls
5. Personal protective equipment

This approach can be applied to chemical hazards. Per the hierarchy, the preferred method is to remove the chemical from the process without adversely impacting the final product. If removal is not possible, then the next method is to evaluate replacing the chemical with one that is less hazardous. For example, replacing a skin-absorbent toxic material with a less toxic material would remove the toxicity exposure hazard from the process. If replacement is not feasible, then engineering controls should be evaluated. **Engineering controls** are designed to remove or divert the hazard from the worker at the source, such as ventilation systems or closed reaction vessels. The benefit of an engineering control is that it functions independent of the worker. If an engineering control is not feasible, then an administrative control should be examined for its effectiveness. **Administrative controls** include policies and procedures to reduce exposures, such as standard operating procedures and work/rest cycles. If no other control is feasible or while other controls are being implemented, **personal protective equipment** in the form of chemical protective clothing and chemical resistant gloves can be used to reduce the exposure potential. Personal protective equipment is the least favored as it does nothing to address the hazard and is dependent on proper selection, donning, and use.

## Target Organ Toxicity

**Target organ toxicity** refers to chemicals that cause damage or adverse effects to specific organs or organ systems. Although damage may occur to multiple systems, certain chemicals impact specific organs or organ systems more than others. Symptoms of target-specific substance exposure are delayed due to the chronic nature of the exposure. The degree of damage to the organ is dependent upon the **dose**: a function of the **duration** of the exposure and **concentration** of the chemical.

- **Hepatotoxin**: a substance that is toxic to the liver. The liver is the primary organ responsible for cleaning the blood and is especially susceptible to damage from chemicals. Ethanol and carbon tetrachloride are hepatotoxic chemicals.
- **Neurotoxin**: substances that target the brain or nervous system and disrupts normal nerve function by blocking or interfering in neuron firing. Lead and mercury are classified as neurotoxins.

- **Hematotoxin**: substances that destroy red blood cells, interfere with the normal clotting mechanism, or destroy the lining of capillaries, resulting in hemorrhaging. Aniline and carbon monoxide are hematotoxic chemicals.
- **Nephrotoxin**: substances that cause damage to the kidneys. Mercury salts and dimethyl sulfate are classified as nephrotoxins.

### Selection of Airborne Hazard Controls

Proper selection of airborne hazard controls is dependent on the concentration or level of the contaminant in the atmosphere. Knowing the level of contaminants allows a safety professional to determine if a control method is needed and, if necessary, what type would be effective, such as selecting between an air-supplied respirator or an air-purifying respirator. The two most common methods for measuring air contaminants are grab samples and air monitoring.

A **grab sample** is when a portion of the atmosphere to be analyzed is collected using a pump, either into a sample bag or canister. The container is sent to a laboratory to determine what is in the sample and the concentration of contaminants. The advantages to this method are that the results are accurate and can conclusively identify all contaminants. The disadvantages are the time delay for results, the need for calibrated pumps, the cost of sample-collection devices, and the fact that results are representative of the time when the sample was collected.

**Air monitoring** is when a portion of the atmosphere is tested on a continuous basis using hand-held or mounted instruments. Area monitors can be installed to provide real-time analysis of the atmosphere and can be preset to alarm at action levels. Colorimetric tubes can be used for specific chemicals to give a semi-quantitative measure of contaminants. Combustible gas indicators can measure explosive/flammable limits and can be outfitted with oxygen sensors and dedicated gas sensors to provide nearly instantaneous readings. The benefits of air monitoring are in the rapid response time, lower cost, and the ability to measure changes in levels as they occur. However, air monitoring instruments tend to be less specific, have a higher degree of error, and may not identify all contaminants in the atmosphere.

### Signs and Symptoms of Chemical Exposure

A **chemical exposure** symptom is the body's reaction to a chemical. Symptoms may become evident immediately after an exposure, while others may take years to develop. Common symptoms of exposure to a chemical can be found on the safety data sheet for the substance. The signs and symptoms of chemical exposure depend on the chemical itself and also the route of exposure, whether it be a dermal exposure, inhalation, or ingestion.

- Symptoms of a **dermal contact** can include dryness, itching, cracking, burns, blisters, or redness near the point of contact.
- **Inhalation** of chemicals are usually identified by a smell or taste followed by coughing, sneezing, itching or burning in throat, detectable chemical odor, shortness of breath, dizziness, lack of concentration, or cognitive difficulties.
- **Ingesting** chemicals can lead to abdominal pains, nausea, vomiting, or acid reflux-like symptoms.

## Exposure Limits

### Threshold Limit Values (TLV)

The American Conference of Governmental Industrial Hygienists, Inc (ACGIH) has developed guidelines, called Threshold Limit Values, some of which have been adopted by OSHA, that estimate the limit that a worker may be exposed to a substance during a standard, 40-hour workweek without experiencing undesirable effects. The guidelines are based on inhalation data obtained from scientific journal articles. The two most common units are $mg/m^3$ and parts per million (ppm). The formula for converting between the two units is: $ppm = \frac{\frac{mg}{m^3} \times 24.45}{MW}$, where MW references the molecular weight of the substance. Molecular weight formula: $MW = \Sigma(atomic\ mass \times atomic\ subscript)$. The units of MW are gram/mole. Care needs to be taken in interpreting reported TLV values. Some values are averaged over typical 40-hour work week (TWA), some are taken as 15 min (STEL) snapshots, four times a day. The **ceiling TLV** is the maximum exposure at any time for any duration.

### Permissible Exposure Limits (PEL)

The major distinction between Permissible Exposure Limits and Threshold Limit Values is TLVs are guidelines set by an organization, while PELs are regulations set by OSHA. They are both valuable in ensuring a safe workplace, but PELs have the power of legal enforcement behind them. The PEL is measured and reported as a time weighted average (TWA). The OHS ACT (General Duty Clause) was enacted in 1970 and requires employers to provide a safe working environment, which includes ensuring toxins are maintained below the PEL (or other guideline if OSHA has not determined a PEL for the substance) determined for the chemical.

### Immediately Dangerous to Life and Health (IDLH)

IDLH stands for Immediately Dangerous to Life and Health. This term is used by the National Institute of Occupational Safety and Health to indicate the concentration of a substance that poses an acute and immediate danger to human life. Examples of IDLH situations are benzene exposure at 500 ppm, ammonia exposure at 300 ppm, and hydrogen sulfide exposure at 100 ppm.

### Action Level (AL)

An organization must regularly test for the level of regulated substances to determine the existing exposure level. If the level of a substance is at or above the action level, determined by OSHA to be half of the PEL, the employer must take action to monitor the health of employees, frequently measure the current exposure levels, and lower the level of the hazardous material. If the situation does not improve or gets worse, including the monitored substance reaching or exceeding the PEL, further action is required. In the interest of full compliance, the safety professional should regularly monitor both the exposure levels of any regulated substances known to exist in the workplace, keep current with the action levels of those substances, and maintain clear and proper documentation of all organizational actions regarding safety.

## Routes of Entry

An individual can be exposed to a chemical hazard by one of the four **routes of entry**: injection, ingestion, absorption, and inhalation.

**Injection** is the subcutaneous exposure of a chemical, which allows it to bypass the protective layer of the skin. An example of an injection exposure would be a broken chemical container that pierces the skin, allowing the chemical to enter the bloodstream.

**Ingestion** is exposure to a chemical by mouth, which causes an exposure by way of the digestive system. A person who has touched a hazardous material and then eats, drinks, applies cosmetics, takes medication, or smokes can transfer the material from their hands into their mouth, resulting in an exposure.

**Absorption** is the movement of a chemical through the intact skin. Skin absorption can occur when certain chemicals are spilled or splashed on unprotected flesh. As the concentration of the chemical is higher on the surface of the skin than it is on the inside of the body, the chemical will move to the area of lower concentration—a process called diffusion.

**Inhalation** is the most common route of entry for hazardous materials. High concentrations of water-soluble chemicals can overwhelm the protection of the **upper respiratory system** and enter the lungs. Chemicals that are not water-soluble can bypass the protective mucosa in the upper respiratory system and pass into the lungs. Once in the lungs, chemicals can damage the lung tissue or pass into the blood through the **alveoli** where they can negatively impact the body.

### ASSIGNED PROTECTION FACTOR

The Occupational Safety and Health Administration (OSHA) defines a respirator's **assigned protection factor (APF)** as the level of protection that a respirator is expected to provide the wearer.

The APF is determined by the manufacturer by measuring the **level of contaminants** outside of the respirator compared to the concentration inside the respirator. This difference represents leakage at the face seal and exhalation valves. The concentration inside the respirator represents the worker's exposure. The APF is calculated as a ratio of the outside versus inside contaminant concentration.

The APF determines whether a respirator will adequately protect an employee and is critical for a robust respiratory protection program. If the measured concentration of the contaminant in the environment divided by the APF exceeds the published **exposure limit**, then the respirator is not providing adequate protection and another control measure or respirator configuration must be selected. If the outside level divided by the APF is lower than the exposure limit, then the respirator is providing adequate protection and can be used in that environment.

## Acute and Chronic Exposures

Exposures to a hazard can be described as either acute or chronic depending on the frequency, duration, and concentration of the exposure.

An **acute exposure** is described as a short-term exposure, lasting seconds to hours. The exposure is typically infrequent in occurrence. The degree of exposure is typically large, such as breathing in large amounts of solvent vapors. Effects of an acute exposure usually manifest in a short period of time, such as dizziness, irritation, coughing, or fainting. Because of the infrequent nature of acute exposures, the body may be able to recover from even large dose exposures. However, the health effects are substance-dependent, as some acute exposures can be fatal.

A **chronic exposure** refers to a long-term exposure, from months to years. The exposure is typically more frequent than an acute exposure and tends to be in smaller amounts. Effects of a chronic exposure are typically latent, not manifesting until months or years later, and are typically permanent due to the body's repeated exposure. Lung cancer attributed to cigarette smoke could be described as the result of a chronic exposure.

Some chemical exposures can have both acute and chronic health effects. An employee may get dizzy while using paint thinner over a period of days and develop liver cancer in later years.

## Hazard Additive Effect

The **additive effect** of hazard exposures means that the health effects of any two hazards is the **sum** of the two. This means that the body experiences a combined effect of the two exposures. This can be illustrated by representing the toxic effect of substance A as 20% and the effect of substance B as 30% resulting in a combined toxicity of 50%. A common example of this effect is the use of a depressant, such as a sleeping pill, and alcohol, also a depressant, which would make a person sleepier together than either of the substances on their own.

## Chemical Synergistic Effect

The chemical **synergistic effect** refers to the toxicity of two chemicals being **multiplied** when combined. Unlike the additive effect where the effects are combined, synergy means the effects are much more severe. This can be illustrated by representing the toxic effect of chemical A as 5% and the effect of substance B as 20%, resulting in a combined toxicity of 80%. The multiplier for the resultant hazard is difficult to predict and depends on the substances that are combined, their amounts and concentrations, among other variables. An example of such an effect is the combination of chlorine bleach and ammonia. Separately, both have relatively low toxic effects. However, when they are mixed, they react to form chloramine and hydrazine, which are highly toxic and can be fatal in high doses.

## Chemical Antagonistic Effect

The **antagonistic effect** is when the toxicity of one chemical is reduced by the exposure of another chemical. This can be illustrated by representing the toxic effect of substance A as 30% and the effect of substance B as 50%, resulting in a combined toxicity of 10%. This effect depends on the substances that are combined, their amounts and concentrations, among other variables and is the core concept behind antidotes—the use of one chemical to reduce the toxicity of another.

A frequently cited example is providing dimercaprol to an employee exposed to mercury—the dimercaprol binds with the mercury to facilitate excretion of the toxin. While the dimercaprol may cause hypertension, this is less severe than the potential damage caused by mercury bioaccumulating in the kidneys.

## Chemical Potentiation

**Chemical potentiation** occurs when a non-toxic chemical is combined with a toxic chemical to create a more toxic exposure. This can be illustrated by representing the toxic effect of substance A as 0% and the effect of substance B as 30% resulting in a combined toxicity of 50%. Similar to synergy, the multiplier is often difficult if not impossible to predict and depends on the substances that are combined, their amounts and concentrations, among other variables. An example of potentiation would be the large increase in the hepatoxicity of carbon tetrachloride when the worker is also exposed to isopropanol.

Potentiation involves a non-toxic and a toxic chemical, whereas synergism is the increase in effects from two toxic materials.

# Noise

The primary hazard of noise is **hearing loss**. Noise-induced hearing loss is related to the amount of time a person is exposed to the noise, the decibel level, the frequency, and whether the noise is continuous or intermittent. Types of noise-induced hearing loss include the following:

- **Temporary threshold shift** is caused by a short exposure to loud noise.
- **Permanent threshold shift** is caused by continuous exposure to noise.
- **Temporary or permanent acoustic trauma** is caused by a loud noise, as from an explosion.

In addition to hearing loss, noise can also interfere with communication. Noise can make it difficult to hear warnings and sirens and even to communicate normally. It also interferes with learning, causes a startle response and other physiological problems such as high blood pressure and ulcers, and makes people irritable and frustrated.

A **baseline audiogram** is a valid audiogram done after a quiet period and used as a comparison for future audiograms to see if hearing thresholds have changed. **Decibel** (dB) is a unit that defines the intensity of sound. **Hazardous noise** is any sound that can cause permanent hearing loss in a specified population. OSHA has established allowable daily amounts of noise that workers can safely be exposed to. The **noise dose** is the percentage of this daily exposure that a particular sound meets. A **noise-induced hearing loss** is any sensorineural hearing loss that can be linked to noise and for which no other cause can be identified. **Threshold of hearing** is 1 dBA. This is the weakest sound that a healthy human can hear in a quiet setting. **Threshold of pain** is 140 dBA. This is the maximum level of sound that a human can hear without pain.

**Review Video: Noise Hazards in Occupational Health**
Visit mometrix.com/academy and enter code: 279189

## Continuous and Impact Noise

Since decibel levels of noise and duration of exposure are primary factors which indicate the type and degree of noise level protection required for construction site workers, it is important to know the difference between "impact" and "continuous" noises as OSHA regulations describe them. When sound levels are measured at a construction site, permissible worker exposures are clearly described in OSHA tables.

- For a full 8-hour work-day, a worker must not be exposed to noise greater than an 85-decibel level. As the level of sound begins to exceed that level, so does the level of permitted exposure begin to decline. If continuous sound levels rise to 115 decibels, a worker is permitted no more than 15 minutes of exposure, according to the OSHA table.
- Impact noise levels are short duration sounds emitting from such equipment as nail guns, air hammers, or punch press equipment. A worker must not be exposed to decibel levels which exceed 140 dB of impact noise.

## Measuring Noise Levels in a Work Area

There are two basic types of noise metering instruments available for onsite noise measurement to ensure compliance with OSHA noise regulations:

- General area noise meters are designed to measure the noise level in the areas where they have been placed. These instruments may be moved to other areas but have the disadvantage of providing only generalized data. Workers are often moving through a construction site where the noise levels vary according to the types of activity and machinery being used. A generalized metering scheme provides little data about the individual exposure record.
- Personal Noise Meter devices are designed to be worn by working personnel. Personal noise meters obtain individual readings. This type of noise metering has a practical advantage since it is common for workers to move through various work areas with different levels of noise production.

Whatever type of device is used, it is important to follow proper handling procedures:

- Check batteries prior to use. Batteries should be removed from any sound meter which will be stored for more than 5 days.
- Use a windscreen to protect the microphone in areas where dust and airborne debris may be lifted into the air by excavating machinery or equipment.
- Never cover the microphone pickup with plastic or other material which will distort reception and invalidate the readings.
- Calibrate the meter periodically using the manufacturer recommended calibration device.

## Hearing Protection for Workers Exposed to High Noise Levels

All employees exposed to an 8-hour time-weighted average of 85 dB noise or greater should be provided with appropriate hearing protection at no cost to them.

- Employers must ensure that hearing protection is being worn by workers subject to high decibel sound levels (85 dB) during an 8-hour time-weighted period.
- Hearing protection is required of any employee or worker who has experienced a threshold shift in hearing level.
- Employees must be allowed to select the type of hearing protectors which they need from a variety of approved protectors.
- It is the employer's responsibility to reevaluate and inspect hearing protection effectiveness when changes in work activity expose the worker to greater levels of sound.

## Control Methods for Exposure to Excessive Levels of Noise

Engineering controls are the first consideration for control of excessive exposure to noise. Sound-dampening foam products can be used to line enclosures and dampen noise from machinery. Where noise can't be avoided, its effects can be reduced by grouping and enclosing noisy processes in a soundproof area so that people working in other areas are not bothered. Design features that can help reduce noise include the following:

- Controlling the direction of the source
- Reducing flow rates
- Reducing driving forces
- Controlling vibrating surfaces

- Using barriers and shields
- Building with sound-absorbing materials

In addition to controlling the noise source itself, you can also protect the workers by requiring **protection** such as earplugs or muffs.

## Radiation

There are three types of radiation: alpha, beta and gamma. Proper shielding is the best protection from the harmful effects of radiation.

**Alpha radiation** is made up of small, positively charged particles. Due to an alpha particle's size and characteristics, it cannot travel great distances and is easily stopped by clothing, gloves, or a piece of paper. Care must be taken not to breathe alpha particles into the lungs, as they will damage the lungs and potentially cause cancer.

**Beta radiation** has a higher energy level than alpha radiation and therefore a greater ability to penetrate surfaces. However, it can be easily blocked by a layer of aluminum foil or similar material.

**Gamma radiation** has the highest energy level and has the most ability to penetrate the human body. Lead is the most common shielding used for gamma radiation; several centimeters is usually sufficient to shield from gamma radiation. Water can also be used for shielding; nuclear reactors and power plants use water shielding. Several feet of water are needed to shield from gamma radiation.

### Non-Ionizing Radiation

OSHA defines **non-ionizing radiation** as a series of energy waves from electric and magnetic fields. As with other radiation sources, these types of radiation travel at the speed of light. There are several sources of non-ionizing radiation:

- Power lines, electrical equipment, and household electric wiring produce extremely low frequency (ELF) radiation.
- Radio frequency and microwave radiation may be absorbed through the skin and body. At high levels, this type of radiation can cause tissue damage due to the heating of the body. Radio transmitters and cell phones are examples.
- Infrared Radiation is emitted from such sources as heat lamps and lasers that operate from this wavelength.
- Visible Light Radiation can damage eyes and skin if it is too intense. The visible light spectrum is what we normally see with our eyes.
- UV or ultraviolet radiation sources come from welding arcs and UV lasers.

### Ionizing Radiation

**Ionizing radiation** is radiation that can produce ions when it interacts with atoms and molecules. Types of ionizing radiation include x-rays, alpha particles, beta particles, gamma radiation, and neutrons. Ionizing radiation can come from natural sources, such as cosmic radiation and radioactive soils, and from artificial sources, such as television sets, diagnostic x-rays, and nuclear fuels. Exposure to ionizing radiation damages human cells, especially rapidly developing cells. It is especially dangerous for infants and children who have the most rapidly developing cells. Exposure to high doses of ionizing radiation causes radiation sickness characterized by weakness, sleepiness, stupor, tremors, convulsions, and, eventually, death. Low doses may cause more delayed effects, such as genetic effects, cancers, cataracts, and shortened life span.

## PREVENTING DAMAGE CAUSED BY RADIATION

The damage caused by ionizing radiation depends on the type and dose of the radiation, the tissue and organs exposed, and the age of person being exposed. The best way to control potential damage is to limit the amount of radiation people are exposed to by limiting the amount of source material. It is also important to limit the amount of time people are exposed to radiation. Other ways to reduce exposure to ionizing radiation include the following:

- Increasing the distance between people and sources of ionizing radiation.
- Using shielding such as air, hydrogen, and water to protect people from sources of radiation. The material used as a shield depends on the type of radiation.
- Using barriers such as walls and fences to keep people away from sources of radiation.
- Use liners and protective materials to keep contaminated waste from leaching into groundwater.

A key concept in radiation protection is to keep the radiation dose "As Low as Reasonably Achievable (ALARA)". Regardless of whether the radiation is alpha, beta, or gamma particles, both time and distance can be used to reduce the amount of exposure. Work schedules should be arranged so that exposure time is limited. Reducing the time exposed to radiation reduces the absorbed dose in a directly proportional manner. Distance away from the radiation source can also be used as a means of reducing absorbed radiation. As one moves away from the radioactive source, the exposure decreases according to the inverse square of the distance as illustrated by the following formula: intensity is proportional to $1/x^2$ where $x$ is the distance from the radiation source.

## SAFETY CONTROLS FOR RADIATION

**Warnings** need to mark any areas where ionizing radiation is located as well as equipment that uses ionizing radiation. In addition to signs on these areas, flashing lights and audio signals can serve as additional warnings. **Evacuation** is a tool used to remove people from an area where a significant amount of ionizing radiation has been released. **Security procedures** need to be in place to keep sources of ionizing radiation from getting into the wrong hands. Procedures can include physical monitoring, controlled entry and exit, and manifest systems. **Dosimetry** measures people's exposure to ionizing radiation. It is necessary because we cannot see or feel this radiation. People who work with or near ionizing radiation need training about its hazards and how to protect themselves and others. **System design and analysis** can help prevent dangerous exposure to ionizing radiation by anticipating and preventing possible sources of failure.

## RADIATION COUNTERS

There are several different methods and devices for detecting and determining exposure levels of ionizing radiation. Common devices used to determine exposure to individuals are dosimeters or film badges which are worn by the person. When exposed to ionizing radiation, elements within the film react and, when developed, result in a permanent radiation exposure record. Dosimeters similarly react to the ionizing radiation and register a measurement of the exposure and in the case of a pocket dosimeter, which uses an ionization chamber, can be read immediately. Ionization chambers measure radiation exposure by the conductivity created by interaction of radiation with the enclosed gas. These chambers are used by themselves, in dosimeters, and are modified for use in Geiger-Mueller Counters. Scintillation instruments, which use phosphors or crystals to produce light in reaction to radiation, have been found to be extremely sensitive and useful when detecting low levels of exposure.

# Heat and Cold Stress

## Health Hazards Associated with Hot Weather Work

**Heat exhaustion** and **heat prostration** are different names for the same illness. They are caused by a victim failing to drink enough water to replace fluids lost to sweat when working in a hot environment. Symptoms include the following: cold, clammy skin; fatigue; nausea; headache; giddiness; and low volume, highly concentrated urine output. Treatment requires moving the victim to a cool area for rest and replacing fluids. **Heat cramps** are muscle cramps during or after work in a hot environment. They occur because of excess body salts lost during sweating. Treatment involves replacing body salts by drinking fluids such as sports drinks. **Heat fatigue** occurs in people who aren't used to working in a hot environment. Symptoms include reduced performance at tasks requiring vigilance or mental acuity. Victims need time to acclimate to the hot environment and training on ways to work safely in a hot environment.

A **heat illness** is any illness primarily caused by prolonged exposure to heat. **Heat stroke** occurs when a person's thermal regulatory system fails. Symptoms include lack of sweating, hot and dry skin, fever, and mental confusion. Victims need to be cooled immediately or loss of consciousness, convulsion, coma, or even death can result. **Sunstroke** is a type of heat stroke caused by too much sun exposure. **Heat hyperpyrexia** is a mild form of heat stroke with lesser symptoms. **Heat syncope** affects individuals who aren't used to a hot environment and who have been standing for a long time. The victim faints because blood flows more to the arms and legs and less to the brain. The victim needs to lie down in a cool area. **Heat rash** is also called prickly heat. It occurs when sweat glands become plugged, leading to inflammation and prickly blisters on the skin. Treatment can include cold compresses, cool showers, cooling lotion, steroid creams, and ointments containing hydrocortisone. During treatment, victims must keep their skin dry and avoid heat.

### *Heatstroke and Appropriate First-Aid Measures*

Heatstroke is an affliction often occurring in construction zones. Workers must be able to recognize its symptoms and to deliver an appropriate first-aid response. The human body afflicted with heatstroke loses its ability to adapt to heat stresses and to regulate itself appropriately.

Heatstroke is characterized by:

A markedly elevated body temperature—generally greater than 104 °F

- A loss of mental alertness and disorientation are likely to occur
- Hot and dry skin in some instances, though sweating may be profuse
- Headache, rapid heartbeat, rapid and shallow breathing, and blood pressure vacillation

Immediate treatment for heatstroke:

- Move the person out of the sun and into a shady area.
- Direct air onto the person with a fan or newspaper. It is necessary to cool the person and lower the body temperature. Cool, damp cloths or sheets may be used, or cool water sprays.
- Attend the heat stroke victim until professional help arrives. Do not leave the heat stroke victim unattended. Unless instructed by a physician, a heat stroke victim should never be sent home alone.

### Conducting a Worksite Investigation of Heat Stress

Safety officials conducting an investigation into a worksite where heat stress injuries are reported should take the following steps:

- Review the onsite OSHA Log or any other existing reports of heat stress injury.
- Interview employees to determine if the employer has taken action to protect workers from heat stress. Are water supplies adequate? Are cooling areas available? Does the employer provide training in heat stress indicators?
- Make a visual inspection of the site by walking around it to assess potential problems. Determine the location of heat sources like machinery, furnaces, or boilers.
- Take heat measurements at various locations. Use the heat stress index to determine the WBGT.

### Measuring for Heat Stress Response

Individual heat stress monitoring is recommended when the worker is under heavy loads (burning 500 kcal/hr) and the temperature is at least 69.8 °F. Oral temperature and water loss must be measured, along with heart rate monitoring.

- Oral temperature must be taken before the employee drinks water. Drinking water before taking the temperature will have the effect of "cheating" the thermometer. The work cycle should be shortened for any worker whose oral temperature exceeds 37.6 °C or 99.68 °F.
- Body water loss measurements are taken by weighing the worker at the beginning and end of each day. Body water weight loss should not be more than 1.5 percent of total body weight per day. Fluid intake should be increased if loss approaches that amount.

### Controls for Reducing and Eliminating Heat Stress and Thermal Injuries

The keys to reducing heat stress and thermal injuries are stated below:

- Control the source by keeping heat sources away from occupied areas.
- Modify the environment through ventilation, shielding, barriers, and air conditioning.
- Adjust activities by making the work easier, limiting time spent in hot environments, and requiring periodic rest breaks.
- Provide protective equipment such as water-cooled and air-cooled clothing, reflective clothing, protective eyewear, gloves, and insulated materials.
- Incorporate physiological and medical examinations and monitoring to identify high-risk people.
- Develop a training program to help workers acclimatize to hot environments and learn safe work habits.

## Health Hazards Associated with Cold Weather Work

**Trenchfoot** occurs when a person spends an extended time inactive with moist skin, at temperatures that are cold but not freezing. Bloods vessels in the feet and legs constrict, causing numbness, a pale appearance, swelling, and pain. Treatment involves soaking the feet in warm water. However, the numbness can last for several weeks even after the feet are warmed. **Chilblains** are an itching and reddening of the skin caused by exposure to the cold. Fingers, toes, and ears are the most susceptible. Gentle warming and treatment with calamine lotion or witch hazel can lessen chilblains. Itchy red hives can occur in some people when their bodies develop an allergic reaction to the cold. The hives may be accompanied by vomiting, rapid heart rate, and swollen nasal passages. Cold compresses, cool showers, and antihistamines can help relieve the symptoms.

Frostbite and hypothermia are the most dangerous cold hazards. **Frostbite** occurs when the temperature of body tissue goes below the freezing point. It leads to tissue damage. The amount of damage depends on how deeply the tissue is frozen. Severe frostbite can lead to the victim losing a damaged finger or toe. Frostbitten skin is usually white or gray and the victim may or may not feel pain. To treat frostbite, the damaged body part must be submerged in room-temperature water so it can warm up slowly. **Hypothermia** occurs when a victim's body temperature drops below 95 °F (35 °C). Symptoms include shivering, numbness, disorientation, amnesia, and poor judgment. Eventually, unconsciousness, muscular rigidity, heart failure, and even death can result. Warm liquids and moderate movement can help warm a victim who is still conscious. An unconscious victim needs to be wrapped warmly and taken for medical treatment.

### *Controls for Reducing and Eliminating Cold Stress and Thermal Injuries*

A cold environment can be measured according to the air temperature, humidity, mean radiant temperature of surrounding surfaces, air speed, and core body temperature of people in extremely cold temperatures. The keys to preventing injury from **cold environments** are as follows:

- Modifying the environment by providing heat sources and using screens or enclosures to reduce wind speed.
- Adjusting activities to minimize time in cold areas and requiring regular breaks in a warm area.
- Providing protective clothing with insulated layers that both wick moisture away from the body and provide a windscreen.
- Providing gloves, hats, wicking socks, and insulated boots to protect vulnerable extremities.
- Allowing employees time to become acclimated to the cold environment.
- Training employees on practices and procedures for staying safe in a cold environment.

# Environmental Management

## Environmental Hazards Awareness

### Health Hazards Posed by Exposure to Mold

Some types of mold emit toxins (**mycotoxins**) into the air that cause respiratory symptoms and can initiate or aggravate asthma in sensitive individuals. Other symptoms include nasal stuffiness, eye irritation, and wheezing. Exposure to mold can also cause pneumonitis, which has symptoms similar to pneumonia. Assessment for mold can be conducted by visual inspections that focus on identifying moist conditions that promote mold growth and visually assessing the presence of mold. Mold spores in the air can be assessed by standard industrial hygiene air sampling; however, there are no occupational health exposure standards for comparison purposes. Therefore, sampling is not generally recommended. However, if sampling is conducted, one must compare the indoor air sample quantity and type of mold spores to an outdoor background location for comparison.

### Health Effects Posed by Exposure to Solid Waste or Vermin

Exposure to solid waste or vermin can occur during occupational settings for employees engaged in trash hauling, recycling, landfill operations, or janitorial services. Exposure can also occur in developing countries to those engaged in material recovery at landfills. **Solid waste** can contain physical hazards (e.g., sharp objects, glass shards, and discarded needles). Decomposition of food waste can lead to bacterial exposure that can contain pathogenic bacteria. Poor personal hygiene of workers can result in ingestion of bacteria. Solid waste can also contain human or animal feces (e.g., in diapers or from cleaning up after pets) that will also cause exposure to bacteria. **Vermin** such as rats and mice also create exposure to bacteria and fecal matter when they occur, either in solid waste or in buildings. Exposure to vermin can also be a respiratory irritant when exposed to dust containing fecal matter particulates.

## Water

### Regulatory Programs Governing Storm Water

Although there is a **US Environmental Protection Agency (EPA) Multi-sector General Industrial Stormwater Permit**, most states are responsible for implementing their own versions of the requirements. There are common provisions of these permits. Companies must identify the potential pollutants from their activities that may impact storm water runoff, must identify discharge locations, and must develop a **storm water pollution prevention plan (SWPPP)**. **Best management practices (BMPs)** must be implemented to control and prevent pollutants from entering storm water runoff. Regular inspections of the facility for BMP implementation and effectiveness must be conducted, along with sampling of storm water runoff to determine whether the pollutant levels in the runoff comply with EPA benchmark values. Deficiencies must be corrected with appropriate documentation. Annual reports must be filed that include the inspection and monitoring results.

### Industrial Wastewater Permitting

Industrial operations that produce wastewater and discharge the water to the sanitary sewer (publicly owned treatment works [POTW]) must obtain a **wastewater discharge permit**. Industries that are in certain standard industrial codes must meet **US EPA categorical treatment standards** for pollutants in their wastewater. Companies that are not covered under a categorical treatment standard must comply with their local **POTW wastewater discharge limits**. These vary depending on the locale and how strict the POTW needs to be with its influent quality to meet its National Pollutant Discharge Elimination System (NPDES) permit limits. Typically, limits are imposed for metals (such as arsenic, lead, cadmium, chromium, iron, copper, nickel, zinc, etc.), biological oxygen demand (BOD), chemical oxygen demand (COD), oil and grease, pH, and total suspended solids.

### US EPA Basic Requirements for Drinking Water Systems

The US EPA governs the regulation of drinking water systems and sets **Maximum Contaminant Levels (MCLs)** for primary health standards. States are authorized to implement these regulations. Public water systems are required to provide water that meets all MCLs and that meets the secondary drinking water standards. The secondary standards are elements that affect taste or odor but do not pose a health risk. Drinking water systems must regularly test for the presence of bacteria (coliforms) according to their system size and report the result to their state agency. Repeat sampling and corrective actions are required for positive coliform results. In addition, the system must compile a consumer confidence report to its customers annually that provides information on the testing results from the year.

### Controls to Prevent Storm Water Pollution

Engineering controls for controlling storm water pollution are designed to prevent pollutants from entering storm water runoff. For example, berms can be installed around storage areas to capture runoff that may potentially be contaminated. It can then be tested and released if it is uncontaminated or treated if necessary. Filter socks and drain inserts can be installed that can filter out and trap pollutants. The filters can be stocked with pollutant-specific media to filter out specific pollutants (e.g., zeolites for dissolved metals, activated carbon for oil and grease, etc.). A roof can be constructed over exposed materials to prevent storm water from impacting materials stored outdoors.

## Air

### Indoor Air Quality (IAQ) Assessments

IAQ (e.g., in an office building) is important to health and comfort. **IAQ assessments** should first start with an inspection, and rarely is sampling for any toxic chemicals required. The assessment should include a walk-through of the entire property to identify potential problems that may contribute to poor air quality. For example, is there any mold or moisture present or evidence of wet carpet? Is the building clean? Are there any chemicals stored that may be off-gassing into the environment (e.g., in a janitor's closet)? The fresh air intake location for the heating, ventilation, and air conditioning (HVAC) system should be examined to ensure it is not located too near the exhaust air duct or is not located where it can be affected by vehicle exhaust or where cars and trucks are idling. Ensure that the HVAC system is maintained as recommended and the system is properly balanced. Sampling for specific contaminants should be conducted only if there is direct evidence of a chemical exposure and for which actual standards are available to compare the results to. Without a standard for comparison, there is no actionable information to be gained from air sampling.

### Requirements for Federal Title V Air Permits and New Source Review

"Title V" refers to Title V of the federal **Clean Air Act**, and it is the permits section. For a regulated air pollution source to need a permit under the Clean Air Act, it must be considered a major source located in an air basin that is designated "nonattainment" for one or more priority pollutants (carbon monoxide, nitrogen oxides, sulfur dioxide, volatile organic compounds, or particulate matter). **New Source Review** refers to the process of evaluating the proposed project to determine whether it meets the requirements of the Clean Air Act or whether the project needs modification or additional control technology to comply. General requirements are for an emission estimate and project description to be submitted to the permitting agency that includes a demonstration of how the project meets the Best Available Control Technology (BACT) requirements. If the project emissions are large enough, air dispersion modeling may be required to demonstrate that health risks from the emissions are not too large. Public notice of the draft permit is required prior to the agency granting the permit, as is review by the overseeing regional EPA office.

## Best Available Control Technology (BACT)

BACT is an acronym for Best Available Control Technology. It is used in any regulatory system that requires pollution to be controlled by the best engineering means available. In the case of air pollution permits, any source considered to be significant by the local air pollution control agency will be required to install air pollution control that is considered the best available. In some cases, the district will have a compilation of accepted BACT. For example, natural gas combustion sources must be equipped with low NOx burners to meet the BACT requirements. There are provisions for considerations of economic feasibility when considering what type of control must actually be installed.

## Control Techniques for Particulate Pollution

Particulates are produced in many types of processes, especially when any cutting, grinding, sizing, or polishing is done. Basic control techniques require that the particulates be captured by using hoods and ventilation ducts that are under negative pressure to capture the dust into a control device. Commonly used **control devices** are as follows:

- **Cyclones** are conical devices that swirl the airstream in a cyclonic fashion. The heavier particulates fall to the bottom of the cone and can be collected in a drum.
- **Baghouses** are filtration devices that operate much like a large vacuum cleaner. The dust-laden air is sucked through the filtration device (baghouse), and the particulates become trapped on the filtration media (generally bags or socks). Clean air is discharged, and the particulate that is trapped on the bags is discharged into a drum. Baghouses generally achieve 95 to 99 percent efficiency but can achieve higher efficiency with use of a high-efficiency particulate air (HEPA) filter.
- An **electrostatic precipitator** is a device that induces a charge on the particles being filtered out to capture them in the control device. These are useful for very fine particles such as smoke.

## Control Techniques for Volatile Organic Emissions

Volatile organic compounds or chemicals **(VOCs)** must be controlled from industrial processes because many are carcinogenic, and others contribute to global warming. Following are the main control strategies for these compounds:

- **Adsorption**: these VOCs can adsorb either physically or chemically on to a substrate, commonly activated carbon, or alumina. The VOCs can be recovered by reheating the material to liberate them, or the filter can be discarded as waste.
- **Incineration**: this involves combustion of the exhaust stream that contains VOCs at such a high heat that complete combustion of the toxic chemicals to carbon dioxide and water is achieved.

- **Condensation**: this involves cooling the exhaust gas stream that contains the VOCs back into the liquid state. This is generally cost-effective when the VOCs are valuable to recover and can be reused.
- **Gas absorption**: this involves passing the exhaust gas stream through a liquid that dissolves the VOCs in the gas. This can be effective when the VOC of concern is water soluble (e.g., acetone).

### VENTILATION

Ventilation serves many purposes. It keeps flammable gases and vapors and toxic contaminants below dangerous levels. It also provides air movement that can cool workers and help prevent heat stress. Ventilation also reduces odors and helps control microorganisms and dust. Finally, ventilation limits carbon dioxide buildup in closed spaces and tightly sealed buildings. The main types of ventilation are thermal control and general ventilation. **Thermal ventilation** is designed to change the temperature of an area, usually to cool it but occasionally to warm it. **General ventilation**, also called dilution ventilation, uses clean air to reduce the level or concentration of contaminants in an area. This type of system is best for processes that generate about the same low level of contaminants every day. For systems that generate large amounts of contaminants or contaminants that are very toxic or flammable, general ventilation may not be able to keep contaminant levels low enough for safety.

### RECIRCULATATION OF AIR

Once it is cleaned, formerly contaminated air should be **recirculated** only if it has no potential health consequences for anyone breathing the air. If the air is recirculated, contaminants must be less than the recommended concentrations for health hazards. In addition, the following procedures must be followed:

- The cleaning system must include equally efficient primary and secondary systems or a primary system accompanied by a fail-safe monitor.
- The cleaning system must include a warning system to indicate failures or inefficiencies.
- If a problem occurs, contaminated air must be diverted outside or the process generating the contaminant must be shut down.
- The recirculated air must be tested regularly to ensure that it is safe and that the cleaning system is working properly.

## Land and Conservation

### PREVENTING LAND POLLUTION BY HAZARDOUS MATERIALS

Prevention of pollution to land by hazardous materials storage can be prevented by best management practices (BMPs) and inspection programs. **Prevention of spills** is much more cost-effective than a costly cleanup later. Storage of hazardous materials should be done indoors whenever possible on a concrete slab that is free of large cracks that might allow spilled material to seep into the soil beneath. Whether storage is indoors or outdoors, secondary containment should be provided to ensure that spilled material does not travel to an area that can impact the soil. Secondary containment can be constructed concrete berms or portable spill control pallets. Secondary containment structures can also be fitted with leak detection systems for remote sensing of leaked material. A regular inspection program should be implemented to look for evidence of leaks or spills outside of the containment structures. Inspections should also ensure spilled material within the containment structure is cleaned up promptly.

## Remediation

Remediation is the act of cleaning up toxic spills and restoring the environment to its unpolluted state. For example, if a site has been subject to a spill of petroleum products such as gasoline or diesel, one must **remediate** the soil to avoid impacts to human health or the groundwater. In this case, the soil with free-flowing product is removed and disposed of as hazardous waste. The remaining soil can be remediated with injected oxidation reactants to break down the petroleum products more quickly, or if the levels are low enough, one can let natural biological processes degrade the chemicals over time. In the case of toxic chemicals spilled in water, the water may have to be remediated through a treatment process. For example, volatile chemicals can be removed from water by air sparging to transfer the pollutant chemicals into the air phase, where they can be captured and removed.

## Recycling Commonly Generated Materials

The most recyclable material commonly generated in industrial settings is metal. There is a strong and robust recycling infrastructure set up to collect and recycle metals of all kinds, especially steel, aluminum, lead, copper, brass, and zinc. This is partly motivated by the strong price obtained for metal scrap. Other commonly recycling materials include glass and plastic. Glass has a robust municipal collection and recycling program in many parts of the country but is unfortunately not greatly cost-effective due to the low cost of glass raw materials (sand and minerals). However, recycled glass has much lower energy requirements than glass manufactured from sand. Plastic is recyclable but problematic in that it needs to be segregated by type, and the recycling feedstocks can easily be contaminated by foreign materials. In many parts of the country, there are not facilities available to recycle plastics other than the type found in milk and soda bottles. On an industrial scale, solvents, oil, and batteries can all be recycled fairly easily.

## Corporate Sustainability Program

A corporate sustainability program is a way to demonstrate to customers and shareholders that a company is considering the environment in their products and operations. As an added benefit, sustainability can result in cost savings. The first consideration should be the *nature* of the products or services made and what the environmental impacts of these products are. For example, what types of raw materials are needed? How sustainable is the supply chain, and how can this be improved? What natural resources are used, and where do they come from? How can the product be made with less energy or with energy that comes from a renewable source? The sustainability program should then set achievable *targets* for reducing the environmental impact of the product. Once the sustainability program is underway, it must be communicated to stakeholders (customers, shareholders, and employees) and improved upon each year.

# Hierarchy of Conservation

## Environmental Benefits of Reduce, Reuse, and Recycle

Environmental sustainability principles include employing a hierarchy of reduce, reuse, and recycle. The environmental benefits of each of these strategies are as follows:

- **Reduce** the use of materials or products in general. For example, purchasing one television instead of one for each room reduces the carbon footprint and energy use overall.
- **Reuse** is the next-best strategy to environmental sustainability and refers to reusing materials rather than discarding them. For example, giving clothing to another family to use rather than discarding it saves resources.
- **Recycle** refers to making a discarded product into new materials. For example, discarded metal can be remelted and re-refined into new metal that can be manufactured into new items. Recycling generally uses less energy than making materials from virgin sources, but it can be labor intensive to segregate materials into a form that can be recycled.

# Environmental Management System Standards

## ISO 14001 Series of Environmental Management System Standards

### *Purpose*

The **ISO 14001 series of environmental management standards** is a voluntary environmental management system standard that sets a broad framework that any type of organization can use to improve environmental performance. It is a management system that requires commitment from top management to be truly effective. It is up to the organization to assess its environmental aspects and use a ranking process to determine its significant environmental impacts. Those significant environmental impacts are used to guide the establishment of environmental performance objectives. An example objective would be to reduce energy consumption of a processing facility by 10 percent over the next two years. The objective would have a written set of planned activities to achieve the objective, and the organization would periodically assess its progress toward meeting the objective. Over time, environmental performance (measured environmental impact) is improved with systematic implementation of an ISO 14001 environmental management system.

### *Elements*

The ISO 14001 environmental management system is built upon the **Plan, Do, Check, Act model**. It requires management commitment for its implementation. The clauses of the standard require that the organization establish an environmental policy, that they commit to compliance with all applicable environmental regulations, that they communicate their environmental programs to employees and make their policy available to the public, that they properly train their employees to do their tasks and to understand their role in the organization's achievement of its environmental objectives, that specific and measurable environmental objectives are established, that the organization maintain document and record control, that the organization conduct periodic internal audits to determine conformance with the standard, and that a system of corrective and preventive actions be implemented. The capstone of the system is the **management review process**, in which top management periodically review the organization's environmental performance and set objectives and allocate resources for the upcoming year.

# Waste Removal, Treatment, and Disposal

## Hazards and Controls for Hazardous Waste

Hazardous waste can be flammable, corrosive, and toxic. In addition, it poses a threat to the environment: it can contaminate water and soil, destroy natural habitats, kill fish, animals, and birds, damage crops, and contribute to air pollution. A key factor to controlling hazardous waste is to eliminate or reduce its production. When possible, processes need to be changed to substitute less hazardous materials or to use materials that don't produce hazardous waste. It is also possible to recycle and reuse some hazardous materials such as solvents. When hazardous materials cannot be eliminated or recycled, they must be safely contained, stored, treated, and disposed of. Containment minimizes contact between the hazardous waste and air, water, soil, and people. Storage may be in tanks, open lagoons, or waste piles. Hazardous materials should always be kept separate from other waste.

### *Treating and Disposing of Hazardous Waste*

There are three main methods for treating hazardous waste: biological, chemical, and physical. **Biological treatment** uses microorganisms such as bacteria to break down organic wastes. **Chemical treatment** uses acids or bases to adjust the pH of substances in order to extract oils and heavy metals. **Physical treatment** isolates or concentrates materials through evaporation, adsorption, solidification, cementation, polymerization, or encapsulation. There are two main methods for disposing of hazardous waste: burial and incineration. Hazardous waste can only be **buried** in secure landfills that meet EPA standards. This is to prevent the waste from leaching into water or surrounding soils. **Incineration**, or burning, can be a safe form of disposal for many hazardous wastes, excluding heavy metals. Incinerators typically include scrubbers downstream from the combustion process to ensure that contaminated materials don't escape.

### *Special Hazard Controls Regulated by the DOT for Transporting Hazardous Materials*

The transporting of hazardous materials poses special threats to life and property. Anyone transporting hazardous materials needs to be familiar with DOT definitions for hazardous materials. To reduce the hazards, DOT regulates the following:

- The type of transportation allowed (For example, radioactive materials cannot be transported on planes, and some hazardous materials cannot be transported on passenger planes or trains).
- The quantity of hazardous material allowed to be shipped at one time.
- Packaging of hazardous materials for transportation.
- Labeling of hazardous materials.
- Transportation routes allowed.
- Shipping papers required.
- Incident reports required.
- Training required of anyone designing packaging, preparing shipments, managing shipments, or driving hazardous materials.

# Training, Education, and Communication

## Adult Learning Theory and Techniques

### Difference in Learning Between Adults and Children

Occupational health and safety training is presented to adults, who learn quite differently from the way that children learn. Therefore, to craft more useful training courses, it is important to consider how adult learning differs from that of children. Adults learn from and apply their experience, whereas children have limited experience and are more receptive to the authority of the teacher. Adults are more self-directed in their learning, as they often see the benefits of learning and can pursue their interests. Children learn through play and are more likely to follow their play interests than to actively seek out information that they can apply in a novel way. Finally, adults are more goal-oriented in their learning than children are. Children are starting from a smaller base of knowledge and absorb whatever material is presented to them at an age-appropriate level. An understanding of these differences between adult learners and children can be used to craft more relevant training courses.

### Effective Teaching Techniques for Adult Learners

Well-designed training courses for adults will have at least three qualities: the training will be relevant to the group, it will provide current information not already known to the participants, and it will build upon their experience. Techniques that have proven useful to promote these three qualities include using hands-on experiences or exercises as a group or in small subgroups (for example, assembling a respirator), providing opportunities for discussion that honors the participants' experience, and allowing participants to demonstrate their newly acquired knowledge in a safe and nonjudgmental environment (for example, running a mock emergency scenario after the participants learn the principles of emergency response).

## Presentation Tools

### Training Delivery Methods

#### *Classroom Training*

Classroom training is often used for safety training, but it has its pros and cons. On the positive side, it offers a chance for workers to dedicate their attention to the task without distractions. It allows for questions to be asked to clarify concepts. Some types of information are best presented in a classroom; for example, hazard communication and toxicology of chemical exposures are best presented in a classroom setting. On the negative side, it can be difficult to make the training class lively and engaging and the participants may get sleepy. It may not be interactive enough. Some people do their best learning by doing and not by listening to another person give a presentation.

#### *On-the-Job Training*

On the job training refers to training given outside of the classroom setting in the work area. It is usually for teaching the actual mechanics of a production job; however, it is also a great opportunity to present **risk and hazard information** in a real-world setting. A positive reason to do on the job training is to provide an opportunity for **interaction and hands-on training**. This can help solidify the concepts and make the training more relevant. A negative aspect of doing on-the-job training is that it is not well-suited to providing information about academic concepts such as chemical exposures or hearing conservation. It is also not a good method for large groups or noisy work areas.

### *Online Training*

Online, web-based training classes are useful because they are available any time and do not require scheduling the physical space and the trainer. They can be very cost-effective and can be tailored to the specific topic to be delivered. Programs purchased from a training program vendor can also keep track of the training records. They can also have built-in **competency assessments**. On the negative side, they provide little interaction and may be difficult for some people to pay attention to. They do not provide an opportunity for the student to ask questions and get clarification on concepts that aren't understood. Some people may not be familiar with how to use a computer, depending on literacy levels and background.

### *Training Delivery Mediums and Technologies*

Safety training can be difficult and tedious, but it is critical for worker health. Classroom training is beneficial because content can be tailored to the audience and work environment. It also allows for personal interaction and hands-on training activities that enhance learning. The disadvantages include the difficulty of scheduling a class that can accommodate everybody who needs to take the class. Usually multiple times and locations must be offered. Online training classes are an attractive option because they can be completed whenever the individual has the time. However, they tend to be generic and not tailored to the audience or specific work environment. Sitting in front of a computer terminal is often boring, and it is more difficult for employees to understand and retain information delivered this way.

### *Choosing Appropriate Training*

A variety of training techniques should be used to teach and reinforce concepts. The best training programs use a combination of all three methods. Traditional classroom lecture-style training is useful when the topic is academic in nature. For example, it can be helpful to explain lockout/tagout regulations and procedures in a classroom setting. Demonstration training is best when the topic involves physical manipulation of an object. An example of demonstration training is teaching the use of a respirator, how to disassemble and maintain it. On-the-job training refers to training in specific tasks and occurs in the actual work environment. Written reference material and job aids should be available to reinforce the proper performance of each task. In the example of lockout/tagout above, on-the-job training should be conducted with each piece of equipment to show employees where the lockout points are, and to demonstrate proper isolation of the energy source.

## Well-Designed Presentations

Developing effective training presentations begins with understanding the information to be conveyed, and why it needs to be taught. Is it a regulatory requirement? What are the consequences if employees do not understand the information? Next, consideration needs to be given to the needs of the audience. For example, what is the educational level, literacy level, and native language of the employees to be trained? The presentation must be tailored to their needs. For example, native Spanish speakers prefer to have training classes delivered in Spanish. Any slides used in the presentations should have plenty of visual elements and minimize wordiness. Finally, consideration should be given to developing presentations that use a variety of techniques all in the same class. There should be multimedia elements, hands-on activities, group break-out sessions, and group discussions to engage the audience and to retain interest in the topic.

# Safety Culture

The Occupational Safety and Health Administration (OSHA) describes a **safety culture** as the shared beliefs, practices, and attitudes toward safety that guide the behavior of an organization. The culture is demonstrated by the importance both management and employees place on working in a risk-averse environment. Robust safety cultures have **engaged leadership** that expects employees to work safely by providing the training and resources necessary to do so. In those organizations, safety is explicitly stated as a **guiding principle**. Safe work practices are encouraged and rewarded while unsafe practices are quickly corrected. In a mature safety culture, every employee, from upper management to the line employee, is responsible for the safety of themselves and every other employee.

## Establishing a Safety Culture

A **safety culture** is the way safety is managed in the workplace. It consists of attitudes, beliefs, and perceptions of staff and management toward working in a safe manner. A safety culture must be encouraged and supported by top management to demonstrate the importance safety holds in the company. Incorporating safety into the company's mission statement as a **core value** and establishing a budget for safety initiatives conveys the importance of safety to the staff and the value of safety to management.

A safety culture is established by defining responsibility and accountability. Written policies and procedures clearly assign responsibility for acting safely and providing for a safe environment. The culture of safety is expanded by including everyone in the company. From top management to the newest employee, it must be communicated that safety is the responsibility and expectation of everyone. When management is on the floor, they must wear the same protective equipment and obey the same rules as any other employee. In addition to supporting safety, violations must be immediately corrected to demonstrate management's expectation of a safe environment. Peers, supervisors, and managers are responsible for calling out unsafe behavior. Chronic or serious violators must have consequences to illustrate that shortcuts and risky behaviors will not be tolerated. Finally, positive reinforcement is critical to recognize compliance and effort by a reward or recognition system celebrating safe behaviors.

The **safety professional** plays a critical role in establishing and maintaining a safety culture within an organization. The safety professional acts as the liaison between staff and management. By analyzing injury trends, near misses, and training statistics, the safety professional reports on the status of the safety system to upper management. Relying on their expertise, the safety professional is a resource to staff on all safety topics. The safety professional also acts as the day-to-day model to staff for the expectations of working safely. Finally, the safety professional strives to continually improve the safety culture by identifying opportunities to improve policies, procedures, and control methods to minimize the risk within the organization.

## Communicating a Safety Culture to Staff

A strong safety culture is nurtured in everything a company does. From putting safety on the agenda for every meeting to prominent posters at the workstations, there are multiple ways that the expectation of a safe work environment can be communicated to staff.

**Periodic newsletters** or **emails** can be used to reinforce specific topics—either on a predetermined schedule or as a result of an incident. **Safety posters** can be strategically placed around the work area to remind employees of general or specific safety behaviors. **Pre-shift meetings** should include safety topics and task-specific reminders. **Comment cards** allow employees to communicate concerns or corrections to management. Whenever management and safety professionals are on the floor, they must **model safe behavior**, regardless of the duration of their stay. **Training courses**, even if they are not safety-specific, should always emphasize safe behaviors. Finally, employee **performance reviews** should include a safety metric to provide feedback to individuals regarding how management perceives their adherence to the safety culture.

## How Management Promotes Safety Culture

The management team is critical in establishing and promoting a safety culture within an organization. Management is ultimately responsible for establishing both the priorities and the acceptable **risk level** within an organization. If management emphasizes employee safety by establishing a low risk threshold and prioritizing safe behavior, this conveys to employees the expectation to work safely. Additionally, management determines funding levels for programs. Therefore, when management directs limited financial resources to safety programs, this conveys to staff the importance they place on employee safety. When a company provides safety equipment, conducts training, and accepts feedback from staff regarding the safety system, staff feel obligated to follow procedures, feel valued by management, and feel empowered to make the workplace safer. The actions of management are crucial in establishing the safety culture.

## Responsibility of Employees for Safety Culture

Although top management is responsible for promoting a safety culture, it is every employee's responsibility to nurture the culture. Employees must be actively engaged in safety committees, work groups, and hazard analysis. Organizations with a mature safety culture have engaged employees at every level that support and encourage safe behavior. Employees must attend all trainings and implement what they have learned. If employees have a question about safety, they are responsible for seeking assistance.

## Causes of Poor Safety Culture

A safety culture is the overall attitude toward safety within an organization. A strong safety culture takes time, effort, and resources. A **poor safety culture** is an environment that is ripe for injuries, accidents, and losses.

A poor safety culture may be a result of a lack of support from top management. Executives may see safety as a cost with no return or may not understand the hard and soft costs associated with injuries and failed regulatory inspections. When safety is not regularly addressed during trainings and meetings, staff do not receive constant messaging about the importance of safety and may not know what the expectations are for their behaving. Accidents that are covered up for fear of retaliation or punishment are another sign that safety is not valued. If the approach to incident investigations is fault-finding and not fact-finding, the company is looking for someone to blame and not to correct the underlying problem. Employees who work in fear of being blamed for an injury will not report injuries or near misses, which sets the stage for additional or even more severe injuries. Companies with poor safety cultures value profits over safety and, when financial decisions must be made, will sacrifice safety initiatives. Lastly, a company that does not investigate incidents to address the root cause perpetuates a poor safety culture by demonstrating to the staff that their safety and well-being are not valued.

## Behavior-Based Safety

**Behavior-based safety** is a method of evaluating the overall safety of a workplace. This method focuses on identifying **at-risk behaviors** that need to be corrected and safe behaviors that need to be reinforced. Assessments typically include observing workers in their environment to understand the influences that result in the choice to work unsafely. In order to minimize unsafe choices, behavior-based safety examines the interactions of three domains: the person, the environment, and the behavior.

The **person** refers to the knowledge and abilities of the individual workers. Evaluations of the person can include whether the worker is adequately trained for the task and whether they have the right personality for the job.

The **environment** addresses not only the physical environment and its impact on safe choices, but also the culture of the organization. Items to examine include whether risky behaviors are explicitly or implicitly rewarded, as well as if there are negative consequences for risky behaviors.

**Behavior** describes how an employee interacts with their environment and the motives behind their actions. Facets of behavior can include employees believing that safe behavior is punished (mocking those who choose to wear proper PPE) or rewarding product output even when safety policies may have been ignored.

## Data Collection, Needs Analysis, Gap Analysis, and Feedback

### Gap Analysis Methodology

Gap analysis is a tool for determining what steps need to be taken to move from the present situation to an improved future situation. It is performed by identifying the current situation, identifying the goal situation, and then figuring out what actions need to be taken to realize the goal. In the context of workplace safety, perhaps a construction site averages three incidents or injuries per month and has a goal of only one incident per month. The "gap" would be the difference between the current number and the desired one. For the example workplace, perhaps employee training or safety protocols would reduce incident rates.

### Training Courses

#### *Determining Effectiveness in Communicating Information*

In determining whether a training course is an effective means of solving a specific problem faced by an organization, the organization should conduct a **needs assessment**. The first question to be answered is, what is the problem we are trying to solve? Once the problem is accurately identified, the organization can decide how best to solve it. Responses other than training courses that should be considered are:

- Designing **visual aids** to prompt workers to remember certain tasks; for example, one could post pictorial job procedures if employees continually forget the order of complex operations.
- **Engineering solutions**, such as providing different tools or equipment to do the task more safely. An example of this is to employ carts to move material rather than train people on proper lifting techniques.
- Redesigning the work sequence or procedure to eliminate hazards.

**Review Video: Training, Education, and Communication**
Visit mometrix.com/academy and enter code: 943679

#### *Basic Elements of Well-Designed Training Courses*

A well-designed training course first must meet a demonstrated need for the organization to accomplish its objectives. For example, it must meet a regulatory requirement or convey information the organization has determined necessary to meet its production or financial goals.

The course presentation should begin with a statement of the learning objectives so the course participants can obtain an overview of the course and the expectations. Secondly, the course leader should outline the regulatory or business objective the course will meet. The well-designed training course should use a variety of teaching methods to convey the information, such as slide show presentations, small group activities, interactive discussions, and experiential learning. Using a combination of techniques keeps participants engaged and allows participants with different learning styles to benefit from the course material. Finally, all well-designed training courses have an assessment module to determine whether the participants have assimilated the information presented.

#### *Effective Evaluation Methods*

There are several effective methods to evaluate the effectiveness of a training course. The most well-known and traditional method is to administer a written quiz or exam at the end of the course that covers the information presented in the course. Some types of learning are best evaluated by requiring the course participant to demonstrate a newly acquired skill to the course instructor, such as how to perform CPR or how to wear an SCBA respirator. Requiring a team of coworkers to apply newly acquired knowledge in a tabletop exercise is also an effective method of evaluating the effectiveness of a training course. An example of this type of evaluation is to require a group that has just received disaster planning training to plan for a specific disaster scenario as assigned by the instructor. What is important to remember when planning training evaluation tools is that methods other than written quizzes can be equally as effective and more useful to the participants.

## Assessing Competency

### Methods of Assessing Employee Competency

**Competency** (defined as possessing sufficient knowledge or skill) should be assessed to determine whether an employee requires supplemental training or resources to work safely. The following four methods can be used to assess competency:

- **Test**: the most common method is giving an employee a test to evaluate their knowledge of the topic. This method is inexpensive and easy to execute. The shortcoming of testing is that it only evaluates knowledge, not ability.
- **Self-assessment**: the employee provides feedback of their own evaluation of their abilities. The benefit of a self-assessment lies in the fact that the employee can identify areas they feel they need to improve. This method can suffer from an employee's fear of consequences if they appear sub-standard or provide an unrealistic assessment of their shortcomings.
- **Feedback**: the supervisor or co-workers provide feedback on the abilities of the employee. Feedback has the advantage of being objective and is based on past performance. This method suffers from the potential of bias because personal feelings can impact the truthfulness of the assessment.
- **Skills test**: the employee demonstrates their abilities in a controlled environment. This method is beneficial in that the assessment demonstrates what the employee can do, does not bias against those who struggle with written tests, and can test the ability of an employee to adapt to unusual situations. However, this method can be expensive if a test laboratory must be constructed or if the observation slows the production line.

### Competency-Based Training

**Competency-based training (CBT)** is a method of safety training that requires employees to demonstrate their ability to perform the skills conveyed during training. Instead of only verifying that an individual has received the information (typically evaluated using a written test), this method relies on performance-based assessments that allow the employee to demonstrate their understanding and application of the knowledge. For example, instead of having an employee complete a written exam on the steps needed to check a respirator prior to use, the evaluator would give the employee a respirator and observe them conducting the checks while donning the respirator.

**Learning** is the process of acquiring new information and retaining it for future use. This learning may be used to develop skills and abilities, but is primarily used for non-specific and unexpected situations.

**Training** is the process of acquiring new skills for a specific scenario. The goal is to provide the learner with the expectation of how a task is to be performed so that it can be individually performed in the future.

## Assessing the Effectiveness of Training

The goal of any training program is to **modify behavior**. Whether the intent is to stop an unsafe behavior or to instill a safe behavior, change is the desired outcome. In order to determine whether training would be appropriate, the safety professional would conduct a **needs assessment**. If training is determined to be a potential method of behavior modification, then the safety professional would either conduct or coordinate the training.

In order to determine the effectiveness of the training, the safety professional would have to compare the state of the organization after the training to its state before the training. Such evaluations could include examining injury or near miss data, or by observing behavior to determine if the training was effective at modifying behavior.

A **competency assessment** is a method to evaluate the ability of an employee to execute the skills for a given task. The assessment can be a **checklist** that denotes the desired skills or **performance objectives** an employee should be able to achieve in order to conduct the job effectively. The employee is **observed or tested** to determine their competency for each skill on the checklist. Such an assessment provides opportunities for employee coaching as well as identifying areas of competency.

# Law and Ethics

## Legal Liability

**Liability** is a legal concept concerning when one party fails to meet its obligations and when damages, including injury, have occurred to another party. Liability is often associated with responsibility. Lawsuits surrounding liability require the injured party to prove that the other party had responsibility for the damages or injury.

Liability may be attributed to acts or omissions. The **acts or omissions doctrine** refers to any direct action or inaction that brings about a result. Thus, an employer can be found liable if they acted in a matter that caused damages (instructing employees to remove machine guards) or if their inaction resulted in damages (a supervisor knew that a guard had been removed but took no action to replace it and a worker subsequently got injured).

### Personal Liability

**Personal liability** means that any legal settlement is satisfied by the personal assets of an individual defendant. If an individual agent of a company is found personally liable for their own actions that resulted in damages, they must use their own assets and not those of the company for payment. A partner in a corporation can be found personally liable in cases of fraud, personal negligence, or intentional unlawful acts committed during the course of business. For example, the Environmental Protection Agency has pursued corporate officers in cases where they personally directed employees to violate hazardous material disposal regulations.

Protection of officers and agents of a company from personal liability is typically achieved by **incorporation**. Once incorporated, the individuals who comprise the company have their personal assets protected from debt obligations and claim settlements. Another form of protection is by securing liability insurance. General liability, professional liability, and product liability policies can be purchased as a vehicle to pay for defense costs and claims against the company, thereby protecting the financial assets of the individual and the company.

### Joint Liability

**Joint liability** is where more than one entity (person or company) is found liable for damages. Typically, the damages are the result of multiple acts of negligence by the named parties. Under this legal theory, a judgement is rendered against all parties as a single entity and all parties are responsible for damages. However, if one party is unable to pay, then the other defendants are responsible for the entire judgement amount.

### Joint and Several Liability

**Joint and several liability** is a legal theory of determining who is responsible for damages and payment in a lawsuit. It is applicable when there are multiple defendants found responsible for damages. Under this concept, the plaintiff seeks damages from all ("joint") or some ("several") of the defendants and the ultimate responsibility for paying is dependent on each party's ability to pay. If a single party has the resources, then they would be responsible for paying the settlement in whole, regardless of their degree of fault. In some instances, defendants may pursue recompense from non-paying co-defendants after the settlement has been paid. Joint and several liability is designed to protect the plaintiff by increasing their chances of receiving payment for damages. This theory has been used for environmental damage caused by improper hazardous waste disposal under the Comprehensive Environmental Response Compensation and Liability Act (CERCLA).

The application and interpretation of this theory is decided at the state level and varies across the country. Some states have replaced this with the theory of "several" liability, meaning defendants pay only their share of the damages, regardless of financial ability. Under several liability, co-defendants may not sue one another after the decision to recoup costs.

## Determining Liability

**Liability** is the determination of responsibility for an injury or damages that arise out of acts or omissions. Acts and omissions refer to a doctrine that determines whether a result was caused by a party's actions or failure to act. If a company acts in a manner that causes an injury to an employee by directing them to work in a dangerous environment or fails to provide proper hazard controls to prevent an injury, the company can be found liable.

In order for liability to be determined, it must be established that the accused party was directly responsible for the loss or harm to person or property (tort), violated a statute, or assumed responsibility by way of contract. Liability can be determined by insurance companies or in court.

## Tort

**Tort** is the body of civil law that allows financial recovery of an injured party from another. Also known as **personal injury**, the result is typically a monetary award to the injured party. Responsibility for the injury can be attributed to an act (something the defendant did) or to an omission (something the defendant failed to do). If an employer knowingly allowed employees to work in unsafe conditions, that employer could be found civilly liable and ordered to pay money to the injured worker for all costs related to the injury, such as medical costs, lost wages, or future earnings.

## Situations in Which an Employer is Liable for Employee Actions

An employer may be **liable** for harm that an employee causes a third party while discharging their duties. The company may be held financially responsible for any action or misconduct of an employee that occurs during the course of business. For example, if a delivery driver is involved in an accident while working, the company may be responsible for all damages. Legal reasoning can include **negligent hiring,** wherein an employer is held liable for failing to perform a background check on an employee who has a criminal record. The related concept of **negligent retention** refers to an employer who, after the discovery that a current employee could pose a danger to others, does not take action against the employee. Businesses can defend themselves by conducting reference or background checks and acting immediately upon any information they receive about current employees. Additionally, **liability insurance** is a vehicle to protect the financial resources of the business for accidents that involve employees.

## Employer's Responsibility for Employee Health and Safety

Employers have an ethical and legal responsibility to provide a hazard-free workplace.

Employers have an ethical obligation to provide a safe work environment. This obligation is based on understanding the mutual dependency of the employer-employee relationship—an employer needs the employee to work as much as the employee needs their job. Thus, it is important for companies to value employees and provide a safe work environment—without the employee, there is no work product that generates revenue. A company that adopts a protective attitude towards employees by prioritizing safety will be rewarded with loyalty, less turnover, and a higher level of employee motivation.

Employers also have a legal responsibility for employee safety. The Department of Labor's Occupational Safety and Health Administration (OSHA) establishes the health and safety regulations employers must follow. As OSHA is a federal agency, their regulations have the power of law. States have the authority to establish their own regulatory body. Failure to adhere to the regulations can result in fines and, in extreme cases, criminal proceedings.

### Workers' Compensation and Employer Liability Insurance

**Workers' compensation** is a program that an employer purchases that provides for medical care and wages for an employee who is injured on the job and unable to work. Workers' compensation is considered a "no-fault" insurance in that the employer does not take the blame for the injury, nor does the employee have to prove the employer caused the injury. Workers' compensation coverage applies immediately after the injury and will cover treatment and recovery. If the employee misses work due to the injury, the program will also pay a portion of the wages lost.

Under **employer liability insurance**, an injured worker or their spouse can seek payment for medical treatment, as well as pain and suffering. Where workers' compensation claim amounts are set, there is no limit for liability claims. Additionally, the burden is on the employee to prove that the employer was **negligent** and responsible for the injury. Claims are typically pursued as **lawsuits** and judgement is delayed until a jury renders a verdict. In order to prove a liability claim, the plaintiff must show that the employer had a duty to protect the employee, the employer's acts or omissions breached that duty, the employee was injured as a direct cause of that breach, and the breach caused damages to the employee. Under liability insurance, there is a chance that no award will be given to the injured worker, and they may even have to pay for the company's legal costs if no award is given.

## Ethical Behavior

### Standards Development Processes

International standards are developed in many different areas; a well-known standard for environmental management is ISO14001 developed by the International Standards Organization, and for health and safety in the workplace is OHSAS 18001 developed by the British Standards Institute. However, there are also other organizations that produce standards. The development process for all is similar. First, the standard must meet a need in the marketplace that is beneficial to businesses and customers. Technical subject matter experts in the field of the standard meet and draft the written language of the standard. The standard is developed through global expert opinion and is written to apply to a broad range of industries. The standards are developed through a multi-stakeholder process through consensus by the subject matter experts. There are also opportunities for comment by the broader public before the standards are finalized.

### Ethical Considerations of Audits

There are several ethical considerations that come into play when auditing. First, auditors must sign and observe nondisclosure agreements that require them to keep confidential any observations, documents, and processes witnessed during the audit. This applies to both external and internal audits. Auditors must remain objective and always have objective evidence to support audit findings. Auditors who are auditing for third-party certifications such as ISO14001 and OHSAS 18001 are not allowed to offer consulting or requirements to correct audit deficiencies. Auditors must fully disclose audit findings during the audit or in the audit closing meeting so that the company is not surprised by the findings in the audit report. This allows for transparency and gives the auditee an opportunity to present all relevant evidence that may help avoid a finding.

### *ISO 19011*

The document "Guidelines for Quality and/or Environmental Management Systems Auditing, ISO 19011" is part of the ISO series of standards, but is not a stand-alone standard to which a company can be certified to. Instead, it sets out best management practices for auditors to use when planning an audit, selecting the audit team, executing the audit, and following up on audit findings. It sets expectations for conducting a quality audit by first defining what the scope of the audit will be and what the audit criteria are. The document then discusses the qualifications of auditors, specifies that the auditors should be independent from the work they are auditing, that audit findings must be grounded in objective evidence, and that auditors must conduct themselves in an ethical and professional manner. The document also discusses the differences between first-, second-, and third-party audits, the responsibilities of the auditor, and the elements that should be included in a well-prepared audit report.

## BCSP Code of Ethics

The Board of Certified Safety Professionals (BCSP) has established a code of ethics and professional conduct that must be followed by individuals who are awarded certificates by this organization. The first two standards of this code promote the need for certificate holders to support and promote integrity, esteem, and influence of the safety occupation. The code prioritizes human safety and health as the top concern in any scenario. Additional focus should also be given to environmental safety and the protection of property. Each of these priorities can be promoted by safety professionals in warning people of hazards and risks. These standards also include the promotion of honest and fair behavior toward all individuals and organizations and the avoidance of any behavior that would dishonor the esteem or reputation of the safety profession.

**Standard 1** focuses on the primary responsibility of a safety professional to protect the safety and health of humans. A specific component of this responsibility is the need to notify appropriate personnel, management, and agencies regarding hazardous or potentially hazardous situations. An example might be a scenario in which a safety professional is analyzing company records of employee exposures to potentially hazardous materials on a consultant basis. The safety professional discovers a calculation mistake in transferring readings from a personal monitor into a formula that calculates the daily exposure rate. This mistake has resulted in underestimating the exposure rate by as much as 50%. The safety professional immediately notes these findings in an urgent communication to the company. He then follows up with the company on correcting the calculation errors immediately for present and future employees and determining actions taken for employees that might already have received hazardous levels of exposure.

**Standard 2** specifically deals with the safety professional's character. The safety professional should "be honest, fair, and impartial; act with responsibility and integrity..." The safety professional has to balance the interests of all involved parties, and represent the profession in all business dealings.

**Standard 3** focuses on appropriate public statements and contact. This standard notes that honesty and objectivity are required in all communications and statements. Safety professionals should only make statements related to areas or situations about which they have direct expertise.

**Standard 4** of this code focuses on the professional status and actions of safety professionals. A safety professional should only engage in projects or activities for which they are highly qualified in terms of knowledge, training, and experience. Additionally, ongoing education and professional advancement activities should be pursued by all safety professionals to maintain and improve knowledge and skill level as well as to maintain certification. The Board of Certified Safety

Professionals supports annual conferences that enable safety professionals to receive valuable training and education while accumulating required points to keep their certification current.

**Standard 5** focuses on integrity and honesty in the presentation of professional qualifications. This includes areas such as education, degrees, certification, experience, and achievements. Not only must safety professionals be careful to clearly and honestly state all qualifications, but any exaggeration or misrepresentation by omission must also be avoided. When applying for jobs, providing references, or testifying in court, a safety professional must not lie about their employment history, professional relationships, or professional qualifications and experience. A safety professional with knowledge about violations of this standard should report the information to the Board of Certified Safety Professionals.

**Standard 6** specifies that the safety professional should avoid all conflicts of interest in order to maintain the integrity of their profession.

**Standard 7** focuses on avoiding discrimination and bias. It is specifically noted that safety professionals must not discriminate or demonstrate bias based on gender, age, race, ethnicity, country of origin, sexual orientation, or disability. These areas are also regulated by local, state, and federal agencies enforcing civil rights and other related anti-discrimination legislation.

**Standard 8** of this code promotes the need for safety professionals to be involved in community and civic events and use their professional qualifications to promote safety within their own community. Examples of this include instructing public safety personnel in handling hazardous materials, teaching public safety classes in areas of fire prevention, home safety, and accident prevention. Safety professionals can work cooperatively with organizations and agencies already working in the community such as the Red Cross, fire departments, and police departments.

A safety professional should adhere to the impartiality principle in all interactions and engage the advice and support of supervisors in determining appropriate actions. One area of concern is to avoid conflicts of interest or promoting oneself beyond actual expertise or competence. For example, if asked to testify in a lawsuit that revolves around an incident involving a former employee of a company affiliated with the safety professional's employer, the safety professional should defer to avoid conflict of interest. Another example would be a safety professional who is asked to testify to the appropriateness of safety procedures related to radioactive materials. Although the safety professional received general instruction in this area in a course, he has no direct experience. He should decline to avoid presenting himself as an expert in that area.

The Code of Ethics and Professional Conduct for safety professionals notes that the primary responsibility of a safety professional is to safeguard the health and safety of humans as well as providing for the safety of the environment and property. In a typical construction site, numerous organizations, individual, and entities are working jointly to complete the project. Ultimately, each organization or company bears responsibility for making sure its workers are well trained and have a safe work environment. A main function in ensuring a safe worksite is to include safety stipulations in the contracts of all involved individuals or organizations.

## Protection of Worker Privacy

**Worker privacy** refers to the extent to which an employee can search an employee's possessions, monitor their actions, monitor their correspondence, and have access to information regarding their personal lives. While employees do have a right to maintain a degree of privacy at work, company policies may eliminate some of the expected degree of privacy, such as by monitoring phone calls or emails.

Laws regarding worker privacy vary by state. The most important factor in employee privacy is that the employer clearly outlines the rules and expectations for privacy and informs the employee of the expectations. **Written policies** outlining allowable practices and stating how the employer will monitor specific employee activities can protect an employer from lawsuits.

### Employer's Responsibility to Protect Personal Information

During an individual's relationship with a company, an employer will collect and hold a variety of personal information. Social Security numbers, bank account numbers, names of family members, medical examinations, and discipline records may be kept within a personnel file. The employee has a certain degree of trust that the employer will properly secure and maintain that information. Whether the files are physical or electronic or both, the employer has an obligation to protect that information.

Physical files should be maintained in secure locations. Locked or limited access rooms or locked file cabinets can be used to limit access to the files. The use of a check-out system will allow the company to track who accesses the files and where they are located at any point of time. In addition to a security protocol, companies should also have a document destruction policy to properly and securely dispose of files that are no longer required to be maintained. Having a secure file system and written procedures on how to track files will protect the company from litigation in the event confidential information gets released.

Electronic files should also be secure. The use of passwords, secure servers, and limited access to the drives will decrease the likelihood of having employee data compromised. Other methods of security include stand-alone servers, encrypted files, constant file access monitoring, and file deletion protocols to protect sensitive employee information.

## HIPAA

The **Health Insurance Portability and Accountability Act (HIPAA)** is a federal law that created national standards for the protection of an individual's sensitive medical information. The intent was to prevent the release of **protected health information (PHI)** without the consent or knowledge of the individual. The Department of Health and Human Services (HHS) issued the Privacy Rule as a result of HIPAA.

The **Privacy Rule** identifies which bodies, referred to as "covered entities," must adhere to the Act. Covered entities include companies that provide medical services to employees or manage workers' compensation claims as a self-insured entity. The Privacy Rule establishes how PHI is properly protected while information necessary for decisions or treatment is transmitted. The Privacy Rule also sets forth when an individual's information can be released without consent, such as for public health emergencies, released to law enforcement, or when required by law.

### Protected Health Information

**Protected health information (PHI)** is a concept that arises from the Health Insurance Portability and Accountability Act (HIPAA). PHI is any health data that is created, stored, or transmitted by an entity covered by HIPAA. Information that is classified as PHI is any information regarding past, present, or future physical or mental health condition; health care being administered to an individual, or payment for health care of an individual that is maintained or transmitted by the covered entity. This includes demographic data and anything that identifies the individual, medical history, test results, insurance information, or treatment information. Information that identifies an individual includes name, social security number, date of birth, contact information, IP addresses, or anything else, other than a code, that could result in uniquely identifying the individual.

## Drug Testing

Applicants can be drug tested as a **condition of employment**, but the process and selection must be applied to all applicants without prejudice. With recent changes in drug laws, the topics of drug testing and the related results are being revisited.

Federal law allows periodic testing of **safety-sensitive positions**, such as bus drivers, and when there is **reasonable suspicion** of an employee being under the influence. Caution must be exercised in reasonable suspicion cases in that supervisors should be trained to identify signs of drug or alcohol use. Management must also consider underlying medical conditions that can cause altered behavior (such as a diabetic episode or stroke) that can mimic substance abuse.

The Occupational Safety and Health Administration (OSHA) has cautioned against mandatory drug testing following occupational accidents because they may dissuade employees from seeking medical assistance. Employers should establish criteria that is rigorously adhered to when determining the need for a post-accident drug test.

## Security Cameras

As costs have decreased, the presence of security cameras has increased in the workplace. Cameras can be used as a deterrent to theft, to assist security teams in monitoring the premises, and to monitor employee productivity. Cameras are prohibited in restrooms, locker rooms, break rooms, or other areas where there is an expectation of privacy.

With their increased area of coverage, the placement and monitoring of video cameras has resulted in capturing employee activities that may be undesirable to management. Video evidence has also been used to analyze workplace accidents which may result in employee discipline.

By law, employers are required to notify employees and the public when cameras are present. Also, federal law requires that video cameras cannot have audio recording, as this would violate wiretap laws.

## Employer's Responsibility for Medical Record Privacy

Both the Health Insurance Portability and Accountability Act (HIPAA) and Americans with Disabilities Act (ADA) address the topic of medical record privacy. Employers who maintain medical records for employees must keep the information private and confidential, viewed only by those who need the information. Medical records must be kept separate from personnel files. Medical information can only be provided to safety and first aid workers and only as it relates to special needs for evacuations.

## Electronic Vehicle Tracking

In the United States, it is legal for a company to use the **Global Positioning System (GPS)** to electronically track its vehicles. The conditions for use are that the company owns the vehicle and the driver has been notified of the tracking system. GPS systems can benefit a company in that they can provide clients with accurate arrival times, assist in optimizing vehicle or route usage, and locate vehicles that may be having a mechanical problem.

However, most states do not allow tracking systems to be used on personal vehicles. Each state has laws regarding specific conditions for electronic fleet monitoring that, if violated, can result in criminal charges against the employer.

## Electronic Privacy

**Electronic privacy** refers to the degree which an employer monitors an employee's use of **email, computers,** and **cell phones**. Methods of electronic monitoring can be as simple as blocking certain websites from being accessed by work computers or as involved as mirroring employee monitors. Companies may have a legitimate concern or need to monitor devices, such as when there is a concern of stealing company secrets. Other concerns may include employees using company-provided devices for personal use or to sabotage the company on social media.

Companies have rights to monitor the use of any equipment they provide individuals. Specifically, the **Electronic Communication Privacy Act (ECPA)** allows a company to monitor phone and email systems. Regardless, policies regarding electronic monitoring must be documented, well-defined, and should have some sort of written acknowledgement for every employee.

## Employer Access to Employee Medical Information

Every employer has the right to access certain medical information, regardless of whether they are subject to the Health Information Portability and Accessibility Act (HIPAA) or not. Such information would include the need for accommodations due to an injury or a pre-existing condition, any special requirements that would need to be considered during an emergency, or any information that an employee voluntarily provides the employer about their health.

Employers must maintain any medical information they receive related to the Americans with Disabilities Act (ADA) or Workers' Compensation claims in a file separate from the employee's personnel file. Information in the medical file can only be released to parties within the organization with a need to know the information. For example, a supervisor needs to know if a worker recovering from a back injury needs help lifting heavy loads but does not need to know that they are recovering from a slipped disc. Medical information can also be released outside of the organization to comply with a lawful subpoena or with the employee's consent.

# ASP Practice Test

**1. There exists a gaseous mixture of 20% hydrogen and 80% propane. What is the lower flammability limit (LFL) of the mixture if the flammable range of hydrogen is 4–75% and the flammable range of propane is 2.2–9.5%?**

a. 2.42%
b. 2.56%
c. 3.56%
d. 6.20%

**2. Transformational learning theory works on the principle that adults will retain information if _______ meaning is attached to an earlier _________.**

a. new, experience
b. literal, lesson
c. positive, example
d. another, definition

**3. Which of the following is a TRUE statement regarding occupational safety training in the workplace?**

a. Experienced workers should be given priority over new hires to receive training.
b. Accidents are statistically likely to occur when workers have recently started a new job.
c. OSHA standards typically do not outline required training.
d. Accidents always increase soon after accident-prevention training.

**4. Which of the following is generally NOT true regarding worksite safety inspections?**

a. Inspectors typically do not have a direct affiliation with the organization or entity undergoing inspection.
b. Inspections are usually conducted by personnel who have robust knowledge, training, and/or experience within the subject area that the inspection is concerned with.
c. Inspections can either be scheduled or unscheduled.
d. Inspections, by design, should only be detail-oriented in nature.

**5. A sound workplace security plan should have measures in place to ____________ visitors in the effort to control site access and increase employee safety.**

a. frisk and disarm
b. screen and restrict
c. interview and photograph
d. train and certify

**6. An effective incident reporting system typically includes all of the following facets EXCEPT:**

a. mechanisms for reporting near misses
b. clear direction on how, when, and to whom injuries should be reported
c. remote electronic access capabilities in the field
d. processes for commencing incident investigations and filing insurance claims

**7. Which of the following would be activated in response to a potential local emergency resulting from a tornado or flood?**

a. a facility contingency charter
b. a facility emergency action plan
c. a US NOAA mitigation response beacon
d. a US FEMA emergency condition notice

**8. Which of the following is typically NOT a rationale for investigating a workplace accident or incident?**

a. to determine the extent of damage or loss associated with the event
b. to assess or attain objective evidence for potential upcoming litigation
c. to reduce the potential for future similar recurrences by identifying the underlying cause of the event itself
d. to assign culpability for rendering disciplinary action

**9. Which of the following is a major benefit that can result from undergoing an external audit versus an internal audit?**

a. benchmarking of audit findings against industry competitors
b. lower overall levels of cost and resource expenditures for the audit
c. more expeditious initiation of corrective action and lessons-learned protocols
d. direct national certification (e.g., ISO) opportunities being more readily available

**10. Which of the following tactics is NOT typically employed as an enforcement measure for ensuring compliance with safety program protocols?**

a. disciplinary action for blatantly disregarding safety rules
b. incentives for proactively following safety rules
c. training regarding safety requirements
d. mandatory participation in safety program activities and initiatives

**11. What is andragogy?**

a. a chemical carcinogen
b. a type of fall protection apparatus
c. an elbow joint condition caused by repetitive motion
d. adult learning theory

**12. A sample of californium-250 has an initial mass of 1 gram. If 637 milligrams remain after 8.5 years, what is the half-life of Cf-250?**

a. 6.42 years
b. 12.65 years
c. 12.96 years
d. 13.06 years

**13. Which of the following is NOT true with regard to hazardous wastes?**

a. Some hazardous wastes can be recycled and reused.
b. Storage of hazardous wastes in open pools or piles is permitted.
c. Hazardous wastes may regularly be combined with other waste types.
d. Wastes that are hazardous can be categorized as toxic, corrosive, and/or flammable.

**14. A key strategy for reducing the risks associated with an explosion hazard is to implement ______________.**

a. material accountability custodians
b. an explosive material disposal (EMD) plan
c. explosive dust sniffers/detectors
d. barriers and distance

**15. Which of the following is a potential positive outcome of an accident or incident?**

a. A shift in workforce safety awareness
b. A decrease in workers' compensation premiums
c. A net increase in workforce camaraderie and morale
d. An increased trust in management

**16. Which of the following is NOT typically utilized as a material to shield against exposure to gamma- or X-ray radiation?**

a. concrete
b. titanium
c. water
d. lead

**17. Which of the following elements of workplace design is NOT related to an increase in the risk of workplace violence incidents?**

a. poor lighting
b. isolated workers
c. lack of communication devices
d. poor internet service

**18. A mutagen is a chemical that affects ________.**

a. the respiratory system
b. the DNA of cells
c. a blood-forming organ
d. part of the lymphatic system

**19. Which of the following is NOT a recognized benefit of computer-based safety training (CBT)?**

a. Employees have more control over the learning process.
b. CBT is easier to understand than in-person lectures.
c. Training can occur on the employee's schedule.
d. Employees can review the material without fear of embarrassment.

**20. Which of the following is NOT considered a useful tool for reducing or eliminating exposures to infectious material hazards in the workplace?**

a. robotics
b. physical separation/barriers
c. personal protective equipment
d. first-aid response

**21. Which of the following is an appropriate measure to follow for the safe handling of flammable and combustible materials?**

a. Plunger cans should be used for dispensing small quantities of material.
b. ISO standards for storage cabinet design and configuration should be followed.
c. Pressurized vacuum pumps should be used for dispensing large quantities of material.
d. Static electricity conductor mechanisms should be employed where flammable or combustible materials are stored or utilized.

**22. Which of the following is NOT a typical means by which hazards arise during the conduct of maintenance activities?**

a. Poorly written maintenance procedures are being used.
b. Incorrect maintenance schedules are being followed.
c. Energy sources do not have a lockout or tagout capability.
d. Systems are not designed for user-friendly maintenance.

**23. A sling has a working load limit (WLL) of 1000 lb when used in a vertical hitch. When the same sling is used in a 60-degree basket hitch with a sling angle factor of 0.866, what is the new WLL?**

a. 866 lb
b. 1,732 lb
c. 1,155 lb
d. 500 lb

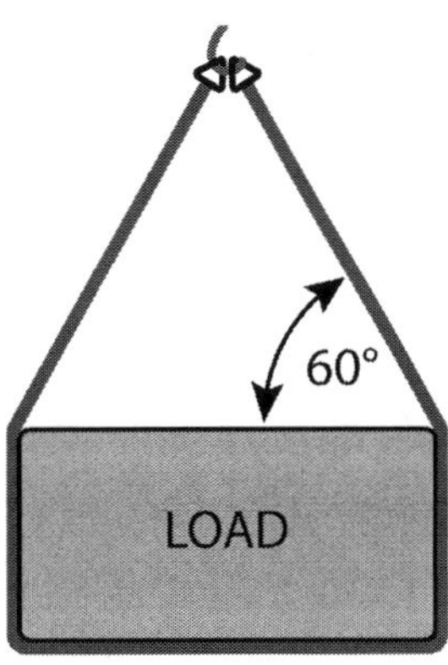


**24. Which of the following is a method widely employed in industry for significantly reducing hazardous noise levels?**

a. using sound-reflective materials in building construction
b. increasing vibrational frequencies
c. wearing earmuffs over earplugs
d. reducing the distance between the source of a noise and workers

**25. Which of the following exposure limits is based on 8-hour days, 40-hour workweeks, and a lifetime of work?**

a. PEL
b. TLV
c. REL
d. IDLH

**26. A certain fire sprinkler is rated to protect 180 $ft^2$ of a light-hazard occupancy, 130 $ft^2$ of an ordinary-hazard occupancy, or 100 $ft^2$ of an extra-hazard occupancy. How many of this sprinkler would be required to protect a single area with low combustibility and a moderate quantity of combustibles if it is 70 feet long by 38 feet wide?**

a. 15
b. 19
c. 21
d. 27

**27. What is the minimum distance a combustible fuel gas cylinder must be stored away from an oxygen cylinder?**

a. 0.2 ft
b. 2 ft
c. 20 ft
d. 200 ft

**28. Which of the following is NOT a widely implemented control for reducing potential heat-stress-related injuries in the workplace?**

a. wearing reflective and insulated clothing
b. regular hose spray-downs of work areas
c. specialized training programs geared toward proper heat management techniques
d. physical examinations for determining employees of high cardiovascular risk

**29. In regard to workplace violence events such as active shooters or bomb threats, employees should be trained to either __________ or __________**

a. shelter-in-place, evacuate
b. distract, deploy
c. observe, record
d. communicate, defuse

**30. A certain frictionless pipe is 6 inches in diameter on one end and 8 inches in diameter on the other end. If water enters the smaller end at a rate of 10 feet per second, what is the velocity of the water as it exits the larger end of the pipe? The density of water is approximately 62.43 $lb/ft^3$.**

a. 0.82 ft/s
b. 5.63 ft/s
c. 7.50 ft/s
d. 13.33 ft/s

**31. To reduce the likelihood of workplace violence, employers should implement a __________ and notify workers that all claims of workplace violence will be investigated promptly.**

a. drug rehabilitation program
b. zero-tolerance policy
c. group counseling program
d. vacation deferral program

**32. Scaffolding must be inspected on which of the following frequencies?**

a. hourly
b. twice daily
c. before each shift
d. weekly

**33. Which of the following project management tools emphasizes how much time should be spent on each project step and orders those steps by priority?**

a. project plan
b. work breakdown structure (WBS)
c. scope of work (SOW)
d. time and materials balance sheet

**34. __________ are standards for right versus wrong that act as moral principles used to guide decisions.**

a. Regulations
b. Standards
c. Rules
d. Ethics

**35. A logic diagram that depicts potential failures in each individual segment or component of a system is:**

a. a fault-tree analysis
b. an event-tree analysis
c. a system reliability and test evaluation
d. a probabilistic risk assessment (PRA)

**36. Which of the following is NOT typically employed when identifying potential risks in the workplace?**

a. accident history evaluations
b. quantitative risk assessments
c. employee feedback
d. cost-benefit analyses

**37. Which of the following four-step continuous improvement models is highly utilized within occupational safety and health programs?**

a. stop-look-assess-learn
b. observe-evaluate-respond-report
c. plan-do-check-act
d. education-engagement-implementation-accountability

**38. Which of the following is NOT considered a tangible benefit of commencing an accident investigation as soon as possible?**

a. The sooner the causes are found, the sooner the lessons can be shared within the organization to prevent recurrences.
b. A rapidly commenced investigation usually sends a message of robust corporate response and engagement.
c. Liability costs can be reduced by rapid fact-finding and root cause determination.
d. Witness accounts are more reliable soon after the incident, and accurate recollection can fade as time passes.

**39. Which of the following is NOT generally true with regard to hazards associated with improper work area illumination?**

a. A dim work area can lead to conditions related to vitamin D deficiency.
b. Bright light can damage the eyes' receptor cells.
c. Lighting diffusers can be installed to protect eyes from glare and strobing.
d. Many illumination-related accidents occur because workers do not take enough time to adjust when moving between lighter and darker areas.

**40. __________ is the legal concept of responsibility for damages that have occurred to another party due to a failure to meet obligations.**

a. Ex parte
b. Liability
c. Pro per
d. Due diligence

**41. Which of the following is NOT a typically implemented protocol for protecting workers from bloodborne pathogens?**

a. regular employee health screenings and medical monitoring
b. assuming all bodily fluids are potentially infectious
c. not permitting eating or drinking in areas where pathogens may be present
d. requiring handwashing after removal of soiled gloves

**42. In which of the following regards is ANSI Z490.1 of vital importance?**

a. It is the OSHA-mandated guidance for the proper design and use of protective eyewear.
b. It is the professional standard for the planning and conductance of health and safety training programs.
c. It contains essential criteria for the erection and maintenance of scaffolding.
d. It outlines general industry standards for the proper treatment, handling, and disposal of combustible materials used in the workplace.

**43. What is the sample standard deviation for the following dataset?**

(4, 7, 15, 17, 26, 53, 59, 75)

a. 32
b. 10.1
c. 26.7
d. 5.9

**44. What is the conventional definition of *lower flammable limit* (LFL)?**

a. the lowest concentration of vapor in air at which the vapor will ignite
b. the lowest temperature at which a gas is flammable
c. the lowest pressure at which a gas is able to ignite at standard temperature (20°C)
d. the amount of heat (energy) that one mole of gas is able to produce at standard temperature and pressure (STP)

**45. Which of the following is NOT typically true with regard to positioning-device systems?**

a. They are usually employed for supporting workers who are working on an elevated vertical surface.
b. The system consists of equipment, connectors, and a body harness or body belt.
c. A worker is able to have both hands free to work while wearing a positioning-device system.
d. Positioning-device systems are not typically attached to lifelines or lanyards.

**46. Experiential adult learning theory believes that adults learn best by ________.**

a. hearing
b. reading
c. doing
d. watching

**47. In terms of waste reduction, what does *P2P* stand for?**

a. plan, prevent, practice
b. pollution prevention plan
c. parallel production process
d. process pollution pricing

**48. In legal terms, *strict liability* is conventionally defined as which of the following?**

a. when a corporate entity is forced to pay compensatory damages associated with a product or service the entity provided, irrespective of fault
b. when a corporate entity has failed to invoke reasonable standards (criteria) of care to prevent injuries or death in the workplace
c. a legal charge resulting from a worker injury or death that occurs due to improper implementation of worker safety criteria
d. an intentional act of neglect during the administration of reasonable care

**49. Thorium-233 has a decay constant of $5.292 \times 10^{-4}$ disintegrations per second. What is the source strength for 1 milligram of Th-233? Note that 1 curie equals $37 \times 10^{9}$ becquerels and that Avogadro's number is $6.02 \times 10^{23}$ units/mole.**

a. $3.695 \times 10^{4}$ curies
b. $3.699 \times 10^{2}$ curies
c. $8.61 \times 10^{-4}$ curies
d. $3.67 \times 10^{-3}$ curies

**50. If the air temperature is 85 °F, the natural wet-bulb temperature is 78 °F, and the globe thermometer temperature is 87 °F, what is the wet-bulb globe temperature (WBGT) outside?**

a. 80.5 °F
b. 83.3 °F
c. 85.0 °F
d. 79.8 °F

**51. Which of the following is NOT a technology used to control industrial particulate air emissions?**

a. electrostatic precipitation
b. mechanical separation
c. flare systems
d. condensation scrubbing

**52. In the circuit below, calculate the current $I_1$.**

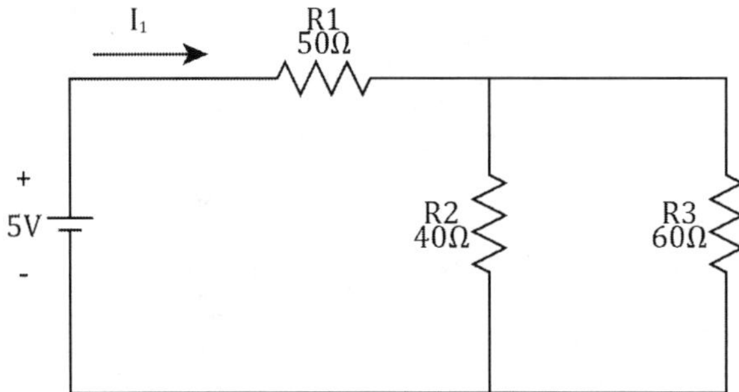


a. 68 mA
b. 100 mA
c. 192 mA
d. 14.8 A

**53. Which of the following is NOT a health effect associated with exposure to occupational noise?**

a. acoustical trauma
b. shifts in threshold
c. tinnitus
d. fibromyalgia

**54. The XYZ Construction Company has 127 full-time workers. Each employee works a full year, or 2,000 hours, at the company. During this time, six recordable incidents occur. What is the incident rate of the company?**

a. 3.38
b. 4.72
c. 7.62
d. 2,116.7

**55. Which of the following is NOT a method of reducing the risk of excavation cave-ins?**

a. shoring
b. benching
c. sloping
d. paneling

**56. Which of the following is NOT generally considered a fundamental principle of ergonomics as it relates to safety engineering?**

a. "People differ from one another."
b. "Whenever possible, the job should be changed and not the worker."
c. "Output should never trump common sense."
d. "People should work smart."

**57. The ____________ effect is when an exposure to two hazardous chemicals results in a multiplicative or compounded effect on the body.**

a. additive
b. synergistic
c. antagonistic
d. subtractive

**58. Which of the following is a control strategy for protecting against hazards associated with confined space work?**

a. A continuous air supply
b. Use of a buddy system
c. Evaluating potential hazards of the space immediately after entry
d. Use of a portable lighting system with redundant power supplies

**59. Regarding ergonomics, most items are designed to accommodate populations in what range of heights?**

a. 1st percentile female – 99th percentile male
b. 5th percentile female – 95th percentile male
c. 10th percentile female – 90th percentile male
d. 0.1 percentile female – 99.9 percentile male

**60. Hazardous wastes are usually disposed of either through _________ or _________.**

a. incineration / burial in permitted landfills
b. transmutation / reprocessing
c. recycling / stabilization
d. dissolution / enzymatic hydrolysis

**61. Autoignition temperature is defined as the temperature at which ________.**

a. a volatile gas will explode
b. one watt of heat is produced per cubic centimeter of burned fuel
c. a fuel will combust without being exposed to an ignition source
d. a volatile material is in equilibrium phase between gas and flammable vapor

**62. Which of the following is NOT generally true regarding chemical irritants?**

a. The skin is usually easily affected by these agents.
b. Permanent tissue damage often occurs as a result of exposure.
c. Mucus membranes are usually easily affected by these agents.
d. The degree of irritation depends on concentration and duration of contact.

**63. Which of the following is NOT generally true regarding biohazards?**

a. Biohazards can be either animal- or plant-based.
b. Biohazards include certain types of bacteria, viruses, and fungi.
c. Biohazards, by definition, are not allergenic in nature.
d. Biohazards of human origin are usually transmitted by some type of bodily fluid.

**64. ________ is/are an airborne biological hazard associated with damp environments.**

a. Mold spores
b. Ebola virus
c. Valley fever
d. Hantaviruses

**65. All the following are stages of experiential adult learning theory EXCEPT:**

a. cooperative reflection
b. concrete experience
c. reflective observation
d. abstract conceptualization

**66. Workplace violence can be defined as including both ________ assault and ________ assault against employees in the workplace.**

a. mental, physical
b. actual, hypothetical
c. verbal, virtual
d. physical, threats of

**67. Safety professionals should enforce rules under which of the following conditions?**

a. only for those groups who are known to not follow the rules
b. evenly to all staff and management at all times
c. for everyone except close friends and supervisors
d. more at the beginning of a project and less as the project progresses

**68. Which of the following is NOT typically considered an effective presentation tool for safety training?**

a. slide show presentations
b. hands-on exercises
c. small group exercises
d. independent review of safety manuals

**69. Which of the following is NOT generally true with regard to building evacuation plans?**

a. Plans should be designed so that personnel know where to exit even when visibility is limited.
b. Plans should include the systems used to communicate the need to evacuate, such as alarm systems.
c. Plans should specify locations of outdoor mustering areas.
d. Plans should include procedures on how to activate emergency response teams in tandem with an evacuation.

**70. Legal liability can be attributed to a party based on what doctrine?**

a. acts or omissions
b. prime contractor responsibility
c. ex post facto
d. prima facia

**71. Which of the following is NOT generally true of recirculated-air system operational requirements?**

a. Cleaning systems must have a secondary filtration module that maintains an efficiency of at least 75 percent of the primary module.
b. Contaminated air must be routed outdoors in the event of an incident.
c. Recirculated air must undergo regular sampling and evaluation to verify that cleaning systems are functioning normally.
d. Cleaning systems must have audiovisual warning indicators to advise personnel of potential issues.

**72. Which of the following is NOT an example of an electrical switching device that is typically used in the workplace for reducing electrical hazards?**

a. a cutout
b. a knockout
c. a lockout
d. an interlock

**73. In a group safety training session, the facilitator must be careful to avoid all the following EXCEPT:**

a. one person dominating the discussion
b. introverts not participating
c. groupthink
d. slide format

**74. Which of the following is NOT typically a workplace control utilized for protecting against bulk-material hazards such as asphyxiation and cave-ins?**

a. lifelines
b. guardrails
c. shoring at angles greater than repose angles
d. sloping at angles less than repose angles

**75. Standards promulgated by OSHA must be treated as which of the following?**

a. suggestions to make a workplace as safe as economically feasible
b. requirements for employees but optional for managers who are only periodically in hazardous areas
c. rules for large employers but recommendations for small employers
d. mandatory provisions for regulated activities in a workplace

**76. Which of the following is NOT a typical approach used in industry for asbestos abatement?**

a. enclosure
b. encapsulation
c. removal
d. relocation

**77. A robust auditing program utilizes ____________ to address the ____________ of issues found during an audit.**

a. checklist protocols / categories
b. corrective action programs / root causes
c. quality assurance criteria / severities
d. ISO 14009 mandates / extent of condition

**78. A metal stamping machine produces spoons, forks, and knives. Approximately 4% of the spoons, 3% of the forks, and 0% of the knives are defective. If three spoons, three forks, and three knives are inspected at random, what is the probability that none of the pieces are defective?**

a. 0.79
b. 0.81
c. 0.90
d. 0.93

**79. A new car costs $12,000. It costs $400 per year for gas and $600 for maintenance for the first year. Each subsequent year, maintenance costs $25 more than it did the previous year. The car is expected to last eight years. After eight years, the dealership will pay $2,000 for it. What is the life-cycle cost of owning the car?**

a. $10,000
b. $12,000
c. $17,525
d. $18,700

**80. Effective safety training courses based on adult learning theories should incorporate which of the following?**

a. presentations, tests, and feedback
b. presentations, exercises, and scenarios
c. videos, notes, and stories
d. roundtables, exercises, and tests

**81. Which of the following NOT is considered a leading indicator for safety management system performance?**

a. pre-employment physical results
b. training courses conducted
c. number of audits performed
d. employee surveys

**82. Which of the following analytical tools would a safety engineer NOT normally employ?**

a. sequential timed events plotting analyses
b. failure modes and effects analyses
c. hazard totem poles
d. IEEE Standard 1004-1A

**83. What should be the first step implemented when developing a facility emergency action plan?**

a. submitting a plan license mandate request to a regional FEMA office
b. assembling a team from a variety of organizational functions and disciplines
c. creating a first-tier disaster-response outline or template
d. constructing a charter for the plan to be approved by the facility's general manager

**84. What is typically regarded as the most vital reason for conducting a workplace safety analysis?**

a. to avoid accidents by noting existing hazards and devising controls to mitigate them
b. to enhance corporate cost-effectiveness over the long term
c. to fulfill OSHA requirements per 29 CFR 1910.46
d. to be able to qualify for most workers' compensation insurance plans

**85. What is typically regarded as a very effective method or model for conducting a root-cause analysis?**

a. the single variance method
b. the prevention-occurrence-prevention model
c. the five whys method
d. the triple event tree model

**86. Which of the following types of electromagnetic radiation usually emanates from sources such as heaters, stoves, and fires?**

a. infrared
b. microwave
c. X-ray
d. thermal

**87. Which of the following materials does NOT act as a good electrical insulator?**

a. mica
b. wood
c. water
d. glass

**88. Which of the following is NOT an indication that an exposure assessment for respiratory hazards may be necessary?**

a. The workplace contains visible fumes, dusts, aerosols, or other emissions.
b. A process uses a substance that has a specific OSHA standard, such as methylene chloride or lead.
c. Employees complain of respiratory irritation or odors.
d. Employees experience tinnitus.

**89. Electrical fires can often occur due to electrical ________ or poor _________.**

a. bonding / grounding
b. short-outs / connectivity
c. inductance / capacitance
d. reactivity / impedance

**90. Which of the following chemicals or types of chemicals does NOT present the hazard of chemical skin burns or irritation?**

a. sodium hydroxide
b. degreasers
c. paint thinners
d. potassium chloride

**91. What is the calculated risk of an accident event that has a frequency of 0.0001/year and an associated consequence of 2.5 fatalities?**

a. 2.5 fatalities/year
b. 0.0001 fatalities/year
c. 0.00025 fatalities/year
d. 0.000040 fatalities/year

**92. What is a GANTT chart?**

a. A project management tool used for presenting a logical breakdown of task requirements.
b. A project management tool used for planning purposes, which graphically depicts a project plan via a bar-chart layout.
c. A project management tool that graphically tracks a project's budgetary trends via a line-chart layout.
d. A project management tool that calculates a project's ongoing performance metrics in the way of meeting budgets, schedules, and performance criteria/deliverables.

**93. Within the Incident Command System, the command staff consists of the _____________, the Safety Officer, and the Liaison Officer.**

a. Finance Chief
b. Public Information Officer
c. Intelligence Chief
d. Incident Commander

**94. Which of the following is an appropriate response from an organization when an unsafe condition is found during a voluntary internal audit?**

a. initiate corrective action measures
b. file a report with management
c. delay action until the following budget year
d. conduct a follow-up audit the next year to determine if the condition still exists

**95. At what noise level does pain typically begin to be felt in the ears?**

a. 100 dBA
b. 120 dBA
c. 140 dBA
d. 160 dBA

**96. What end-product tool is conventionally derived from a failure modes and effects analysis?**

a. an action list
b. a reliability plan
c. a fault tree
d. a frequency/severity concept summary

**97. An emergency evacuation plan should include the location of _______, alarm pull stations, and assembly areas.**

a. fire extinguishers
b. landline telephones
c. fire sprinklers
d. evacuation routes

**98. A bicycle is suspended at the peak of two slanted attic rafters. The bottom ends of the rafters are bolted to a joist that runs perpendicular to the roofline. If the bicycle weighs 30 lb and the rafters come together to form a 60-degree angle at the peak, what is the tension applied to the joist? (Neglect the weight of the rafters.)**

a. 8.7 lb
b. 12.8 lb
c. 17.3 lb
d. 30 lb

**99. Which of the following is NOT typically evaluated within the domain of accident prevention?**

a. accident severity or consequence
b. accident responsibilities
c. accident financial impacts
d. accident frequency

**100. Which of the following best describes an effective slide show presentation?**

a. It contains images, covers one topic per slide, and uses a minimal amount of text.
b. It is funny, has thorough descriptions, and has sounds.
c. It covers as many points as possible, uses complete sentences, and has moving graphics.
d. It has multiple images, contains a variety of effects, and uses technical terms.

**101. What is a gap analysis?**

a. an examination of the organization's safety violations
b. a comparison of the safety performance of one organization with that of another
c. a method used to identify areas for improvement in a safety program
d. an evaluation of injury data

**102. Which of the following is NOT typically addressed through a separate safety-related program in most industrial settings?**

a. Fair Labor Standards Act
b. substance abuse
c. employee wellness or medical monitoring
d. workplace violence

**103. Which of the following is generally NOT true with regard to proper workstation configurations?**

a. An employee's chair and desk should be set at heights to enable the employee's legs to be bent within a range of 90–110 degrees (at the knees) while seated.
b. The top of a workstation computer screen should be set at eye level.
c. Keyboards should be placed above the height of the elbows, keeping the employee's wrists moderately bent upwards.
d. Footrests should be used by shorter employees to help maintain proper leg-to-torso angles.

**104. A type C-rated fire extinguisher is effective against which type of fire?**

a. a fire of flammable liquids
b. a fire involving electrical equipment
c. a trash, wood, or paper fire
d. a kitchen fire

**105. Using Kirchhoff's voltage law, calculate the voltages across R2 and R3 in the circuit below.**

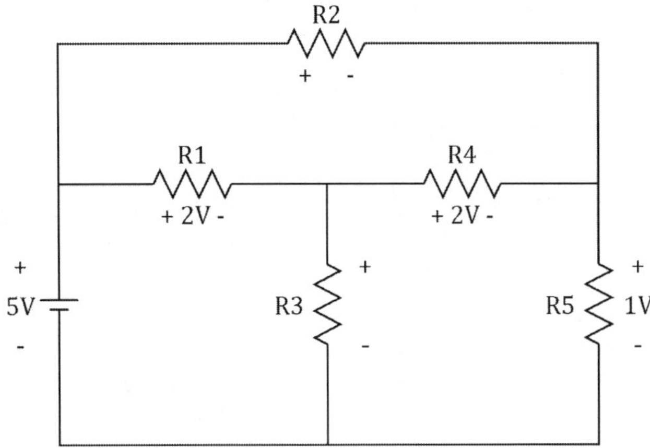


a. 2 V, 5 V
b. 4V, 3 V
c. 5 V, 2 V
d. 7 V, 4 V

**106. A 38 g mixture is composed of 12 g of compound A, 8 g of compound B, and 18 g of compound C. Compound A has a toxic equivalency factor (TEF) of 0.1, compound B has a TEF of 0.03, and compound C has a TEF of 0.01. What is the toxic equivalency (TEQ) of the mixture?**

a. 5.32 g
b. 0.00114 g
c. 1.62 g
d. 1.34 g

**107. Performing a(n) ________________ is an effective way of determining whether a specific training regimen is a means of solving a particular organizational problem.**

a. training audit
b. fishbone analysis
c. event-tree evaluation
d. needs assessment

**108. Which of the following acids would be considered the most dangerous to overall human health?**

a. 15 M nitric acid
b. 0.1 M hydrochloric acid
c. 20 M acetic acid
d. 0.01 M sulfuric acid

**109. Within the topic of fleet safety, which of the following is NOT an area that has an impact on reducing losses associated with accidents?**

a. crash or collision investigations
b. vehicle inspections
c. driver behaviors
d. timely license renewals

**110. What does the ergonomics-related acronym *RULA* stand for?**

a. repetitive user lifting assessment
b. rapid upper limb assessment
c. realized under leverage activity
d. repetitive user ligament assessment

**111. Which of the following elements is NOT part of the fire tetrahedron?**

a. fuel
b. oxygen
c. smoke
d. chain reaction

**112. Balance the following reaction between sulfuric acid and aluminum hydroxide by filling in the correct stoichiometric values for each chemical:**

$$\_\ H_2SO_4 + \_\ Al(OH)_3 \rightarrow \_\ Al_2(SO_4)_3 + \_\ H_2O$$

a. 3, 2, 1, 6
b. 2, 3, 1, 3
c. 3, 3, 2, 6
d. 1, 2, 1, 4

**113. What are the three *Rs* associated with waste reduction and environmental resource conservation?**

a. regenerate, recycle, resources
b. recycle, reduce, reuse
c. rectify, replenish, replicate
d. replace, reuse, restart

**114. Which of the following benefits of good housekeeping contributes to fire prevention?**

a. reduction of fuel available to start or sustain a fire
b. better appearance of work area for visitors
c. easy location of tools in the event of a fire
d. lower insurance premiums due to clean workspaces

**115. Mandatory drug testing is commonly used in all the following instances EXCEPT:**

a. a pre-employment screening
b. after a workplace injury
c. a periodic check for a safety-sensitive position
d. when a supervisor has reason to suspect impairment

**116. Per trenching safety program protocols, if a 6-foot-deep trench is dug in a gravel-sand environment, what angle must the trench wall(s) not exceed?**

a. 46 degrees
b. 40 degrees
c. 34 degrees
d. 28 degrees

**117. A worker is connected to a 6-foot-long lanyard while working on a ledge 40 feet above the ground. The lanyard is connected to the building 10 feet above the ledge. If the maximum elongation of the lanyard is 42 inches and the worker's D-ring is attached at a height of 5 feet 6 inches, what is the fall clearance from the connection point? Add a 3-foot margin of safety.**

a. 18 feet
b. 21 feet
c. 28 feet
d. 58 feet

**118. Which of the following is NOT a recognized phase of learning under transformational learning theory?**

a. identification of a dilemma
b. establishment of benefit
c. critical reflection
d. discovering the answer

**119. Which of the following can be modified in advance of an OSHA inspection to prevent citations or reduce fines?**

a. injury logs
b. internal audit reports with negative findings
c. training records
d. none of the above

**120. Which of the following environmental media does NOT typically require a state regulatory permit?**

a. wastewater
b. facility air emissions
c. stormwater runoff
d. petroleum

**121. All the following actions increase the risk of workplace violence and assault at a business EXCEPT**

a. working with cash
b. working late at night
c. contact with the public
d. working in pairs or groups

**122. Which of the following is the most common route of chemical exposure?**

a. inhalation
b. ingestion
c. injection
d. absorption

**123. A permit-required confined space safety program typically consists of all the following elements, EXCEPT:**

a. unauthorized entry prevention
b. cost-benefit analyses
c. hazard controls
d. entry permit requirements

**124. A(n) ________________ assessment, often requested by employers, primarily serves to determine whether physical or psychological limitations will prevent a candidate or employee from performing requisite job duties.**

a. anthropometric baseline
b. functionality
c. fitness-for-duty
d. Myers-Briggs

**125. Which of the following is NOT required on a container label that is compliant with the Globally Harmonized System of hazard communication?**

a. Storage temperature
b. Pictogram
c. Name
d. Hazard Statement

**126. Which of the following is NOT typically associated with excessive exposure to vibrating machinery?**

a. carpal tunnel syndrome
b. white finger
c. diminished hand dexterity or grip
d. osteoarthritis

**127. Per the Environmental Protection Agency, the term *NESHAP* refers to which of the following?**

a. National Effluent Sampling and Hazard Abatement Plan
b. National Environmental Statistical Hazards Assessment Protocol
c. National Emission Standards for Hazardous Air Pollutants
d. National Environmental Stewardship Historical Annex Policy

**128. Which of the following is NOT generally true with regard to adult learners compared to children?**

a. Adults generally take responsibility for their own learning.
b. Adults usually challenge new information that is offered to them.
c. Adults are typically self-directed when it comes to education.
d. Adults usually learn by cognitive means, whereas children tend to favor kinesthetic techniques.

**129. A ________ is a substance that impacts a developing fetus and can result in abnormalities.**

a. mutagen
b. carcinogen
c. teratogen
d. reproductive toxin

**130. A ____________ is a regimented and methodical evaluation of a planned or existing undertaking or process that attempts to identify and assess potential issues that may ultimately cause a risk to workers, equipment, and/or operational efficiencies.**

a. hazard and operability study (HAZOP)
b. failure modes and effects analysis (FMEA)
c. job safety analysis (JSA)
d. fishbone analysis

**131. The following are all examples of workplace violence EXCEPT:**

a. threatening behavior, such as vandalism, theft, and throwing objects
b. deleting a threatening email
c. verbal or written threats
d. harassment, including bullying, rumors, and intimidation

**132. Which of the following materials is NOT commonly utilized as a fire suppressant?**

a. carbon dioxide
b. halon
c. sodium bicarbonate
d. magnesium sulfate

**133. To reduce the risk from the threat of explosive devices, employees should be trained to report any suspicious object that is "HOT," which stands for __________, __________, or __________.**

a. handmade, open, ticking
b. haphazard, obvious, tempting
c. hidden, obviously suspicious, not typical
d. here, orderly, tainted

**134. Which of the following is NOT a part of emergency response plan preparation?**

a. planning
b. publishing
c. practicing
d. evaluating

**135. If there is a 100-curie source of the radioactive isotope cobalt-60 at time $t_0$, approximately what percentage of the source will be remaining after 21.2 years if the half-life of cobalt-60 is 5.3 years?**

a. 25.0 percent
b. 18.5 percent
c. 6.3 percent
d. 1.6 percent

**136. Per OSHA, energy control programs shall include procedures for the sequential steps necessary to ______________ machines or equipment.**

a. de-energize, stabilize, and lockout
b. shut down, isolate, block, and secure
c. redirect, ground, and bond
d. discharge, lockout, tagout, and reinitiate

**137. General ergonomic requirements, per OSHA, are enforced per ______________.**

a. OSHA 29 CFR 1910.95
b. OSHA General Duty Clause, Section 5(a)(1)
c. OSHA Ergonomic Hazards Policy, OSHA-ETS-416P.2
d. OSHA 29 CFR 1926.54

**138. What are the five letter-based classes of portable fire extinguishers?**

a. A, B, C, F, and X
b. A, B, C, D, and Z
c. A, B, C, D, and K
d. A, B, C, AA, and O

**139. Per EPA guidelines, which of the following is NOT typically designated as an essential element of an environmental management system (EMS)?**

a. maintaining employee environment-related competencies and knowledge
b. regularly assessing associated EMS legal requirements
c. regularly reviewing an organization's environmental objectives
d. implementing corrective-action protocols in support of continuous improvement initiatives

**140. Which of the following exposure limits is legally enforceable by OSHA?**

a. PEL
b. REL
c. TLV
d. STEL

**141. If a heat-generating source within a work setting has an operational lifetime of 500 kilowatt-hours, what is the equivalent amount of heat that is generated in joules during this operational lifetime (assuming no efficiency-related losses)?**

a. 138.9 J
b. 500,000 J
c. $7.2 \times 10^6$ J
d. $1.8 \times 10^9$ J

**142. In fault-tree analyses, what types of logic gates are applied for linking together event sequences?**

a. IF/THEN
b. AND/OR
c. YES/NO
d. IN/OUT

**143. Which of the following is NOT typically utilized as an ergonomic hazard control?**

a. work hardening
b. job rotation
c. work conditioning
d. task tiering

**144. The ignition of organic materials in the absence of a readily observable initiator, which is usually due to internal heat generation via oxidation, is commonly referred to as ____________________.**

a. spontaneous combustion
b. acute exothermia
c. thermodynamic excitation
d. volatile organic compound (VOC) transition

**145. Which of the following is NOT a method listed on the EPA's hierarchy of hazard controls?**

a. Elimination
b. Engineering
c. Risk Management
d. Personal Protective Equipment

**146. A well-constructed training course typically includes a(n) ____________________ to verify that the trainees have absorbed the vital informational components of the course.**

a. feedback questionnaire
b. retention review tool
c. assessment module
d. self-examination exercise

**147. If a storage shelf has a weight-limit capacity of 500 pounds and a safe utilization surface area of 10 $ft^2$, how many cube-shaped 8-$ft^3$ boxes weighing 50 pounds each can be safely stored on the shelf? (No stacking of boxes is permitted.)**

a. 2
b. 5
c. 7
d. 10

**148. Which types of records does HIPAA regulate access to?**

a. employment
b. payroll
c. medical
d. none of the above

**149. Within the domain of ergonomics and related injuries, the term *CTD* typically refers to which of the following?**

a. carpal tunnel dysfunction
b. cumulative trauma disorder
c. cystic tissue degeneration
d. chronic tendon dysplasia

**150. What is defined as "a solid material composed of distinct particles or pieces, regardless of size, shape, or chemical composition, which presents a fire or deflagration hazard when suspended in air or some other oxidizing medium over a range of concentrations?"**

a. volatile particulate matter
b. explosive PM10
c. combustible dust
d. unstable airborne residuals

**151. Which of the following is NOT true regarding the Environmental Protection Agency's hazardous waste identification (HWID) process?**

a. An initial determination must be made by a generator as to whether subject waste is solid waste.
b. The EPA must perform a codified audit series before officially approving a generator's hazardous waste inventory.
c. A determination must be made by the generator as to whether subject waste is RCRA hazardous waste.
d. Waste generators may petition to have a specific type of waste delisted from their hazardous waste record.

**152. Besides providing an exam at the end of a training course to measure the effectiveness of the training course, what is another method that can be employed to measure course efficacy?**

a. having trainees apply their knowledge in a skills test
b. having trainees critique the training course
c. having trainees complete instructor feedback questionnaires
d. having trainees draft a mock installment outline for the subject training program

**153. Which of the following groups should be exempted from an organization's zero-tolerance policy for workplace violence?**

a. management
b. contractors
c. visitors
d. none of the above

**154. Employee feedback on safety performance should be ________.**

a. positive, generalized, and offered at a convenient time
b. presented during annual reviews
c. given in front of the group
d. timely, specific, and factual

**155. Which of the following is a recommended approach for proper chair adjustment in a workstation?**

a. to move the chair as close as reasonably possible to the work area while seated
b. to move the elbow rests of the chair a forearm's length away from the edges of the workstation
c. to set the chair's back support to approximately 10 degrees away from the desk and keep it fixed
d. to set the chair's recline limit to approximately 10 degrees away from the desk

**156. What is a method of discharging static electricity from one's person?**

a. walking on a concrete floor while wearing rubber-based shoes or insoles
b. briefly touching any conductive metal that is grounded and non-energized
c. washing one's hands
d. changing one's clothes

**157. Within the realm of industrial air emissions, what does the abbreviation *BACT* stand for?**

a. breathable airborne contaminant test
b. biotic aerobic classification technique
c. best available control technology
d. bacterial antivirus cleanup technique

**158. Which of the following is NOT a method for preventing combustible dust explosions?**

a. bag collector
b. routine equipment maintenance program
c. ignition source control plan
d. general ventilation fan

**159. Which of the following is a reason that safety training in a group setting can be particularly effective?**

a. It allows one member to share all their experiences with the group.
b. It allows members to listen to only what pertains to them.
c. It allows participants to learn from other group members' experiences.
d. Side conversations can increase networking opportunities.

**160. A disaster recovery plan should designate a(n) ________________ who ultimately decides what recovery actions need to be taken and assigns responsibilities for achieving such actions.**

a. recovery coordinator
b. emergency response team task leader
c. disaster preparedness liaison
d. contingency manager

**161. Which of the following is NOT a fire detection system?**

a. smoke detector
b. heat detector
c. flame detector
d. carbon dioxide detector

**162. According to the Federal Emergency Management Agency, an ________________ is a "management system designed to enable effective and efficient domestic incident management by integrating a combination of facilities, equipment, personnel, procedures, and communications operating within a common organizational structure."**

a. incident management integration program
b. incident command system
c. integrated emergency management charter
d. incident management and response system

**163. What are the two primary pieces of legislation enforced by the EPA that prescribe limits to industrial water pollution levels and standards for water quality?**

a. the Federal Water Pollution Control Act and the Federal Water Quality Act
b. the Comprehensive Environmental Response, Compensation, and Liability Act and the Toxic Substances Control Act
c. the Water Quality Standards Act and the Clean Liquid Effluents Act
d. the Clean Water Act and the Safe Drinking Water Act

**164. Based on the BCSP Code of Ethics, a safety professional may accept an assignment outside of their technical knowledge base under which of the following circumstances?**

a. when they reasonably believe they can accomplish the assignment satisfactorily
b. when professionals from the applicable field have been consulted
c. when payment is prorated accordingly
d. a safety professional may never accept an assignment outside their expertise

**165. Find the pressure that 0.500 mol of $H_2$ (g) will exert on a 500.0 mL flask at 300.0 K.**

a. $2.46 \times 10^{-2}$ atm
b. 12.32 atm
c. 24.6 atm
d. 49.3 atm

**166. An employee is regularly situated in an environment that has eight-hour time-weighted-average ambient noise levels just at the OSHA 29 CFR 1910.95 hazardous noise threshold. If the personal protective equipment (PPE) he wears decreases the ambient sound intensity by a factor of 10, what is the intensity level of the sound he hears?**

a. about 8.5 dBA
b. about 60 dBA
c. about 75 dBA
d. about 84 dBA

**167. What is a needs analysis?**

a. a method of determining what must be done at the operations level to meet strategic goals of upper management
b. a way to determine what safety training would address a gap between the current and desired states
c. a process to evaluate how a safety training program should be conducted
d. an evaluation of the personal protective equipment usage in an organization

**168. If an enclosed work area (room) has dimensions of 20 feet × 15 feet × 10 feet, what is the theoretical minimum amount of time it would take for the air in that room to be completely ventilated and exchanged by a ventilation system that operates at a rate of 10 cubic feet per second?**

a. 5 minutes
b. 10 minutes
c. 30 minutes
d. 60 minutes

**169. If errors in manufacturing cost $1,000 to fix, and the plant averages 12 errors per week, which is the plant improvement plan with highest savings-to-cost ratio?**

a. Hiring a supervisor prevents 6 errors per week and costs $3,200 monthly.
b. Installing an inspection machine prevents 11 errors per week, lasts 10 years, and costs $500,000.
c. Employee training prevents 4 errors per week, lasts one year, and costs $8,000.
d. Hiring an extra worker prevents one error per week and costs $400 weekly.

**170. The US Nuclear Regulatory Commission's annual worker dose limit is 5 rem (10 CFR 20). What percent of this limit would a worker receive if they were exposed to an average daily 10-millirem dose (for an eight-hour workday) over a 2,000-hour work year?**

a. 25 percent
b. 50 percent
c. 75 percent
d. >100 percent

**171. The longest sequence of activities in a project plan that must be completed on time in order for a given project, as a whole, to be completed on time is known as the project's ______________.**

a. target milestone timeline
b. float continuum
c. overrun margin
d. critical path

**172. Which of the following is NOT typically true with regard to the scope of a job safety analysis (JSA)?**

a. A JSA includes safety recommendations associated with a given task.
b. A JSA identifies potential hazards associated with a given task.
c. A JSA outlines traceability requirements associated with a given task.
d. A JSA integrates safety principles with job practices.

**173. Which of the following responses to observing an unsafe behavior should a safety professional NOT employ?**

a. ignore the behavior and hope it goes away
b. inform the employee's supervisor of the need to correct the behavior
c. hold a private discussion with the employee
d. initiate discipline for the employee

**174. Which of the following is a method of risk transfer when painting the exterior of a multistory building?**

a. using properly installed tie-off points for body harnesses
b. renting a boom lift for the maintenance staff
c. hiring a painting subcontractor
d. putting off the paint job for another year

**175. Which of the following is NOT typically included as part of an annual fire extinguisher maintenance inspection?**

a. ensuring adequate amounts of extinguishing agent are present
b. ensuring that all components are in serviceable condition
c. verifying adequate canister pressure levels
d. testing extinguisher performance on a fire

**176. _________ is the process of water-soluble chemicals (such as fertilizers, pesticides, or hazardous waste) migrating through soil via rain or runoff and subsequently polluting nearby surface water or groundwater.**

a. Vadose transpiration
b. Leaching
c. Migration
d. Aquiferic diffusivity

**177. What is the recommended upper weight limit for hand tools?**

a. 0.5 kg (1.1 lb)
b. 1.0 kg (2.2 lb)
c. 1.5 kg (3.3 lb)
d. 2.0 kg (4.4 lb)

**178. Which of the following liquids is considered the most flammable?**

a. diethyl ether
b. diesel fuel
c. kerosene
d. acetic acid

**179. In regard to particulate matter emitted from stacks and other sources, what does the acronym *AMAD* mean?**

a. airborne material ascension dispersion
b. atmospheric measurement adiabatic device
c. allowable modeled atmospheric dilution
d. activity median aerodynamic diameter

**180. Which of the following is NOT typically considered a tactic for reducing the risk of potential injuries that may result from manual materials handling?**

a. proper task designing and/or redesigning
b. task sampling
c. suitable pre-placement procedures
d. workflow protocols

**181. What employee information is an employer obligated to treat as confidential?**

a. medical information, including disabilities or medical conditions
b. personal identifiable information
c. financial information, such as salary or withholdings
d. all of the above

**182. Which of the following is NOT true with regard to the Comprehensive Environmental Response, Compensation, and Liability Act (CERCLA)?**

a. It establishes prohibitions and requirements concerning closed and abandoned hazardous waste sites.
b. It provides for liability of persons responsible for releases of hazardous material at closed and abandoned hazardous waste sites.
c. It has an established trust fund to provide for cleanup when no responsible party can be identified.
d. It created an agency to review insurance policies for hazardous waste haulers.

**183. Excessive periods of standing in the workplace can often lead to the manifestation of _________.**

a. varicose veins
b. plantar nerve damage
c. muscular dystrophic separation
d. sepsis

**184. Which of the following is NOT a concept in adult learning theory?**

a. Learning should be self-directed.
b. Retention occurs regardless of readiness.
c. New material should be associated with experiences.
d. Information that is applicable to a task is easier to retain.

**185. Which of the following naturally occurring substances has a total of only three possible nuclides, with only one being categorized as radioactive?**

a. uranium
b. hydrogen
c. helium
d. radon

**186. Which of the following is NOT a recognized learning style?**

a. auditory
b. kinetic
c. virtual
d. visual

**187. The ________ considers any verbal or physical conduct from which a reasonable person infer "an intent to cause harm" as workplace violence.**

a. FBI
b. DEA
c. EPA
d. TSA

**188. Which of the following is NOT usually regarded as a potential benefit of a robust environmental management system?**

a. reduced training costs
b. resource conservation
c. pollution prevention
d. improved employee morale

**189. Which federal agency is responsible for making current OSHA regulations available to the public?**

a. Department of Labor
b. Government Accountability Office
c. Department of Health and Human Services
d. Government Publishing Office

**190. Emergency evacuation plans should be practiced at least ________.**

a. weekly
b. monthly
c. bi-annually
d. annually

**191. Which of the following parameters is NOT considered pivotal for determining a facility's routine airborne pollutant concentrations?**

a. wind stability
b. facility stack heights
c. precipitation levels
d. damper specifications

**192. Which of the following is a model included in options-based responses to active shooter events?**

a. run, duck, cover
b. fight, call, stay
c. run, fight, hide
d. fight, cover, call

**193. Which of the following activities requires a hot work permit?**

a. using a belt sander
b. oxyacetylene torch cutting
c. using an asphalt kettle
d. warming an area with a space heater

**194. When confronted with an unfamiliar or special hazard (such as asbestos or mold) in a workplace, how should a safety professional proceed?**

a. hire a subcontractor with appropriate expertise
b. research the topic on their own and do the best job they can
c. convince management that the hazard can be avoided
d. train employees to correct the hazard

**195. Which of the following classifications is NOT typically utilized for categorizing deficiencies noted during an environmental management system internal audit?**

a. opportunities for improvement (observations)
b. conditions adverse to quality (nonconformances)
c. corrective actions (areas for concern)
d. violations (breaches of protocol)

**196. What is the recommended upper weight or force limit of an object that is to be horizontally pushed or pulled from a kneeling position?**

a. 42 lb
b. 33 lb
c. 25 lb
d. 16 lb

**197. Which of the following best describes a carcinogen?**

a. an organism that causes a disease
b. a substance that affects the reproductive system
c. a substance that interrupts normal cell death processes
d. a substance that causes premature cell death

**198. Regarding optimal execution of automotive safety features, what is the recommended distance between a driver's chest and the steering wheel?**

a. 7–9 inches
b. 10–12 inches
c. 14–16 inches
d. 16–18 inches

**199. Which of the following mitigation technologies is NOT known to effectively remove water contaminants?**

a. ultraviolet light
b. high-efficiency filters
c. ozonation
d. recirculation

**200. _____________ usually results in pain that affects the back, the hips, and the outside of the legs, and is typically caused by the compression of a spinal nerve root in the lower back area due to a degenerated disk.**

a. Scoliosis
b. Osteoarthritis
c. Sciatica
d. Fibromyalgia

# Answer Key and Explanations

**1. A:** The LFL of a mixture is calculated according to the following formula:

$$LFL_{mix} = \frac{1}{\frac{f_1}{LFL_1} + \frac{f_2}{LFL_2} + \ldots + \frac{f_n}{LFL_n}}$$

Where:

$LFL_{mix}$ = lower flammability limit of the mixture

$f_n$ = fractional concentration of component $n$

$LFL_n$ = lower flammability limit of component $n$

$$LFL_{\text{mix}} = \frac{1}{\frac{0.2}{0.04} + \frac{0.8}{0.022}} = 0.0242$$

**2. A:** Transformational learning theory is rooted in the fact that adults have more life experiences to which new information can be applied. Associating new meaning with an earlier experience allows the information to be cataloged in a familiar location for longer retention and easier recall.

**3. B:** Accidents are statistically likely to occur when workers have recently started a new job; thus, it is most imperative that safety training regimens occur prior to workers commencing a new job or task. Employees conducting unfamiliar work must be shown how to safely perform procedures, be instructed on proper accident response and reporting procedures, and be instilled with the fact that safety is a priority with the organization.

**4. D:** Worksite safety inspections are usually conducted by inspectors who do not have a direct affiliation with the organization or entity being inspected and by personnel who have robust knowledge, training, and/or experience within the subject area that the inspection is concerned with. Moreover, inspections can be either scheduled or unscheduled, and can be either detail-oriented or general in nature.

**5. B:** A sound workplace security plan should have measures in place to screen and restrict visitors in the effort to control site access and increase employee safety. Limiting access helps to prevent unauthorized personnel from wandering around the facility where they can pose a hazard to themselves or cause harm to others. Security measures should include regular site assessments to identify and control vulnerabilities, such as windows, garages, rooftops, and ventilation shafts.

**6. C:** A robust incident reporting system typically includes reporting mechanisms for recording near misses. It also includes clear directions on how to report an injury, when an injury should be reported, and whom the injury should be reported to. Finally, it typically includes processes for commencing incident investigations and filing insurance claims. Remote electronic access capabilities in the field are not a mandatory element of such a system and are thus seldom implemented.

**7. B:** A facility emergency action plan would be activated in response to a potential local emergency resulting from a tornado or flood. The plan outlines evacuation procedures, medical treatment, and contact information.

**8. D:** Potential rationales for investigating a workplace accident or incident typically include determining the extent of damage or loss associated with an event, assessing or attaining objective evidence for potential upcoming litigation resulting from the event, and reducing the potential for future similar recurrences by identifying the underlying cause of the event itself. A root-cause analysis is often employed as a tool to support the investigation in a fact-finding—not fault-finding—effort. Assigning blame should never be a fundamental goal of an accident investigation.

**9. A:** A major benefit that can result from undergoing an external audit is the collection and comparison of benchmarking information (per audit findings) against that of industry competitors that have undergone similar audits. External audits can have a cost, can take longer for corrective action feedback, and may not directly impact certification eligibility.

**10. D:** Mandatory participation in safety program activities and initiatives (e.g., voluntary protection programs) is not typically employed as an enforcement measure for ensuring compliance with safety program protocols. Such measures may, however, include disciplinary actions for blatant disregard of safety rules, incentives for proactively following safety rules (e.g., gift cards provided to entire staff for having zero lost time over a calendar year), and training on safety requirements.

**11. D:** The term *andragogy* refers to adult learning theory; it is the study of how adults learn and how their learning is different from that of children. Programs geared toward adults should be based on these principles to increase retention.

**12. D:** The half-life of a radioactive isotope can be calculated according to the following formula:

$$\text{half life} = \frac{\text{time} \times \log(2)}{\log\left(\frac{\text{initial mass}}{\text{final mass}}\right)} = \frac{8.5 \text{ years} \times \log(2)}{\log\left(\frac{1\text{g}}{0.637\text{g}}\right)} = 13.06 \text{ years}$$

**13. C:** There are numerous elements in the management of hazardous waste. Some hazardous wastes can be recycled or reused. It is permissible to store hazardous wastes in specially designed open pools or temporarily in piles. Furthermore, wastes that are hazardous can be categorized as toxic, corrosive, reactive, and/or flammable. Hazardous wastes should not be combined with other waste types as doing so increases the total volume of waste that must be properly managed and the associated costs.

**14. D:** A key strategy for reducing the risks associated with an explosion hazard is to implement the use of barriers and distance. Materials that can deflect, block, and contain explosive blasts (e.g., concrete) can usually absorb a large percentage of detonation energy as well as airborne projectiles resulting from such blasts. Additionally, the impact of the overpressure on people, which can result in injuries, decreases as distance from the blast increases.

**15. A:** A potential positive outcome of an accident or incident is a shift in overall workforce safety awareness—specifically regarding levels of focus on safety practices and future incident avoidance. On the negative side, workers' compensation premiums usually increase after the occurrence of an incident. Also, trust in management typically goes down, and camaraderie and morale usually decline.

**16. B:** Titanium is not an effective shielding material for protecting against exposure to gamma- or X-ray radiation. The best shielding materials against these types of ionizing radiations include lead, concrete, and water.

**17. D:** Factors that can increase the risk of workplace violence towards employees include poor interior or exterior lighting, employees who work alone or are otherwise physically isolated from other employees, and a lack of communication devices to summon assistance when needed.

**18. B:** A mutagen is a chemical, material, or form of ionizing radiation that can affect the DNA of a cell. Once the DNA is impacted, the error in the sequence is then replicated and passed on to future cell generations. Such an error can result in tumor formation associated with cancer.

**19. B:** Depending on the type of CBT deployed by an organization, the training may not necessarily be easier than in-person training, but employees can control the pace of the training and the learning process, reviewing information as often as needed. This also avoids any potential embarrassment for asking questions in a group setting. Additionally, employees can take the training as their schedules allow, reducing the need to schedule a time for an entire group to be pulled out of the workplace for training.

**20. D:** Effective tools for reducing/eliminating exposures to infectious materials in the workplace include the use of robotics for remote handling of such hazards, the use of separation (as of clean rooms and rooms that contain these hazards) and physical barriers for staff handling infectious materials, and the use of personal protective equipment. First-aid response is an after-the-fact intervention which does not reduce or eliminate the exposure itself.

**21. A:** Plunger cans can be implemented for safely dispensing small quantities of flammable or combustible materials (such as solvents), particularly for industrial maintenance and cleaning activities. Flammable chemicals should never be highly pressurized and should always be grounded to safely disperse static charges. Safety cabinet design requirements are issued by the National Fire Prevention Association (NFPA), not the International Organization for Standardization (ISO).

**22. C:** Workplace hazards may arise in a number of different ways while conducting maintenance activities, including using poorly written maintenance procedures that do not clearly convey necessary step-by-step protocols, using incorrect or outdated maintenance schedules, and executing work functions on systems that are not of a user-friendly design for maintenance (e.g., limited access/service locations).

**23. B:** The adjusted WLL based on a vertical WLL can be calculated as:

$$Adjusted\ WLL = Vertical\ WLL \times number\ of\ legs \times sling\ angle\ factor$$

Since a basket hitch goes under the load and is connected to the master link or hook at both ends, it has two legs. Therefore, the 60-degree basket hitch has a WLL of $\mathbf{1,000 \times 2 \times 0.866 = 1,732}$.

**24. C:** A method for significantly reducing hazardous noise levels that is widely employed in industry is the wearing of both earplugs and earmuffs. In this configuration, the combination of both items attenuates the noise more than either item would by itself; however, caution must be used to ensure that employees are still able to hear alarms and other warning signals. Other noise reduction strategies include using sound-absorbing materials in building construction, decreasing vibrational frequencies, and increasing the distance between a noise source and workers.

**25. B:** Threshold limit values (TLVs) are established by the American Conference of Governmental Industrial Hygienists and are based on exposures over an 8-hour day and a 40-hour workweek. OSHA's permissible exposure limits (PELs) are based only on an 8-hour workday. Recommended exposure limits (RELs) are based on a 10-hour workday and a 40-hour week. Immediately dangerous to life and health (IDLH) values should never be exceeded for any period of time.

**26. C:** Under NFPA 13, occupancies with low combustibility and a moderate quantity of combustibles are classified as ordinary-hazard occupancies. Thus, the solution is the square footage of the building divided by the sprinkler rating for ordinary-hazard occupancies: $\frac{(70\times38)}{130} = 20.46$. This number is rounded up to the nearest whole sprinkler, 21.

**27. C:** Compressed fuel gas cylinders must be stored at least 20 feet away from oxygen cylinders. Alternatively, the cylinders can be separated by a 30-minute fire rated wall that is 5 feet high.

**28. B:** Regular hose spray-downs of work areas are not a widely implemented control for reducing potential heat-stress-related injuries in the workplace. Although such a measure may temporarily decrease local ambient temperatures by a few degrees, it is not a viable long-term solution to excessive-heat work environments and can create additional concerns such as slipping hazards and a higher degree of relative humidity in the subject work area. Such measures as wearing reflective and insulated clothing, executing training programs geared toward proper heat management techniques, and regular medical monitoring of employees at high cardiovascular risk are generally recommended controls for helping reduce or eliminate potential heat-stress incidents in the workplace.

**29. A:** In the event of a workplace violence event, employees should be trained to either shelter-in-place or evacuate, depending on the situation and directions from law enforcement or management.

**30. B:** Mass flow rate is defined as:

$$M = \rho VA$$

Where $\rho$ is density, $V$ is velocity, and $A$ is cross-sectional area. Since the openings of the pipe are circular, the equation for the area is:

$$A = \pi r^2$$

Because mass flow rate is constant throughout a pipe, the mass flow rate at the small end of the pipe can be set equal to the mass flow rate at the large end of the pipe:

$$62.43 \times 10 \text{ fps} \times (\pi \times (3 \text{ in.})^2) = 62.43 \times V_2 \times (\pi \times (4 \text{ in.})^2)$$

We can solve this for the water velocity at the larger end of the pipe, written above as $V_2$. The result is 5.63 feet per second.

**31. B:** A critical element of a workplace violence prevention program is the implementation of a zero-tolerance policy. A policy that covers employees, contractors, clients, and visitors will provide staff with the understanding that they will have some level of protection from violence at the workplace and that all incidents will be dealt with appropriately.

**32. C:** OSHA construction standard 29 CFR 1926.451 requires that scaffold systems be inspected by a competent person before each work shift and whenever there has been an incident that may have impacted the integrity of the system.

**33. A:** A project plan emphasizes how much time should be spent on each project step and orders those steps by priority. Other project management tools, such as WBSs and Gantt charts, are also robustly effective at laying out project elements and associated timetables, but they do not necessarily emphasize time spent on steps or the priority of each step.

**34. D:** Ethics can be defined as the standards for determining what is right or wrong. Ethics can also act as moral principles used to guide decisions.

**35. A:** A fault-tree analysis is a logic diagram that depicts potential failures in each individual segment or component of a system. Fault-tree analysis can be used to proactively identify potential safety issues in a system or as a root cause analysis tool after an incident has occurred. Event trees, system reliability evaluations, and probabilistic risk assessments (PRAs), as well as failure modes and effects analyses (FMEAs), are also useful tools that are regularly employed in the realm of design-safety engineering. However, these tools do not match the description in the question.

**36. D:** Accident history evaluations, employee feedback, and quantitative risk assessments are regularly employed in industry for identifying potential risks in the workplace. Cost-benefit analyses are usually done to determine the economic viability of a hazard control or mitigation strategy, not to identify potential risks.

**37. C:** The plan-do-check-act continuous improvement model is highly utilized within industrial occupational safety and health programs to evaluate the efficacy of safety control measures and determine if additional measures are necessary.

**38. C:** Benefits of commencing an accident investigation as soon as possible include: the sooner an accident's root cause is discovered, the sooner these lessons can be shared within the organization for preventing recurrences; a rapidly commenced investigation usually sends a message of robust corporate response and engagement; and witness accounts are usually more reliable earlier as opposed to later. Any costs associated with litigation will not be reduced due to the pace of fact-finding.

**39. A:** The following statements are true regarding illumination-related hazards that may exist in the workplace: extended exposure to intense light can damage eye receptor cells; the installation of lighting diffusers can help protect eyes from glares and strobing; and numerous illumination-related accidents occur because workers do not take enough time to let their eyes adjust when moving between lighter and darker areas. Conditions related to vitamin D deficiency (such as rickets) typically involve long-term lack of exposure to sunlight, so they are not associated with improper work area illumination.

**40. B:** *Liability* is the term used when assigning responsibility for damages that have occurred to another party. The damages may be a result of a failure to meet an obligation, such as an element of a contract; or they may result from failure to protect another party from injury.

**41. A:** Typically implemented protocols for protecting workers from bloodborne pathogens include the following: training workers to assume that all bodily fluids are potentially infectious; not permitting eating or drinking in areas where pathogens may be present; and requiring handwashing after removal of soiled gloves. Regular employee health screenings and medical monitoring do not protect workers from bloodborne pathogens, but rather serve to identify infectious diseases that employees have already been exposed to.

**42. B:** ANSI Z490.1 is the professional standard for the planning and conductance of health and safety training programs. It sets the industry benchmark for conducting such programs and conveys best practices for the optimal construction, delivery, and evaluation of these programs.

**43. C:** The sample standard deviation for a dataset is calculated using the following formula:

$$s = \sqrt{\frac{\sum(x - \bar{x})^2}{n - 1}}$$

Plugging in the dataset (4, 7, 15, 17, 26, 53, 59, 75), we can solve for the sample standard deviation:

$$s = \sqrt{\frac{784 + 625 + 289 + 225 + 36 + 441 + 729 + 1849}{7}} = \sqrt{711.14} \approx 26.7$$

**44. A:** The lower flammable limit (LFL), in a standard definition, is the lowest concentration of vapor in air at which the vapor will ignite at a given pressure and temperature. Concentrations below the LFL have too little fuel to ignite—often referred to as a "vapor-lean condition." Vapor concentrations above the LFL exposed to an ignition source will ignite and propagate a flame or, if confined, cause an explosion.

**45. D:** Positioning-device systems are usually employed for supporting workers who are working on an elevated vertical surface, and they consist of equipment, connectors, and a body harness or body belt. Moreover, a worker is also able to have both hands free while wearing such a system in order to perform required tasks efficiently and safely. Positioning-device systems are usually attached to either a lifeline or a lanyard in some capacity. OSHA Standards 1910.140, 1915.160, and 1926.502 address the specific regulatory requirements for these systems.

**46. C:** Experiential learning theory is based on the kinetic (i.e., doing) aspect of adult learning. The theory is founded on the ability of adults to retain new information more easily if, in addition to the cognitive aspects, the muscles or motor skills are engaged.

**47. B:** *P2P* is an acronym the EPA uses for "pollution prevention plan." Pollution prevention (P2) is a method of evaluating all the steps in a process for potential sources of waste or pollution and identifying strategies to reduce both the associated cost and the environmental impact.

**48. A:** In legal terms, strict liability is conventionally defined as a situation in which a corporate entity is forced to pay compensatory damages associated with a product or service it provided, irrespective of fault. During litigation, a claimant only needs to prove that a subject tort actually occurred and that the defendant was responsible. Federal law typically assigns strict liability in situations it considers to be inherently hazardous.

**49. A:** For ionizing radiation, the strength is a measure of how much radiation a particular source is emitting. Source strength can be calculated using the following equation:

$$Q = \frac{K_T M N_A}{W}$$

In the above equation, $K_T$ is the decay constant, $M$ is the mass of the substance, $N_A$ is Avogadro's number, and $W$ is the atomic weight. We can calculate the source strength using the numbers from the question, as follows:

$$Q = \frac{5.292 \times 10^{-4} \times 0.000001 \times 6.02 \times 10^{23}}{233} = 1.367 \times 10^{23} \text{ Bq} = 3.695 \times 10^{4} \text{ curies}$$

**50. A:** Wet-bulb globe temperature (WBGT) measures heat stress on workers and includes the impact of direct sunlight, unlike heat index, which assumes a shaded environment. WBGT is calculated according to the following equation:

$$WBGT = 0.7T_w + 0.2T_g + 0.1T_d$$

In this equation, $T_w$ is natural wet-bulb temperature, $T_g$ is globe thermometer temperature, and $T_d$ is actual air temperature, or dry-bulb temperature. We can calculate the WBGT using the numbers from the question, as follows:

$$WBGT = (0.7 \times 78) + (0.2 \times 87) + (0.1 \times 85) = 80.5°$$

**51. C:** There are several technologies that can be used to control particulate air emissions from industrial processes. An electrostatic precipitator uses static electricity to attract particles to charged plates where they are later removed; mechanical separators, such as high-efficiency particulate air (HEPA) filters and cyclone separators, physically prevent the particulate matter from leaving the exhaust stacks; condensation scrubbing uses water droplets to capture the particles to prevent their escaping into the atmosphere. Flare systems are used for volatile organic chemical (VOC) emissions; they prevent escape from the system by burning nearly all the VOC vapors.

**52. A:** To find the current $I_1$, the equivalent resistance of the circuit must be found. Resistors $R_2$ and $R_3$ are in parallel, and $R_1$ is in series with their equivalent resistance. Therefore, the equivalent resistance of the entire circuit can be calculated as:

$$R_{eq} = R_1 + \frac{R_2 \times R_3}{R_2 + R_3} = 50\ \Omega + \frac{40\ \Omega \times 60\ \Omega}{40\ \Omega + 60\ \Omega} = 74\ \Omega$$

Then using Ohm's law, the current can be calculated as follows:

$$I = \frac{V}{R} = \frac{5\text{ V}}{74\ \Omega} = 0.068\text{ A} = 68\text{ mA}$$

**53. D:** Health effects associated with exposure to occupational noise include the following: acoustical traumas caused by a sudden, extremely loud noises; shifts in threshold due to short- or long-term exposure to noise; and tinnitus (ringing in the ears) caused by short- or long-term exposure to occupational noise.

**54. B:** Incident rate (in the below equation, *IR*) can be calculated using the following formula:

$$IR = \frac{\text{Number of OSHA recordable incidents} \times 200{,}000}{\text{Number of employee hours worked}}$$

We can calculate the incident rate for the company and time period in question using the numbers from the question, as follows:

$$IR = \frac{6 \times 200{,}000}{127 \times 2000} = \frac{1{,}200{,}000}{254{,}000} = 4.72$$

**55. D:** Shoring is the process of installing support members within an excavation. Benching is a method of cutting back the sides of an excavation in a step-like manner. Sloping is a method of cutting back the sides of an excavation in an even, ramp-like style.

**56. C:** There are four fundamental precepts of ergonomics as it relates to safety engineering: "people differ from one another"; "whenever possible, the job should be changed and not the worker"; "people should work smart"; and "people are more appropriate for some tasks than machines are, and vice versa."

**57. B:** Chemical synergy occurs when the effects of exposures to two separate chemicals are a multiple of each exposure. For example, an exposure to a substance that is 2% chemical A and a substance that is 8% chemical B causes a reaction 40 times greater than what either of the two chemicals alone would cause. When the effects are summed, the interaction is termed *additive*. When the effects of the two chemicals are lessened, the interaction is termed *antagonistic*.

**58. B:** Use of a buddy system is an excellent control strategy for protecting against hazards associated with confined space work. The buddy system allows workers to monitor one another for the effects of hazardous atmospheres, heat stress, or supplied air system malfunctions. Other control strategies include assessing confined-space hazards prior to (not after) entry, worker training, installing accessible fire-suppression equipment, and ensuring that sufficient ventilation is available within the space.

**59. B:** In ergonomics, most items are designed to comfortably accommodate populations in the range of height from a 5th percentile female to a 95th percentile male. In the United States, this would be a range of height from about 5 feet 0 inches through 6 feet 3 inches.

**60. A:** Hazardous wastes are usually disposed of either through incineration or burial in permitted landfills. Incinerators often employ downstream scrubbers following combustion to help ensure that toxic gases do not get released into the environment. Landfills permitted for hazardous waste disposal must meet Environmental Protection Agency criteria to ensure that chemicals cannot migrate into groundwater or nearby soil media.

**61. C:** The autoignition temperature for a fuel is defined as the temperature at which the fuel will combust without being exposed to an ignition source.

**62. B:** Chemical irritants are compounds that usually adversely and temporarily affect the skin and mucus membranes, as well as the eyes and possibly the respiratory tract. The degree of irritation is directly related to the concentration of the irritant and the duration of contact. Irritants do not necessarily cause permanent tissue damage as a result of normal exposure. Examples of irritants include ammonia, ozone, chlorine, and nitrogen dioxide.

**63. C:** Biohazards can be either animal- or plant-based. They may include certain types of bacteria, viruses, or fungi. Also, when they originate from people, they are usually transmitted by some type of bodily fluid. In addition, they can be either toxic or allergenic in nature.

**64. A:** Mold is a living organism classified as a fungus that requires moisture and a food source to propagate. Molds reproduce by producing spores that are released into the environment. Inhalation of these spores may cause a reaction in sensitive individuals. Ebola virus is not airborne. Valley fever and hantaviruses do not have a particularly strong association with damp environments.

**65. A:** The experiential adult learning theory incorporates four stages of learning: concrete experience (practicing), reflective observation (watching and analyzing), abstract conceptualization (generalizing to other situations), and active experimentation (applying the knowledge).

**66. D:** Workplace violence includes physical assaults and threats of assault against employees. Workplace violence can range from verbal threats to homicide.

**67. B:** Safety professionals are ethically bound to enforce safety provisions evenly and at all times, regardless of bias, relationship, organizational level, or stage of the project or process.

**68. D:** Effective presentations will leverage adult learning theories. Such tools include slide show presentations, hands-on exercises, and small group exercises. OSHA does not consider handing out safety manuals for independent review an effective method for training.

**69. D:** Building evacuation plans should be designed so that personnel know where to exit in limited visibility conditions. Plans should also include the use of systems to communicate when an evaluation should occur, and they should specify locations of outdoor mustering areas. Items related to emergency response team activations are addressed separately, in emergency response plans.

**70. A:** Legal liability typically follows the doctrine of acts or omissions in that a party can be responsible for injury or damages based on what they did ("acts") or did not ("omissions") do to protect the injured party. For example, telling employees to not put on a fall protection harness would be an act resulting in liability, while not having a required fall protection program would be an omission.

**71. A:** Although OSHA does not administer specific indoor air quality (IAQ) standards, it does maintain a cadre of general ventilation protocols, as well as guidance regarding specific air contaminants that can potentially spawn IAQ issues. According to this guidance, recirculated-air system operational requirements include the following, at a minimum: contaminated air must be routed outdoors in the event of an incident; recirculated air must undergo regular sampling and evaluation to verify that cleaning systems are functioning normally; air-cleaning systems must have audiovisual warning indicators to advise personnel of potential issues; and secondary filtration modules must maintain an efficiency at least equal to that of a subject system's primary filtration modules.

**72. B:** Types of electrical switching devices that are typically used in the workplace for preventing access to hazardous electrical areas or for interrupting electrical power include cutouts, lockouts, and interlocks. Cutouts automatically trip power to electrical equipment when a certain temperature is reached. Lockouts prevent equipment from being switched on. Interlocks essentially preclude employee access to energized equipment or work areas. Knockouts are partially stamped openings in electrical enclosures that allow for the insertion of a wire, cable, or pipe.

**73. D:** In group sessions, facilitators must keep one individual from dominating the discussion and thereby limiting participation of the other members. Introverts may not be comfortable participating or asking clarifying questions, which will impact the effectiveness of the training for them. Also, the facilitator must try to avoid groupthink, wherein participants will, to avoid becoming outsiders, make an effort to agree with each other in spite of the facts or their own personal opinions and beliefs.

**74. C:** Several preventative controls can be utilized in the workplace for protecting against bulk-material hazards such as asphyxiation and cave-ins, including lifelines, guardrails, sloping at angles less than repose angles, and likewise shoring at angles less than repose angles.

**75. D:** OSHA standards are federal regulations, which means they carry the power of law. An employer must identify all activities within the workplace that are regulated by standards and adhere to the applicable provisions.

**76. D:** There are three general approaches used in industry for asbestos abatement: enclosure, encapsulation, and removal. Enclosure involves positioning permanent, airtight walls around the asbestos; encapsulation involves spraying the asbestos with a binding-type sealant that will keep the material in place; and removal involves temporary isolation, negative pressure, application of an immobilization solution, and ultimately, disposal.

**77. B:** A robust auditing program utilizes corrective action programs to address the root causes of issues found during an audit to prevent the issues from recurring.

**78. B:** Three spoons, three forks, and three knives will be inspected. We can view each inspection as an independent event. If spoons are defective 4% of the time, there is a 96% chance a spoon is not defective. Likewise, there is a 97% chance a fork will not be defective. Knives have a 0% or negligible defect rate, and therefore a 100% chance of not being defective. To sum the probabilities of independent events, we multiply them. In this case, we can ignore the probability for non-defective knives since it is 1.00:

$$P_{\text{no defects}} = 0.96 \times 0.96 \times 0.96 \times 0.97 \times 0.97 \times 0.97 = 0.807$$

**79. D:** Life-cycle cost is the total cost of a system or component over its entire lifespan. To calculate it, we subtract the total savings from the total costs. In this problem, the life-cycle cost can be calculated by summing the costs and subtracting the dealership's payment, as follows:

$$\text{Life-cycle cost} = \$12{,}000 + (\$400 \times 8) + \sum_{n=0}^{7} (\$600 + \$25 \times n) - \$2{,}000 = \$18{,}700$$

**80. B:** Safety training courses that are based on adult learning theories should incorporate presentations, exercises, and scenarios to best leverage the common ways in which adults learn.

**81. A:** Leading indicators for safety management system performance include training courses conducted, the number of safety audits performed, and employee surveys to provide feedback. Leading indicators drive safety-related changes while lagging indicators help to evaluate effectiveness.

**82. D:** Safety engineers and professionals have a variety of analytical tools regularly at their disposal for helping to perform safety assessments and risk determinations. Such tools may include sequential timed events plotting (STEP) analyses, failure modes and effects analyses (FMEA), and hazard totem poles.

**83. B:** The first step that should be implemented when developing a facility emergency action plan is selecting team members from a variety of organizational functions and disciplines. This scenario inevitably supplies a diverse set of viewpoints and areas of expertise that will ultimately result in the development of a stronger overall plan.

**84. A:** The most imperative reason for conducting a workplace safety analysis is typically to help avoid accidents by determining what hazards exist and what controls are required to avoid them. In addition, formal safety analyses, such as safety analysis reports (SARs) or technical safety requirements (TSRs), are often mandated by law or by contractual agreement.

**85. C:** The five whys method is typically regarded as a very effective method or model for conducting a root-cause analysis. This approach essentially advocates the use of consecutive, logically connected *why* questions that are used to ultimately reach the root cause or justification behind an occurrence. There is no requirement that the process be limited to five iterations—more or fewer may be used to reach a conclusion.

**86. A:** Infrared radiation usually emanates from sources such as heaters, stoves, and fires. Excessive exposure to infrared radiation can potentially lead to optical-related health effects such as cataracts, scotomas, lesions, hemorrhaging, and swelling.

**87. C:** Electrical insulators are materials that inhibit the free flow of electricity. Good insulating materials include air, wood, glass, plastics, mica, quartz, and rubber. Materials that are not good electrical insulators are those that conduct electricity well, such as copper, aluminum, and water.

**88. D:** The Respiratory Protection Standard (29 CFR 1910.134) requires employers to identify and evaluate respiratory hazards. Potential respiratory hazards can be identified by the presence of visible emissions, the use of specifically regulated substances, or employee reports (such as odors) or symptoms (such as irritation of the nose, throat, or chest). Tinnitus is a condition related to excessive noise.

**89. B:** Electrical fires can often occur due to electrical short-outs or poor connections. A short-out is an instance of electricity bypassing the intended current path and arcing across a gap between two conductive materials (i.e., short-circuiting). A similar phenomenon can occur if two connectors are not properly contacted—the electricity will "jump" the gap. The resultant arcing that occurs in such scenarios can ignite nearby flammable items.

**90. D:** Corrosive chemicals, such as sodium hydroxide, present the risk of a chemical burn. Degreasers and paint thinners, each consisting of a blend of petroleum products, can irritate the skin. Potassium chloride is a neutral salt that is neither a corrosive nor an irritant.

**91. C:** Risk is equal to the product of frequency and consequence (also referred to as severity). The overall calculated annual risk of an accident event which has a frequency of 0.0001/year and an associated consequence of 2.5 fatalities is derived by multiplying these two values. Hence, (0.0001/year) × (2.5 fatalities) = 0.00025 fatalities/year.

**92. B:** A GANTT chart is a project management tool used for planning purposes, which usually depicts a project plan via a bar-chart layout. It is regularly used by project managers, along with work-breakdown structures and other project management tools, to assist in determining project timelines, schedules, budgetary constraints, and critical paths.

**93. B:** Within the Incident Command Systems (ICS), the Command Staff consists of the Public Information Officer, the Safety Officer, and the Liaison Officer. The Command Staff is directed by the Incident Commander, who also directs the efforts of the various Section Chiefs.

**94. A:** OSHA encourages the use of internal audits as a proactive means of identifying unsafe conditions. If an unsafe condition is detected during an audit, the employer is required to take action to correct the hazard. Hazards that are identified during internal audits, that are not corrected, and that are subsequently identified during an OSHA inspection will be cited as "willful" since the employer had prior knowledge and did not act.

**95. C:** A noise level of 140 dBA is generally considered to be the approximate threshold of ear pain due to sound pressure.

**96. A:** Normally, an action list is the sought-after end-product tool that is rendered by conducting a failure modes and effects analysis. Actions receive a risk rank to allow for prioritization. If these actions are executed well, risk in the workplace is often substantially reduced.

**97. D:** An emergency evacuation plan should clearly denote primary and secondary evacuation routes, the location of alarm pull stations, and primary and secondary assembly areas.

**98. A:** The problem is represented in the triangle at left below. As it is easier to work with a right triangle than to work with an isosceles triangle, the triangle has been cut in half, its variables halved, and this half shown on the right. In this format, the bottom leg of the triangle, labeled x, represents the tension in the joist. This allows for the calculation of x as follows:

$$\tan(30) = \frac{x}{15}$$

$$x = 8.66 \text{ lb}$$

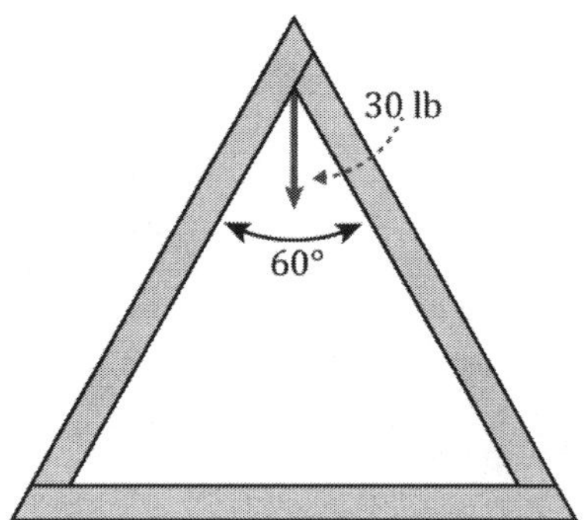


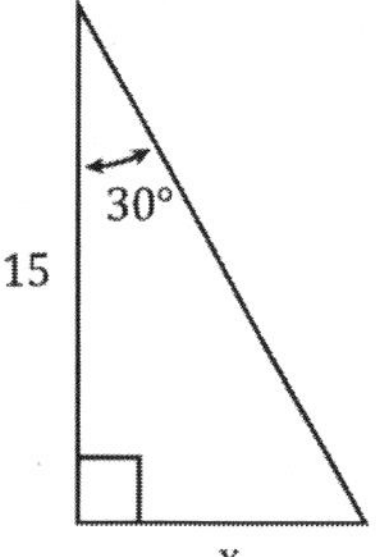


**99. B:** There are three primary categories normally evaluated within the domain of accident prevention: accident severity or consequence, accident frequency or probability, and accident financial impact. Responsibility is not a consideration for prevention.

**100. A:** Effective slide show presentations should not have large amounts of text that require participants to read, diverting their attention from the facilitator. Slides should be engaging, not only to engage visual learners but to avoid boring participants to the point of disengagement. One slide should cover only one topic. This allows the facilitator to present related information before the audience has moved on.

**101. C:** A gap analysis is a method to identify areas of improvement in a safety program. The gap analysis looks to compare the current state of the program to the desired state and identify areas that need to be addressed. The desired state may be compliance with a standard, or it may be identified as the result of an audit.

**102. A:** The Fair Labor Standards Act (FLSA) is typically not treated as a separate safety-related focus area or program within most industrial settings. The FLSA centers on workers' rights regarding working hours, overtime pay, exempt versus nonexempt status, acceptable working conditions, and ensuring that minors are not exploited. The act is usually administered and enforced through human resources and does not fall under the purview of safety and health.

**103. C:** There are several proper workstation configurations that should be procedurally implemented to help ensure that employees regularly retain maximum possible ergonomic benefits. These configurations including the following: setting chair and desk levels at such heights that the employee's legs are bent at a 90- to 110-degree angle at the knee; setting the top of workstation computer screens at levels equivalent to employee eye levels; and encouraging shorter employees to use footrests to help them maintain proper leg-to-torso angles. Keyboards should always be set at the approximate level that elbows are on when the employee is seated and resting their elbows on the desk; wrists should lie flat and straight.

**104. B:** A type C-rated fire extinguisher is effective against a fire involving live electrical equipment. Because of their nonconductive natures, extinguishing agents such as sodium bicarbonate and monoammonium phosphate are typically used in type C extinguishers to fight these types of fires.

**105. B:** Kirchhoff's voltage law states, "The sum of the electrical voltage around any closed network is zero." Reading the voltages around the top loop in a clockwise direction and using the following equation allows the voltage across $R_2$ to be calculated:

$$-2\text{ V} + V_{R2} - 2\text{ V} = 0$$

The voltage across $R_2$ must then equal 4 V.

The same can be done for $R_3$ in the loop containing $R_1$ and $R_3$:

$$-5\text{ V} + 2\text{ V} + V_{R3} = 0$$

The voltage across $R_3$ must then equal 3 V.

**106. C:** The toxic equivalency (TEQ) of a mixture is calculated by multiplying the mass of each dioxin by its corresponding toxic equivalency factor (TEF) and summing the results according to the following formula:

$$TEQ = \sum(m_i \times TEF_i)$$

$$TEQ = (12\text{ g} \times 0.1) + (8\text{ g} \times 0.03) + (18\text{ g} \times 0.01) = 1.62\text{ g}$$

**107. D:** Performing a needs assessment is an effective way for determining whether a specific training regimen is a means of solving a particular organizational issue. A training needs assessment compares the current state of the safety program and the desired state to determine whether training will close any identified gaps.

**108. A:** Compared to 0.1 M (molar) hydrochloric acid (HCl), 20 M acetic acid ($C_2H_4O_2$), and 0.01 M sulfuric acid ($H_2SO_4$), 15 M nitric acid ($HNO_3$) would be the most dangerous to overall human health due to its being a strong acid and having a high molar concentration (15 M). Though HCl and $H_2SO_4$ are also strong acids (comparable to nitric acid), in this example they are less concentrated (0.1 M and 0.01 M respectively). For $C_2H_4O_2$, although the molar concentration is higher than that of $HNO_3$ in this instance, it is a very weak acid in nature at nearly all comparable molarities.

**109. D:** Within the general realm of fleet safety programs, facets such as collision investigations, vehicular inspections, and driver behaviors are associated with loss reduction. Investigations identify areas for program improvement, inspections ensure equipment is working properly, and driver behavior can impact accident frequency and severity. Although maintaining licenses is required for applicable fleet operations, it is not typically associated with the safe operation of vehicles.

**110. B:** The ergonomics-related acronym *RULA* stands for "rapid upper limb assessment." This assessment is performed to quantify potential worker exposures to ergonomic risk factors associated with arm-related musculoskeletal disorders. In the assessment, biomechanical and posture-related load demands on the arms, torso, and neck are evaluated.

**111. C:** The fire tetrahedron consists of four elements: fuel, oxygen, heat, and a perpetual exothermic reaction that sustains combustion—a chain reaction. This reaction, which keeps the fire going, will continue until at least one of the other three elements (fuel, oxygen, and heat) is eliminated. Smoke is not an element of the fire tetrahedron but is of course a dangerous byproduct of a fire event.

**112. A:** By comparing the products to the reactants, we see there must be at least two Al atoms and at least three sulfate groups in the starting material. Therefore, a coefficient of 2 must be placed in front of $Al(OH)_3$ and a coefficient of 3 must be placed in front of $H_2SO_4$. To make the number of hydrogen and oxygen atoms equal on both sides of the equation, a coefficient of 6 must be placed in front of $H_2O$.

**113. B:** The three Rs typically associated with waste reduction and environmental resource conservation are *recycle, reduce,* and *reuse*. Each of these words represents a strategy that reduces the amount of waste that has an opportunity to enter and impact the environment.

**114. A:** Housekeeping entails cleaning and organizing a work area. By sweeping and cleaning up scrap, workers can reduce the amount of fuel available to start or sustain a fire. Placing flammable or combustible materials in proper storage containers reduces an ignition source's access to fuel to start a fire.

**115. B:** OSHA discourages mandatory drug testing after workplace accidents with the reasoning that it may deter employees from reporting occupational injuries. However, if there is a reasonable suspicion that drugs or alcohol may have contributed to the injury, the employer could require a test as long as there is a clear written policy in place.

**116. C:** Per trenching safety program protocols, if a trench with a depth of 6 feet is dug in type C materials (i.e., gravel, sand, or a mixture thereof), the trench wall(s) must not exceed an angle of 34 degrees.

**117. A:** The fall clearance can be calculated by adding the following: the length of the lanyard, height of the worker's D-ring, the elongation distance, and the margin of safety. This gives the following sum:

$$6 + 5.5 + 3.5 + 3 = 18 \text{ ft.}$$

**118. D:** Transformational learning theory postulates that adults learn when they experience radical changes in thoughts, perspectives, or behaviors. This learning takes place in three phases—identifying the dilemma of having incorrect information, establishing the benefit of "correct" knowledge that motivates the learning, and critical reflection of previously held knowledge to evaluate how it was incorrect.

**119. D:** Modifying or altering logs, audits, or records is unethical behavior and potentially violates Standard 2 of the Code of Ethics as set forth by the Board of Certified Safety Professionals: "Act with responsibility and integrity... Avoid all conduct or practice that is likely to discredit the profession or deceive the public.")

**120. D:** State regulatory permits are normally required for wastewater, facility air emissions, and stormwater runoff. While onsite petroleum storage is regulated, the actual usage rate of petroleum does not require a permit.

**121. D:** There are several actions that increase the risk of workplace violence and assault at a business. These include exchanging or working with cash, working late at night or early in the morning, having direct contact with members of the public, and working alone. Assigning employees to work in pairs or groups reduces the risk of workplace violence.

**122. A:** Inhalation is the exposure to a chemical substance by way of the respiratory system and is the most common route of exposure. Ingestion (oral exposure), injection (subdermal exposure), and absorption (dermal exposure) are other routes of chemical exposure.

**123. B:** Permit-required confined space safety programs typically consist of several distinct elements, including unauthorized entry prevention, hazard controls, entry permit requirements, space evaluations, entry team duties, rescue protocol, and training.

**124. C:** A fitness-for-duty assessment, which may be required by employers, primarily serves to determine whether a candidate or current employee is able to perform requisite job duties, or whether physical or psychological limitations will inhibit that ability. Such exams may be part of the hiring process, or they may be used when determining whether an employee can safely return to work after a prolonged, injury-related absence.

**125. A:** As set forth in the Hazard Communication Standard (29 CFR 1910.1200), a label that is compliant with the Globally Harmonized System must contain the following: a product identifier (i.e., a name), a signal word, a pictogram, hazard statement(s), precautionary statement(s), and manufacturer information, such as name, address, and phone number.

**126. D:** Several undesirable physical conditions can manifest over time from excessive exposure to vibrating machinery. Among them are carpal tunnel syndrome, vibration white finger, diminished hand dexterity or grip, and permanent loss of sensation in the fingers due to nerve damage. Osteoarthritis is the breakdown of cartilage in joints, and it has not been linked to vibration exposure.

**127. C:** Per the Environmental Protection Agency's 40 CFR 61, *NESHAP* refers to the National Emission Standards for Hazardous Air Pollutants. These standards outline facilities' annual maximum emissions of several substances, including benzene, polychlorinated biphenyls (PCBs), lead, chromium, volatile organic compounds (VOCs), and mercury.

**128. D:** Adults and children tend to learn in very distinct ways. Adults generally take responsibility for their own learning, they usually challenge new information that is offered to them, and they are typically self-directed when it comes to education. Learning modes (such as visual, auditory, and kinetic) are specific to individuals, and not necessarily to age groups. No learning mode is categorically considered an adult mode rather than a children's mode.

**129. C:** Teratogens, by definition, impact developing fetuses during periods of rapid cell replication and organ development in the womb. Results can include birth defects, abnormalities, or impaired function of organs later in the life of the fetus. Teratogens include cigarette smoke, alcohol, and certain chemicals. Though the other toxins mentioned could indirectly impact a developing fetus, their primary impacts, by definition, are to other areas.

**130. A:** A hazard and operability study (HAZOP) is a regimented and methodical evaluation of a planned or existing undertaking or process that attempts to identify and assess potential issues that may ultimately cause a risk to workers, equipment, and/or operational efficiencies.

**131. B:** Workplace violence includes all forms of threatening behaviors, all forms of threats (both written and verbal), and all forms of harassment meant to demean, embarrass, or humiliate an employee.

**132. D:** Numerous materials or agents are utilized as fire suppressants. Selection of an agent may depend on the type of extinguishing device used or the type of fuel involved in the fire. Common materials and extinguishing agents include carbon dioxide, halon, sodium bicarbonate, potassium bicarbonate, and water.

**133. C:** Employees should report to management any suspicious object that is hidden, obviously suspicious, and not typical for the environment in which it is located.

**134. B:** Effective emergency response plans are prepared by way of planning, practicing, and evaluating. Planning establishes roles and responsibilities in the event of an emergency while practicing allows for practical troubleshooting. Plans should be constantly evaluated for areas of improvement to increase efficiency and reduce losses during an emergency.

**135. C:** A 100-curie source of cobalt-60 at time $t_0$, with an associated half-life of 5.3 years, will have decayed to approximately 6.3 curies after 21.2 years (or 4 half-lives). In the domain of radioactive decay, a half-life period is the amount of time required for half (50 percent) of an original amount of radioactive material to decay to a stable form. Thus, in this case, 4 half-lives (5.3 years $\times$ 4 = 21.2 years) will result in $1/(2)^4$, or 6.3 percent, of the original radioactive material being left.

**136. B:** Per OSHA 29 CFR 1910.147, energy control programs shall include procedures for the sequential steps necessary to shut down, isolate, block, and secure machines or equipment.

**137. B:** OSHA has not promulgated a singular standard targeting ergonomic risk factors and controls. General ergonomic requirements are enforced by way of the administration's General Duty Clause, Section 5(a)(1).

**138. C:** There are currently five classes of fire extinguisher technologies, each designed to handle a different type of fire. The five alphabet-based codes that denote these classes are A, B, C, D, and K. Class A is for ordinary combustibles such as wood, paper, and plastic, and is symbolized by a green triangle. Class B is for combustible liquids such as gasoline, oil, and grease, and is symbolized by a red square. Class C is for live electrical equipment and is symbolized by a blue circle. Class D is for combustible metals such as sodium, potassium, and magnesium, and is symbolized by a yellow decagon. Finally, Class K is for fats and cooking oils and is symbolized by a black hexagon.

**139. D:** Per EPA guidelines, an environmental management system (EMS) can address several distinct elements, including maintaining or sustaining employee environment-related competencies and knowledge bases, regularly assessing associated EMS legal requirements, regularly evaluating potential environmental impacts associated with the EMS, and regularly reviewing an organization's environmental objectives.

**140. A:** Permissible exposure limits (PELs) are established by standard and are enforceable by OSHA. Recommended exposure limits (RELs) are established by the National Institute for Occupational Safety and Health (NIOSH). Threshold limit values (TLVs) are established by the American Conference of Governmental Industrial Hygienists (ACGIH). Short-term exposure limits (STELs) are also established by NIOSH.

**141. D:** The equivalent amount of heat that is generated during the operational lifetime of a heat-generating source that has an operational lifetime of 500 kilowatt-hours (assuming there are no efficiency-related losses) is $1.8 \times 10^9$ J. This can be calculated by converting kilowatt hours to joules. Knowing that a joule is 1 watt per second, we multiply by various forms of 1 until we have canceled out the units we do not want and arrive at a figure in joules, as follows:

$$500 \text{ kWh} \times \frac{3{,}600 \text{ s}}{1 \text{ hr}} \times \frac{1{,}000 \text{ J}}{1 \text{ kWs}} = 1.8 \times 10^9 \text{ J}$$

**142. B:** In fault-tree analyses, AND/OR logic gates are applied for linking together interrelated event sequences.

**143. D:** There are several tactics that are regularly employed in industry as ergonomic hazard controls. These include such strategies as work hardening (a rehabilitation-oriented work mode intended to gradually restore an injured worker's functionality), work conditioning (use of specific conditioning and strengthening tasks to help restore an injured worker's functionality), and job rotation (alternating job tasks to avoid overworking single muscle groups or to avoid repetitive motions).

**144. A:** The ignition of organic materials in the absence of a readily observable initiator, which is usually due to internal heat generation via oxidation, is commonly referred to as "spontaneous combustion."

**145. C:** The EPA's hierarchy of hazard controls lists recommended methods in order of effectiveness: elimination (most effective), substitution, engineering, administrative, and personal protective equipment (least effective).

**146. C:** A well-constructed training course typically includes an assessment module to verify that trainees have absorbed the vital informational components of the course. Assessment modules include examinations, skills demonstrations, or post-training observations.

**147. A:** If a storage shelf has a weight-limit capacity of 500 pounds and a safe utilization surface area of 10 $ft^2$, it will be able to support no more than two 8-$ft^3$ cube-shaped 50-lb boxes, if no stacking of boxes is permitted. Because the boxes are the shape of cubes and have a volume of 8 $ft^3$, each box will have six sides, and every side will have a surface area of 4 $ft^2$ (2 ft × 2 ft). Thus, only two boxes can fit (taking up 8 $ft^2$) within an area of 10 $ft^2$. The two boxes together weigh 100 pounds, which is less than the prescribed 500-pound limit.

**148. C:** The Health Insurance Portability and Accountability Act, better known by the acronym *HIPAA*, is a federal law that regulates who can access an individual's health records and information.

**149. B:** Within the domain of ergonomics and related injuries, the term *CTD* stands for "cumulative trauma disorder," which is defined as excessive wear and tear on soft tissues such muscles, tendons, and nerves usually caused by continuous overuse throughout a protracted time period. Such disorders can also manifest from substandard posture or position during work, or substandard workstation configuration.

**150. C:** OSHA Publication 3371-08 (2009) specifically defines *combustible dust* as a solid material comprising distinct particles or pieces, regardless of size, shape, or chemical composition, that presents a fire or deflagration hazard when suspended in air or some other oxidizing medium over a range of concentrations.

**151. B:** There are several items regularly required of waste generators per the EPA's hazardous waste identification (HWID) process. These include providing an initial determination as to whether subject waste is solid waste, providing a determination as to whether subject waste is Resource Conservation and Recovery Act (RCRA) hazardous waste, and implementing a petitioning process when wanting a specific type of waste to be delisted from hazardous waste records.

**152. A:** Besides providing an exam at the end of a training course to measure the effectiveness of the training course, another method that can be employed to measure course effectiveness is to have trainees demonstrate their new knowledge by way of a skills test.

**153. D:** An effective deterrent to workplace violence is a zero-tolerance policy, meaning no level of potentially aggressive behavior will be allowed in the workplace. This policy should apply to management, contractors, visitors, and anyone else who interacts with employees, in an effort to reduce the risk of employee injury.

**154. D:** Feedback for employees on safety performance should be timely (i.e., prompt), specific (as by providing accurate examples of observed behavior), and factual (so as to avoid the perception by the employee that they are being baselessly attacked).

**155. A:** A strongly recommended approach for proper chair usage in a workstation is to move the chair as close as reasonably possible to the work area while seated. This facilitates neutral body positions and reduces the propensity for overreaching.

**156. B:** Briefly touching any conductive metal that is grounded and non-energized is normally an excellent method of discharging potential static electricity from one's person.

**157. C:** Within the realm of industrial air emissions, the term *BACT* normally stands for "best available control technology."

**158. D:** Combustible dusts present fire, deflagration, and/or explosion hazards depending on the environment the dust is located in. Dust explosions can be controlled by removing the fuel or removing the ignition sources. Bag collectors trap the dust to keep it contained and away from ignition sources. Routine maintenance ensures that wiring and equipment do not spark or overheat and consequently act as ignition sources. Also, a plan that restricts open flames and controls static electricity will help reduce the risk of dust explosions.

**159. C:** Training in a group setting can be effective because group participants can learn from the experiences of other participants. Shared experiences lend context and provide real-world examples of the information being presented.

**160. A:** A disaster recovery plan should designate a recovery coordinator who ultimately decides what recovery actions need to be taken and assigns responsibilities for achieving such actions.

**161. D:** Smoke detectors are designed to detect the particulate matter in the air from smoke. Heat detectors can be used to detect temperature changes in environments where particulate matter, such as dust, may cause false alarms in smoke detector systems. Flame detectors sense radiation (i.e., infrared, visible, and ultraviolet light) associated with combustion. Carbon monoxide—not dioxide—detectors are sensors that may also be incorporated in some fire detection systems.

**162. B:** According to FEMA, an incident command system is a management system designed to enable effective and efficient domestic incident management by integrating a combination of facilities, equipment, personnel, procedures, and communications operating within a common organizational structure.

**163. D:** The two primary pieces of legislation enforced by the EPA that prescribe limits to industrial water pollution levels and overall standards for water quality are the Clean Water Act and the Safe Drinking Water Act.

**164. D:** The BCSP Code of Ethics Standard 4 states that safety professionals should "undertake assignments only when qualified by education or experience in the specific technical fields involved." Thus, safety professionals should never accept assignments which are outside of their technical knowledge base.

**165. C:** To calculate the pressure that 0.500 mol of $H_2$ will exert on a 500.0 mL flask at 300.0 K, we use the ideal gas equation $PV = nRT$, where $R$ is the ideal gas constant of 0.0821 L·atm/(K·mol), $P$ is the pressure in atmospheres, $V$ is the volume in liters, $n$ is the molecular weight in moles, and $T$ is the temperature in kelvins. If we isolate $P$ in this equation, we get:

$$P = \frac{nRT}{V}$$

Now we can calculate the pressure by plugging the numbers from the question them into the equation: $n$ = 0.500 mol, $V$ = 0.500 L, $T$ = 300.0 K, and $R = 0.0821 \frac{\text{L·atm}}{\text{K·mol}}$. This gives use the pressure, as follows:

$$P = \frac{(0.500\text{ mol})(0.0821\text{ L}\cdot\text{atm}/(\text{K}\cdot\text{mol})(300.0\text{ K})}{(0.500\text{ L})} = 24.6\text{ atm}$$

**166. C:** The OSHA 29 CFR 1910.95 hazardous noise threshold is 85 dBA. Sound level intensity is a logarithmic measure of sound intensity relative to the reference level, and it can be calculated according to the following equation:

$$IL(dB) = 10 \times \log\left(\frac{I}{I_0}\right)$$

In this equation, $IL$ is sound level intensity in dBA, $I$ is sound level in watts, and $\boldsymbol{I_0}$ is the reference level in watts. Inputting 85 dBA and solving for intensity using an $\boldsymbol{I_0}$ of $\mathbf{10^{-12}}$ W, the intensity is $\mathbf{3.16 \times 10^8}$ W. If we divide by 10 and then solve for intensity level, we find that the answer is 75 dBA.

**167. B:** A needs analysis is a method used by an organization to determine what safety training should occur for an identified gap. A gap is the difference between the current state and the desired state. Whereas a gap analysis determines how to close a gap, a needs analysis identifies the gap itself.

**168. A:** In an enclosed work area, the minimum amount of time to exchange the air can be calculated by finding the volume of the work area (20 feet × 15 feet × 10 feet = 3000 $ft^3$), dividing that by the volumetric ventilation rate of 10 $ft^3$ per second, and then converting seconds to minutes, as follows:

$$3{,}000 \text{ ft}^3 \times \frac{1 \text{ second}}{10 \text{ ft}^3} \times \frac{1 \text{ minute}}{60 \text{ seconds}} = 5 \text{ minutes}$$

**169. C:** To find the plan with the highest savings to cost ratio, we must evaluate each of the answer choices.

Choice A saves 6 errors per week and costs $800 per week, which gives us the following calculation and ratio: $\frac{6\times1{,}000}{800} = 7.5$. Choice B saves a total of 11 errors per week. Since the $500,000 cost is for 10 years, we will also multiply the savings out for 52 weeks and 10 years. This gives us the following: $\frac{11\times1{,}000\times52\times10}{500{,}000} = 11.44$. Choice C saves 4 errors per week for 52 weeks, and during that same period, it costs $8,000, giving the following ratio: $\frac{4\times1{,}000\times52}{8{,}000} = 26$. Finally, choice D saves 1 error per week and costs $400 per week, which gives us the following: $\frac{1\times1{,}000}{400} = 2.5$. Among these four ratios, choice C is the highest.

**170. B:** Given the US Nuclear Regulatory Commission's annual worker dose limit of 5 rem, we can see that, were a worker exposed to an average daily 10-millirem dose for an eight-hour workday over a 2,000-hour work-year, the worker would receive 50 percent of the NRC limit. This can be calculated by multiplying the daily dose by the hours worked per year and converting millirem to rem, as follows:

$$\frac{10 \text{ millirem}}{8 \text{ hours}} \times 2{,}000 \text{ hours} \times \frac{1 \text{ rem}}{1{,}000 \text{ millirem}} = 2.5 \text{ rem}$$

The resulting 2.5 rem is 50 percent of the NRC limit of 5 rem.

**171. D:** The longest sequence of activities in a project plan which must be completed on time in order for a given project, as a whole, to be completed on time is known as the project's critical path.

**172. C:** The scope of a job safety analysis (JSA) typically encompasses several facets, including the notation of safety recommendations associated with a given task, the identification of potential hazards associated with a given task, and the overall integration of safety principles with job practices associated with a given task.

**173. A:** Employees who behave in unsafe manners endanger themselves and others as well as exposing the organization to liability or citations. Depending on the culture and structure of the organization, the safety professional can inform the employee's supervisor to correct the behavior, discuss the situation directly with the employee, or initiate disciplinary action, particularly if the behavior is egregious or repeated. Safety professionals should never ignore unsafe behavior, as this ignores the actual danger presented by the behavior and sends the message that this behavior is acceptable.

**174. C:** Risk transfer is the act of shifting the responsibility for managing a risk from one party to another. The risk is not eliminated or controlled but simply moved. Subcontracting out a painting operation at heights moves the risk from the building owner to the subcontractor. That subcontractor may then elect to manage the risk using other methods, such as acceptance or control.

**175. D:** There are several items that are normally included as part of an annual fire extinguisher maintenance inspection: ensuring that adequate levels (volumes) of extinguishing agent are present in the extinguisher, ensuring that all the extinguisher's external components are in serviceable condition, and verifying the adequacy of extinguisher pressure levels. During routine maintenance, the extinguisher is not discharged.

**176. B:** Leaching is the process of water-soluble chemicals polluting nearby surface or groundwater after migrating through soil via rain or runoff.

**177. B:** The recommended upper weight limit for hand tools is 1.0 kg (2.2 lb), with lighter tools being recommended as potentially better for older workers. In addition, hand tools should always be designed such that the handle's center of gravity is properly aligned with the center of the hand when held.

**178. A:** Diethyl ether is a Class IA (highest flammability class) flammable liquid and is thus considerably more flammable than diesel, kerosene, and acetic acid, which are Class II flammables. The flammable liquid classification system is used by EPA, NFPA, DOT, and OSHA.

**179. D:** In regard to particulate matter (especially radiological effluents) emitted from stacks and other sources, the acronym *AMAD* stands for "activity median aerodynamic diameter," and is a key parameter used in contaminant dispersion modeling and human uptake assessments.

**180. B:** There are several strategies that can be employed in the workplace for reducing the risk of injuries that may result from manual materials handling, including proper task design and/or redesign, suitable pre-placement (of materials) procedures, and useful workflow protocols.

**181. D:** An employer is obligated to protect all confidential employee information that they collect or maintain. This includes medical information, personal identifiable information (e.g., social security number), and financial information used for payroll purposes. Employers may be held liable if they do not properly protect the information in their possession.

**182. D:** There are several pertinent facets supporting the promulgation and execution of the Comprehensive Environmental Response, Compensation, and Liability Act (CERCLA). Some of these facets include the following: the establishment of prohibitions and requirements concerning closed and abandoned hazardous waste sites; provision for liability of persons responsible for releases of hazardous material at closed and abandoned hazardous waste sites; and establishment of a trust fund (commonly known as the "Superfund") to provide for cleanup when no responsible party can be identified.

**183. A:** Excessive periods of standing in the workplace can often lead to the manifestation of varicose veins in the legs, as well as undue stress and strain on the muscles and soft tissues of the back, knees, hips, ankles, and feet.

**184. B:** Adults will retain information better if the learning is self-directed, the material is associated with past experiences, and the information is applicable to a job or task. Generally, adults will retain information better when they are ready to learn, as by having been given a clear motivation.

**185. B:** Hydrogen has a total of only three nuclides that exist in nature: protium, deuterium, and tritium, with only the third (tritium) being radioactive. Tritium has half-life of approximately 12 years and undergoes beta (β) decay.

**186. B:** There are three widely recognized modes or styles through which adults typically learn: auditory (hearing, listening), kinetic (doing), or visual (seeing). Effective training programs will contain elements to appeal to all three of these learning styles.

**187. A:** The Federal Bureau of Investigation (FBI) produced a report entitled "Workplace Violence – Issues in Response" where it defined workplace violence as any conduct that could be interpreted as showing an intent to cause harm.

**188. A:** Potential benefits associated with the implementation of a robust environmental management system may include resource conservation, pollution prevention, improved employee morale, and emission program cost savings.

**189. D:** The Government Publishing Office (GPO) is responsible for publishing and maintaining the Code of Federal Regulations (CFR). OSHA standards are located in Title 29 of the CFR and can be found on the GPO website.

**190. D:** The National Fire Protection Agency (NFPA) Standard 1 states that evacuation drills must be held frequently enough to familiarize building occupants with the process, but no less once a year.

**191. D:** Several parameters are normally assessed in order to accurately determine a facility's routine airborne pollutant concentrations. These do not include damper specifications, but they do include wind stability and direction, facility stack heights, precipitation levels, particulate deposition velocities, dilution factors, filter efficiencies, stack-exit flow rates and cross-sectional areas, building-wake effects, and original material-at-risk quantities.

**192. C:** Options-based responses to an active shooter event include the run, fight, hide model. Employees are encouraged to decide between evacuating the area, seeking a hiding place, or, as a last resort, confronting the assailant.

**193. B:** The National Fire Prevention Association's standard 51B requires that a competent person issue a hot work permit for welding, cutting, brazing, or any other spark-producing activity.

**194. A:** The BCSP Code of Ethics states that members should only work within their area of expertise. This means that if a certified safety professional is faced with a hazard outside of their expertise or training, they should seek consultation from outside experts.

**195. D:** There are usually three separate classification levels utilized for categorizing deficiencies noted during an environmental management system internal audit. These are (in order of severity) conditions adverse to quality (nonconformances), corrective actions (areas for concern), and opportunities for improvement (observations). In addition, noteworthy practices can also be highlighted as a benchmark or guide for helping implement potential improvements in needed areas.

**196. A:** The recommended upper weight or force limit of an object that is to be horizontally pushed or pulled from a kneeling position is 42 lb.

**197. C:** Cancer is a condition that occurs when the normal cell death processes are interrupted, meaning that cells live longer than intended. These "excess" cells gathered in a localized area can result in an abnormal mass of tissue, referred to as a *tumor*. Carcinogens are by definition cancer-causing agents, known or believed to cause cancer by interrupting normal cell death processes in this fashion.

**198. B:** With regard to optimal execution of automotive safety features (i.e., seatbelts and airbags), it is recommended that there be 10–12 inches of empty space between a driver's chest and the steering wheel.

**199. D:** There are several mitigation technologies used in industry that effectively remove water contaminants such as bacteria, unwanted minerals, and toxic chemicals. Such technologies include the use of ultraviolet light, high-efficiency filters, and ozone.

**200. C:** The condition of sciatica usually results in pain that affects the back, the hips, and the outside of the legs. It is typically caused by the compression of a spinal nerve root in the lower back area from a degenerated disk.

# How to Overcome Test Anxiety

Just the thought of taking a test is enough to make most people a little nervous. A test is an important event that can have a long-term impact on your future, so it's important to take it seriously and it's natural to feel anxious about performing well. But just because anxiety is normal, that doesn't mean that it's helpful in test taking, or that you should simply accept it as part of your life. Anxiety can have a variety of effects. These effects can be mild, like making you feel slightly nervous, or severe, like blocking your ability to focus or remember even a simple detail.

If you experience test anxiety—whether severe or mild—it's important to know how to beat it. To discover this, first you need to understand what causes test anxiety.

## Causes of Test Anxiety

While we often think of anxiety as an uncontrollable emotional state, it can actually be caused by simple, practical things. One of the most common causes of test anxiety is that a person does not feel adequately prepared for their test. This feeling can be the result of many different issues such as poor study habits or lack of organization, but the most common culprit is time management. Starting to study too late, failing to organize your study time to cover all of the material, or being distracted while you study will mean that you're not well prepared for the test. This may lead to cramming the night before, which will cause you to be physically and mentally exhausted for the test. Poor time management also contributes to feelings of stress, fear, and hopelessness as you realize you are not well prepared but don't know what to do about it.

Other times, test anxiety is not related to your preparation for the test but comes from unresolved fear. This may be a past failure on a test, or poor performance on tests in general. It may come from comparing yourself to others who seem to be performing better or from the stress of living up to expectations. Anxiety may be driven by fears of the future—how failure on this test would affect your educational and career goals. These fears are often completely irrational, but they can still negatively impact your test performance.

**Review Video: 3 Reasons You Have Test Anxiety**
Visit mometrix.com/academy and enter code: 428468

## Elements of Test Anxiety

As mentioned earlier, test anxiety is considered to be an emotional state, but it has physical and mental components as well. Sometimes you may not even realize that you are suffering from test anxiety until you notice the physical symptoms. These can include trembling hands, rapid heartbeat, sweating, nausea, and tense muscles. Extreme anxiety may lead to fainting or vomiting. Obviously, any of these symptoms can have a negative impact on testing. It is important to recognize them as soon as they begin to occur so that you can address the problem before it damages your performance.

**Review Video: 3 Ways to Tell You Have Test Anxiety**
Visit mometrix.com/academy and enter code: 927847

The mental components of test anxiety include trouble focusing and inability to remember learned information. During a test, your mind is on high alert, which can help you recall information and stay focused for an extended period of time. However, anxiety interferes with your mind's natural processes, causing you to blank out, even on the questions you know well. The strain of testing during anxiety makes it difficult to stay focused, especially on a test that may take several hours. Extreme anxiety can take a huge mental toll, making it difficult not only to recall test information but even to understand the test questions or pull your thoughts together.

**Review Video: How Test Anxiety Affects Memory**
Visit mometrix.com/academy and enter code: 609003

## Effects of Test Anxiety

Test anxiety is like a disease—if left untreated, it will get progressively worse. Anxiety leads to poor performance, and this reinforces the feelings of fear and failure, which in turn lead to poor performances on subsequent tests. It can grow from a mild nervousness to a crippling condition. If allowed to progress, test anxiety can have a big impact on your schooling, and consequently on your future.

Test anxiety can spread to other parts of your life. Anxiety on tests can become anxiety in any stressful situation, and blanking on a test can turn into panicking in a job situation. But fortunately, you don't have to let anxiety rule your testing and determine your grades. There are a number of relatively simple steps you can take to move past anxiety and function normally on a test and in the rest of life.

**Review Video: How Test Anxiety Impacts Your Grades**
Visit mometrix.com/academy and enter code: 939819

## Physical Steps for Beating Test Anxiety

While test anxiety is a serious problem, the good news is that it can be overcome. It doesn't have to control your ability to think and remember information. While it may take time, you can begin taking steps today to beat anxiety.

Just as your first hint that you may be struggling with anxiety comes from the physical symptoms, the first step to treating it is also physical. Rest is crucial for having a clear, strong mind. If you are tired, it is much easier to give in to anxiety. But if you establish good sleep habits, your body and mind will be ready to perform optimally, without the strain of exhaustion. Additionally, sleeping well helps you to retain information better, so you're more likely to recall the answers when you see the test questions.

Getting good sleep means more than going to bed on time. It's important to allow your brain time to relax. Take study breaks from time to time so it doesn't get overworked, and don't study right before bed. Take time to rest your mind before trying to rest your body, or you may find it difficult to fall asleep.

**Review Video: The Importance of Sleep for Your Brain**
Visit mometrix.com/academy and enter code: 319338

Along with sleep, other aspects of physical health are important in preparing for a test. Good nutrition is vital for good brain function. Sugary foods and drinks may give a burst of energy but this burst is followed by a crash, both physically and emotionally. Instead, fuel your body with protein and vitamin-rich foods.

Also, drink plenty of water. Dehydration can lead to headaches and exhaustion, especially if your brain is already under stress from the rigors of the test. Particularly if your test is a long one, drink water during the breaks. And if possible, take an energy-boosting snack to eat between sections.

**Review Video: How Diet Can Affect your Mood**
Visit mometrix.com/academy and enter code: 624317

Along with sleep and diet, a third important part of physical health is exercise. Maintaining a steady workout schedule is helpful, but even taking 5-minute study breaks to walk can help get your blood pumping faster and clear your head. Exercise also releases endorphins, which contribute to a positive feeling and can help combat test anxiety.

When you nurture your physical health, you are also contributing to your mental health. If your body is healthy, your mind is much more likely to be healthy as well. So take time to rest, nourish your body with healthy food and water, and get moving as much as possible. Taking these physical steps will make you stronger and more able to take the mental steps necessary to overcome test anxiety.

**Review Video: How to Stay Healthy and Prevent Test Anxiety**
Visit mometrix.com/academy and enter code: 877894

## Mental Steps for Beating Test Anxiety

Working on the mental side of test anxiety can be more challenging, but as with the physical side, there are clear steps you can take to overcome it. As mentioned earlier, test anxiety often stems from lack of preparation, so the obvious solution is to prepare for the test. Effective studying may be the most important weapon you have for beating test anxiety, but you can and should employ several other mental tools to combat fear.

First, boost your confidence by reminding yourself of past success—tests or projects that you aced. If you're putting as much effort into preparing for this test as you did for those, there's no reason you should expect to fail here. Work hard to prepare; then trust your preparation.

Second, surround yourself with encouraging people. It can be helpful to find a study group, but be sure that the people you're around will encourage a positive attitude. If you spend time with others who are anxious or cynical, this will only contribute to your own anxiety. Look for others who are motivated to study hard from a desire to succeed, not from a fear of failure.

Third, reward yourself. A test is physically and mentally tiring, even without anxiety, and it can be helpful to have something to look forward to. Plan an activity following the test, regardless of the outcome, such as going to a movie or getting ice cream.

When you are taking the test, if you find yourself beginning to feel anxious, remind yourself that you know the material. Visualize successfully completing the test. Then take a few deep, relaxing breaths and return to it. Work through the questions carefully but with confidence, knowing that you are capable of succeeding.

Developing a healthy mental approach to test taking will also aid in other areas of life. Test anxiety affects more than just the actual test—it can be damaging to your mental health and even contribute to depression. It's important to beat test anxiety before it becomes a problem for more than testing.

**Review Video: Test Anxiety and Depression**
Visit mometrix.com/academy and enter code: 904704

# Study Strategy

Being prepared for the test is necessary to combat anxiety, but what does being prepared look like? You may study for hours on end and still not feel prepared. What you need is a strategy for test prep. The next few pages outline our recommended steps to help you plan out and conquer the challenge of preparation.

## Step 1: Scope Out the Test

Learn everything you can about the format (multiple choice, essay, etc.) and what will be on the test. Gather any study materials, course outlines, or sample exams that may be available. Not only will this help you to prepare, but knowing what to expect can help to alleviate test anxiety.

## Step 2: Map Out the Material

Look through the textbook or study guide and make note of how many chapters or sections it has. Then divide these over the time you have. For example, if a book has 15 chapters and you have five days to study, you need to cover three chapters each day. Even better, if you have the time, leave an extra day at the end for overall review after you have gone through the material in depth.

If time is limited, you may need to prioritize the material. Look through it and make note of which sections you think you already have a good grasp on, and which need review. While you are studying, skim quickly through the familiar sections and take more time on the challenging parts. Write out your plan so you don't get lost as you go. Having a written plan also helps you feel more in control of the study, so anxiety is less likely to arise from feeling overwhelmed at the amount to cover.

## Step 3: Gather Your Tools

Decide what study method works best for you. Do you prefer to highlight in the book as you study and then go back over the highlighted portions? Or do you type out notes of the important information? Or is it helpful to make flashcards that you can carry with you? Assemble the pens, index cards, highlighters, post-it notes, and any other materials you may need so you won't be distracted by getting up to find things while you study.

If you're having a hard time retaining the information or organizing your notes, experiment with different methods. For example, try color-coding by subject with colored pens, highlighters, or post-it notes. If you learn better by hearing, try recording yourself reading your notes so you can listen while in the car, working out, or simply sitting at your desk. Ask a friend to quiz you from your flashcards, or try teaching someone the material to solidify it in your mind.

## Step 4: Create Your Environment

It's important to avoid distractions while you study. This includes both the obvious distractions like visitors and the subtle distractions like an uncomfortable chair (or a too-comfortable couch that makes you want to fall asleep). Set up the best study environment possible: good lighting and a comfortable work area. If background music helps you focus, you may want to turn it on, but otherwise keep the room quiet. If you are using a computer to take notes, be sure you don't have any other windows open, especially applications like social media, games, or anything else that could distract you. Silence your phone and turn off notifications. Be sure to keep water close by so you stay hydrated while you study (but avoid unhealthy drinks and snacks).

Also, take into account the best time of day to study. Are you freshest first thing in the morning? Try to set aside some time then to work through the material. Is your mind clearer in the afternoon or evening? Schedule your study session then. Another method is to study at the same time of day that you will take the test, so that your brain gets used to working on the material at that time and will be ready to focus at test time.

## Step 5: Study!

Once you have done all the study preparation, it's time to settle into the actual studying. Sit down, take a few moments to settle your mind so you can focus, and begin to follow your study plan. Don't give in to distractions or let yourself procrastinate. This is your time to prepare so you'll be ready to fearlessly approach the test. Make the most of the time and stay focused.

Of course, you don't want to burn out. If you study too long you may find that you're not retaining the information very well. Take regular study breaks. For example, taking five minutes out of every hour to walk briskly, breathing deeply and swinging your arms, can help your mind stay fresh.

As you get to the end of each chapter or section, it's a good idea to do a quick review. Remind yourself of what you learned and work on any difficult parts. When you feel that you've mastered the material, move on to the next part. At the end of your study session, briefly skim through your notes again.

But while review is helpful, cramming last minute is NOT. If at all possible, work ahead so that you won't need to fit all your study into the last day. Cramming overloads your brain with more information than it can process and retain, and your tired mind may struggle to recall even previously learned information when it is overwhelmed with last-minute study. Also, the urgent nature of cramming and the stress placed on your brain contribute to anxiety. You'll be more likely to go to the test feeling unprepared and having trouble thinking clearly.

So don't cram, and don't stay up late before the test, even just to review your notes at a leisurely pace. Your brain needs rest more than it needs to go over the information again. In fact, plan to finish your studies by noon or early afternoon the day before the test. Give your brain the rest of the day to relax or focus on other things, and get a good night's sleep. Then you will be fresh for the test and better able to recall what you've studied.

## Step 6: Take a practice test

Many courses offer sample tests, either online or in the study materials. This is an excellent resource to check whether you have mastered the material, as well as to prepare for the test format and environment.

Check the test format ahead of time: the number of questions, the type (multiple choice, free response, etc.), and the time limit. Then create a plan for working through them. For example, if you have 30 minutes to take a 60-question test, your limit is 30 seconds per question. Spend less time on the questions you know well so that you can take more time on the difficult ones.

If you have time to take several practice tests, take the first one open book, with no time limit. Work through the questions at your own pace and make sure you fully understand them. Gradually work up to taking a test under test conditions: sit at a desk with all study materials put away and set a timer. Pace yourself to make sure you finish the test with time to spare and go back to check your answers if you have time.

After each test, check your answers. On the questions you missed, be sure you understand why you missed them. Did you misread the question (tests can use tricky wording)? Did you forget the information? Or was it something you hadn't learned? Go back and study any shaky areas that the practice tests reveal.

Taking these tests not only helps with your grade, but also aids in combating test anxiety. If you're already used to the test conditions, you're less likely to worry about it, and working through tests until you're scoring well gives you a confidence boost. Go through the practice tests until you feel comfortable, and then you can go into the test knowing that you're ready for it.

## Test Tips

On test day, you should be confident, knowing that you've prepared well and are ready to answer the questions. But aside from preparation, there are several test day strategies you can employ to maximize your performance.

First, as stated before, get a good night's sleep the night before the test (and for several nights before that, if possible). Go into the test with a fresh, alert mind rather than staying up late to study.

Try not to change too much about your normal routine on the day of the test. It's important to eat a nutritious breakfast, but if you normally don't eat breakfast at all, consider eating just a protein bar. If you're a coffee drinker, go ahead and have your normal coffee. Just make sure you time it so that the caffeine doesn't wear off right in the middle of your test. Avoid sugary beverages, and drink enough water to stay hydrated but not so much that you need a restroom break 10 minutes into the test. If your test isn't first thing in the morning, consider going for a walk or doing a light workout before the test to get your blood flowing.

Allow yourself enough time to get ready, and leave for the test with plenty of time to spare so you won't have the anxiety of scrambling to arrive in time. Another reason to be early is to select a good seat. It's helpful to sit away from doors and windows, which can be distracting. Find a good seat, get out your supplies, and settle your mind before the test begins.

When the test begins, start by going over the instructions carefully, even if you already know what to expect. Make sure you avoid any careless mistakes by following the directions.

Then begin working through the questions, pacing yourself as you've practiced. If you're not sure on an answer, don't spend too much time on it, and don't let it shake your confidence. Either skip it and come back later, or eliminate as many wrong answers as possible and guess among the remaining ones. Don't dwell on these questions as you continue—put them out of your mind and focus on what lies ahead.

Be sure to read all of the answer choices, even if you're sure the first one is the right answer. Sometimes you'll find a better one if you keep reading. But don't second-guess yourself if you do immediately know the answer. Your gut instinct is usually right. Don't let test anxiety rob you of the information you know.

If you have time at the end of the test (and if the test format allows), go back and review your answers. Be cautious about changing any, since your first instinct tends to be correct, but make sure you didn't misread any of the questions or accidentally mark the wrong answer choice. Look over any you skipped and make an educated guess.

At the end, leave the test feeling confident. You've done your best, so don't waste time worrying about your performance or wishing you could change anything. Instead, celebrate the successful completion of this test. And finally, use this test to learn how to deal with anxiety even better next time.

**Review Video: 5 Tips to Beat Test Anxiety**
Visit mometrix.com/academy and enter code: 570656

## Important Qualification

Not all anxiety is created equal. If your test anxiety is causing major issues in your life beyond the classroom or testing center, or if you are experiencing troubling physical symptoms related to your anxiety, it may be a sign of a serious physiological or psychological condition. If this sounds like your situation, we strongly encourage you to seek professional help.

# How to Overcome Your Fear of Math

The word *math* is enough to strike fear into most hearts. How many of us have memories of sitting through confusing lectures, wrestling over mind-numbing homework, or taking tests that still seem incomprehensible even after hours of study? Years after graduation, many still shudder at these memories.

The fact is, math is not just a classroom subject. It has real-world implications that you face every day, whether you realize it or not. This may be balancing your monthly budget, deciding how many supplies to buy for a project, or simply splitting a meal check with friends. The idea of daily confrontations with math can be so paralyzing that some develop a condition known as *math anxiety*.

But you do NOT need to be paralyzed by this anxiety! In fact, while you may have thought all your life that you're not good at math, or that your brain isn't wired to understand it, the truth is that you may have been conditioned to think this way. From your earliest school days, the way you were taught affected the way you viewed different subjects. And the way math has been taught has changed.

Several decades ago, there was a shift in American math classrooms. The focus changed from traditional problem-solving to a conceptual view of topics, de-emphasizing the importance of learning the basics and building on them. The solid foundation necessary for math progression and confidence was undermined. Math became more of a vague concept than a concrete idea. Today, it is common to think of math, not as a straightforward system, but as a mysterious, complicated method that can't be fully understood unless you're a genius.

This is why you may still have nightmares about being called on to answer a difficult problem in front of the class. Math anxiety is a very real, though unnecessary, fear.

Math anxiety may begin with a single class period. Let's say you missed a day in 6th grade math and never quite understood the concept that was taught while you were gone. Since math is cumulative, with each new concept building on past ones, this could very well affect the rest of your math career. Without that one day's knowledge, it will be difficult to understand any other concepts that link to it. Rather than realizing that you're just missing one key piece, you may begin to believe that you're simply not capable of understanding math.

This belief can change the way you approach other classes, career options, and everyday life experiences, if you become anxious at the thought that math might be required. A student who loves science may choose a different path of study upon realizing that multiple math classes will be required for a degree. An aspiring medical student may hesitate at the thought of going through the necessary math classes. For some this anxiety escalates into a more extreme state known as *math phobia*.

Math anxiety is challenging to address because it is rooted deeply and may come from a variety of causes: an embarrassing moment in class, a teacher who did not explain concepts well and contributed to a shaky foundation, or a failed test that contributed to the belief of math failure.

These causes add up over time, encouraged by society's popular view that math is hard and unpleasant. Eventually a person comes to firmly believe that he or she is simply bad at math. This belief makes it difficult to grasp new concepts or even remember old ones. Homework and test grades begin to slip, which only confirms the belief. The poor performance is not due to lack of ability but is caused by math anxiety.

Math anxiety is an emotional issue, not a lack of intelligence. But when it becomes deeply rooted, it can become more than just an emotional problem. Physical symptoms appear. Blood pressure may rise and heartbeat may quicken at the sight of a math problem – or even the thought of math! This fear leads to a mental block. When someone with math anxiety is asked to perform a calculation, even a basic problem can seem overwhelming and impossible. The emotional and physical response to the thought of math prevents the brain from working through it logically.

The more this happens, the more a person's confidence drops, and the more math anxiety is generated. This vicious cycle must be broken!

The first step in breaking the cycle is to go back to very beginning and make sure you really understand the basics of how math works and why it works. It is not enough to memorize rules for multiplication and division. If you don't know WHY these rules work, your foundation will be shaky and you will be at risk of developing a phobia. Understanding mathematical concepts not only promotes confidence and security, but allows you to build on this understanding for new concepts. Additionally, you can solve unfamiliar problems using familiar concepts and processes.

Why is it that students in other countries regularly outperform American students in math? The answer likely boils down to a couple of things: the foundation of mathematical conceptual understanding and societal perception. While students in the US are not expected to *like* or *get* math, in many other nations, students are expected not only to understand math but also to excel at it.

Changing the American view of math that leads to math anxiety is a monumental task. It requires changing the training of teachers nationwide, from kindergarten through high school, so that they learn to teach the *why* behind math and to combat the wrong math views that students may develop. It also involves changing the stigma associated with math, so that it is no longer viewed as unpleasant and incomprehensible. While these are necessary changes, they are challenging and will take time. But in the meantime, math anxiety is not irreversible—it can be faced and defeated, one person at a time.

## False Beliefs

One reason math anxiety has taken such hold is that several false beliefs have been created and shared until they became widely accepted. Some of these unhelpful beliefs include the following:

***There is only one way to solve a math problem***. In the same way that you can choose from different driving routes and still arrive at the same house, you can solve a math problem using different methods and still find the correct answer. A person who understands the reasoning behind math calculations may be able to look at an unfamiliar concept and find the right answer, just by applying logic to the knowledge they already have. This approach may be different than what is taught in the classroom, but it is still valid. Unfortunately, even many teachers view math as a subject where the best course of action is to memorize the rule or process for each problem rather than as a place for students to exercise logic and creativity in finding a solution.

***Many people don't have a mind for math***. A person who has struggled due to poor teaching or math anxiety may falsely believe that he or she doesn't have the mental capacity to grasp mathematical concepts. Most of the time, this is false. Many people find that when they are relieved of their math anxiety, they have more than enough brainpower to understand math.

***Men are naturally better at math than women***. Even though research has shown this to be false, many young women still avoid math careers and classes because of their belief that their math abilities are inferior. Many girls have come to believe that math is a male skill and have given up trying to understand or enjoy it.

***Counting aids are bad***. Something like counting on your fingers or drawing out a problem to visualize it may be frowned on as childish or a crutch, but these devices can help you get a tangible understanding of a problem or a concept.

Sadly, many students buy into these ideologies at an early age. A young girl who enjoys math class may be conditioned to think that she doesn't actually have the brain for it because math is for boys, and may turn her energies to other pursuits, permanently closing the door on a wide range of opportunities. A child who finds the right answer but doesn't follow the teacher's method may believe that he is doing it wrong and isn't good at math. A student who never had a problem with math before may have a poor teacher and become confused, yet believe that the problem is because she doesn't have a mathematical mind.

Students who have bought into these erroneous beliefs quickly begin to add their own anxieties, adapting them to their own personal situations:

***I'll never use this in real life***. A huge number of people wrongly believe that math is irrelevant outside the classroom. By adopting this mindset, they are handicapping themselves for a life in a mathematical world, as well as limiting their career choices. When they are inevitably faced with real-world math, they are conditioning themselves to respond with anxiety.

***I'm not quick enough***. While timed tests and quizzes, or even simply comparing yourself with other students in the class, can lead to this belief, speed is not an indicator of skill level. A person can work very slowly yet understand at a deep level.

***If I can understand it, it's too easy***. People with a low view of their own abilities tend to think that if they are able to grasp a concept, it must be simple. They cannot accept the idea that they are capable of understanding math. This belief will make it harder to learn, no matter how intelligent they are.

***I just can't learn this***. An overwhelming number of people think this, from young children to adults, and much of the time it is simply not true. But this mindset can turn into a self-fulfilling prophecy that keeps you from exercising and growing your math ability.

The good news is, each of these myths can be debunked. For most people, they are based on emotion and psychology, NOT on actual ability! It will take time, effort, and the desire to change, but change is possible. Even if you have spent years thinking that you don't have the capability to understand math, it is not too late to uncover your true ability and find relief from the anxiety that surrounds math.

## Math Strategies

It is important to have a plan of attack to combat math anxiety. There are many useful strategies for pinpointing the fears or myths and eradicating them:

***Go back to the basics***. For most people, math anxiety stems from a poor foundation. You may think that you have a complete understanding of addition and subtraction, or even decimals and percentages, but make absolutely sure. Learning math is different from learning other subjects. For example, when you learn history, you study various time periods and places and events. It may be important to memorize dates or find out about the lives of famous people. When you move from US history to world history, there will be some overlap, but a large amount of the information will be new. Mathematical concepts, on the other hand, are very closely linked and highly dependent on each other. It's like climbing a ladder – if a rung is missing from your understanding, it may be difficult or impossible for you to climb any higher, no matter how hard you try. So go back and make sure your math foundation is strong. This may mean taking a remedial math course, going to a tutor to work through the shaky concepts, or just going through your old homework to make sure you really understand it.

***Speak the language***. Math has a large vocabulary of terms and phrases unique to working problems. Sometimes these are completely new terms, and sometimes they are common words, but are used differently in a math setting. If you can't speak the language, it will be very difficult to get a thorough understanding of the concepts. It's common for students to think that they don't understand math when they simply don't understand the vocabulary. The good news is that this is fairly easy to fix. Brushing up on any terms you aren't quite sure of can help bring the rest of the concepts into focus.

***Check your anxiety level***. When you think about math, do you feel nervous or uncomfortable? Do you struggle with feelings of inadequacy, even on concepts that you know you've already learned? It's important to understand your specific math anxieties, and what triggers them. When you catch yourself falling back on a false belief, mentally replace it with the truth. Don't let yourself believe that you can't learn, or that struggling with a concept means you'll never understand it. Instead, remind yourself of how much you've already learned and dwell on that past success. Visualize grasping the new concept, linking it to your old knowledge, and moving on to the next challenge. Also, learn how to manage anxiety when it arises. There are many techniques for coping with the irrational fears that rise to the surface when you enter the math classroom. This may include controlled breathing, replacing negative thoughts with positive ones, or visualizing success. Anxiety interferes with your ability to concentrate and absorb information, which in turn contributes to greater anxiety. If you can learn how to regain control of your thinking, you will be better able to pay attention, make progress, and succeed!

***Don't go it alone***. Like any deeply ingrained belief, math anxiety is not easy to eradicate. And there is no need for you to wrestle through it on your own. It will take time, and many people find that speaking with a counselor or psychiatrist helps. They can help you develop strategies for responding to anxiety and overcoming old ideas. Additionally, it can be very helpful to take a short course or seek out a math tutor to help you find and fix the missing rungs on your ladder and make sure that you're ready to progress to the next level. You can also find a number of math aids online: courses that will teach you mental devices for figuring out problems, how to get the most out of your math classes, etc.

***Check your math attitude***. No matter how much you want to learn and overcome your anxiety, you'll have trouble if you still have a negative attitude toward math. If you think it's too hard, or just have general feelings of dread about math, it will be hard to learn and to break through the anxiety. Work on cultivating a positive math attitude. Remind yourself that math is not just a hurdle to be cleared, but a valuable asset. When you view math with a positive attitude, you'll be much more likely to understand and even enjoy it. This is something you must do for yourself. You may find it helpful to visit with a counselor. Your tutor, friends, and family may cheer you on in your endeavors. But your greatest asset is yourself. You are inside your own mind – tell yourself what you need to hear. Relive past victories. Remind yourself that you are capable of understanding math. Root out any false beliefs that linger and replace them with positive truths. Even if it doesn't feel true at first, it will begin to affect your thinking and pave the way for a positive, anxiety-free mindset.

Aside from these general strategies, there are a number of specific practical things you can do to begin your journey toward overcoming math anxiety. Something as simple as learning a new note-taking strategy can change the way you approach math and give you more confidence and understanding. New study techniques can also make a huge difference.

Math anxiety leads to bad habits. If it causes you to be afraid of answering a question in class, you may gravitate toward the back row. You may be embarrassed to ask for help. And you may procrastinate on assignments, which leads to rushing through them at the last moment when it's too late to get a better understanding. It's important to identify your negative behaviors and replace them with positive ones:

***Prepare ahead of time***. Read the lesson before you go to class. Being exposed to the topics that will be covered in class ahead of time, even if you don't understand them perfectly, is extremely helpful in increasing what you retain from the lecture. Do your homework and, if you're still shaky, go over some extra problems. The key to a solid understanding of math is practice.

***Sit front and center***. When you can easily see and hear, you'll understand more, and you'll avoid the distractions of other students if no one is in front of you. Plus, you're more likely to be sitting with students who are positive and engaged, rather than others with math anxiety. Let their positive math attitude rub off on you.

***Ask questions in class and out***. If you don't understand something, just ask. If you need a more in-depth explanation, the teacher may need to work with you outside of class, but often it's a simple concept you don't quite understand, and a single question may clear it up. If you wait, you may not be able to follow the rest of the day's lesson. For extra help, most professors have office hours outside of class when you can go over concepts one-on-one to clear up any uncertainties. Additionally, there may be a *math lab* or study session you can attend for homework help. Take advantage of this.

***Review***. Even if you feel that you've fully mastered a concept, review it periodically to reinforce it. Going over an old lesson has several benefits: solidifying your understanding, giving you a confidence boost, and even giving some new insights into material that you're currently learning! Don't let yourself get rusty. That can lead to problems with learning later concepts.

## Teaching Tips

While the math student's mindset is the most crucial to overcoming math anxiety, it is also important for others to adjust their math attitudes. Teachers and parents have an enormous influence on how students relate to math. They can either contribute to math confidence or math anxiety.

As a parent or teacher, it is very important to convey a positive math attitude. Retelling horror stories of your own bad experience with math will contribute to a new generation of math anxiety. Even if you don't share your experiences, others will be able to sense your fears and may begin to believe them.

Even a careless comment can have a big impact, so watch for phrases like *He's not good at math* or *I never liked math*. You are a crucial role model, and your children or students will unconsciously adopt your mindset. Give them a positive example to follow. Rather than teaching them to fear the math world before they even know it, teach them about all its potential and excitement.

Work to present math as an integral, beautiful, and understandable part of life. Encourage creativity in solving problems. Watch for false beliefs and dispel them. Cross the lines between subjects: integrate history, English, and music with math. Show students how math is used every day, and how the entire world is based on mathematical principles, from the pull of gravity to the shape of seashells. Instead of letting students see math as a necessary evil, direct them to view it as an imaginative, beautiful art form – an art form that they are capable of mastering and using.

Don't give too narrow a view of math. It is more than just numbers. Yes, working problems and learning formulas is a large part of classroom math. But don't let the teaching stop there. Teach students about the everyday implications of math. Show them how nature works according to the laws of mathematics, and take them outside to make discoveries of their own. Expose them to math-related careers by inviting visiting speakers, asking students to do research and presentations, and learning students' interests and aptitudes on a personal level.

Demonstrate the importance of math. Many people see math as nothing more than a required stepping stone to their degree, a nuisance with no real usefulness. Teach students that algebra is used every day in managing their bank accounts, in following recipes, and in scheduling the day's events. Show them how learning to do geometric proofs helps them to develop logical thinking, an invaluable life skill. Let them see that math surrounds them and is integrally linked to their daily lives: that weather predictions are based on math, that math was used to design cars and other machines, etc. Most of all, give them the tools to use math to enrich their lives.

Make math as tangible as possible. Use visual aids and objects that can be touched. It is much easier to grasp a concept when you can hold it in your hands and manipulate it, rather than just listening to the lecture. Encourage math outside of the classroom. The real world is full of measuring, counting, and calculating, so let students participate in this. Keep your eyes open for numbers and patterns to discuss. Talk about how scores are calculated in sports games and how far apart plants are placed in a garden row for maximum growth. Build the mindset that math is a normal and interesting part of daily life.

Finally, find math resources that help to build a positive math attitude. There are a number of books that show math as fascinating and exciting while teaching important concepts, for example: *The Math Curse; A Wrinkle in Time; The Phantom Tollbooth;* and *Fractals, Googols and Other Mathematical Tales*. You can also find a number of online resources: math puzzles and games, videos that show math in nature, and communities of math enthusiasts. On a local level, students can compete in a variety of math competitions with other schools or join a math club.

The student who experiences math as exciting and interesting is unlikely to suffer from math anxiety. Going through life without this handicap is an immense advantage and opens many doors that others have closed through their fear.

## Self-Check

Whether you suffer from math anxiety or not, chances are that you have been exposed to some of the false beliefs mentioned above. Now is the time to check yourself for any errors you may have accepted. Do you think you're not wired for math? Or that you don't need to understand it since you're not planning on a math career? Do you think math is just too difficult for the average person?

Find the errors you've taken to heart and replace them with positive thinking. Are you capable of learning math? Yes! Can you control your anxiety? Yes! These errors will resurface from time to time, so be watchful. Don't let others with math anxiety influence you or sway your confidence. If you're having trouble with a concept, find help. Don't let it discourage you!

Create a plan of attack for defeating math anxiety and sharpening your skills. Do some research and decide if it would help you to take a class, get a tutor, or find some online resources to fine-tune your knowledge. Make the effort to get good nutrition, hydration, and sleep so that you are operating at full capacity. Remind yourself daily that you are skilled and that anxiety does not control you. Your mind is capable of so much more than you know. Give it the tools it needs to grow and thrive.

# Tell Us Your Story

We at Mometrix would like to extend our heartfelt thanks to you for letting us be a part of your journey. It is an honor to serve people from all walks of life, people like you, who are committed to building the best future they can for themselves.

We know that each person's situation is unique. But we also know that, whether you are a young student or a mother of four, you care about working to make your own life and the lives of those around you better.

**That's why we want to hear your story.**

We want to know why you're taking this test. We want to know about the trials you've gone through to get here. And we want to know about the successes you've experienced after taking and passing your test.

In addition to your story, which can be an inspiration both to us and to others, we value your feedback. We want to know both what you loved about our book and what you think we can improve on.

**The team at Mometrix would be absolutely thrilled to hear from you!** So please, send us an email at tellusyourstory@mometrix.com or visit us at mometrix.com/tellusyourstory.php and let's stay in touch.

# Additional Bonus Material

Due to our efforts to try to keep this book to a manageable length, we've created a link that will give you access to all of your additional bonus material.

**Please visit https://www.mometrix.com/bonus948/asp to access the information.**